GAS CHROMATOGRAPHY

A. I. M. KEULEMANS

*Research Chemist, Koninklijke/Shell-Laboratorium,
Amsterdam, Holland*

Edited by
C. G. VERVER

With a foreword by
A. J. P. MARTIN

SECOND EDITION

REINHOLD PUBLISHING CORPORATION
NEW YORK
CHAPMAN & HALL, LTD., LONDON

PRINTED IN THE UNITED STATES OF AMERICA BY
THE WAVERLY PRESS, INC., BALTIMORE, MD.

FOREWORD

It gives me great pleasure to write this foreword to Dr. Keulemans'
book on "Gas Chromatography."

I have been accused by several petroleum chemists of hiding my work
in the *Biochemical Journal*, an offense, of which I, as a biochemist, had not
been aware. It has not, however, hampered Shell's chemists who have for
many years been among the most active investigators of all varieties of
chromatography.

Dr. Keulemans demonstrates in this volume his mastery of this subject,
a mastery which reflects the vast amount of work which he and his colleagues have put into the development of this analytical tool.

Chemists in many fields will be grateful to the author who has assembled
here such an admirably clear account of all the practical and theoretical
aspects of this rapidly growing method.

A. J. P. Martin

PREFACE TO SECOND EDITION

As was to be predicted, much has happened in the very "live" domain of gas chromatography within the short time that has elapsed since the first edition of this book was published. This is evident from the number of well-attended symposia on the subject that have been held in 1957 and 1958 (Michigan, New York and Amsterdam).

The developments to be signalled do not greatly affect the fundamental theory of gas-chromatographic separations. This theory was, apparently, already sufficiently established by the end of 1956 and has undergone little significant change. In particular, the formula developed by Van Deemter, which gives a quantitative form to some of the views expressed in James and Martin's first paper on the subject, has been well substantiated and has proved its value for deducing the measures that must be taken in order to improve separation.

The principal changes included in the new edition are related to practical matters. The most important of these are: the development, for highly critical separations, of columns having an extremely large number of theoretical plates; these columns, which are both of the packed type (Scott) and the coated capillary type (Golay), are described in an addition to Chapter 7; the introduction of new and highly sensitive detection systems, such as the argon β-ray detector of Lovelock and the McWilliam flame ionization detector (Chapter 3); the use of gas-solid chromatography for special purposes, such as the characterization of catalyst surfaces and the separation of isotopes (Chapter 8).

It has been impossible to refer to the vast number of applications that G.L.C. and G.S.C. have recently found. Some of the examples given in Chapter 2 have, however, been replaced by others that may be of more immediate interest. The introduction to Appendix I has been rewritten in accordance with the pressing desirability of restricting the number of stationary liquids used in G.L.C. to a few standard types wherever possible. The former Appendix II, giving constructional details of katharometers, has been omitted from the new edition, since thermal conductivity cells are now obtainable commercially in satisfactory quality. A subject index has been added.

The author has taken the opportunity of remedying a few omissions; *inter alia*, he has now attempted to do fuller justice to the work of Professor Erica Cremer, of Innsbruck, Austria, and her school, on the fundamentals of gas-solid chromatography.

A. I. M. KEULEMANS
C. G. VERVER

Amsterdam, Holland
August 1959

PREFACE TO FIRST EDITION

The methods of gas chromatography are still young. This is particularly true for gas-liquid chromatography, the first account of which was published by Martin and James toward the end of 1952. The new procedures have been—and are still being—developed at a phenomenal rate, and it is obviously a hazardous undertaking for anyone to write a book on so unfinished a subject. The author has nevertheless undertaken the task, stimulated as he was by the great interest shown in these delicate and versatile methods of separation, which in many cases have already provided easy solutions for analytical problems that previously seemed impossibly difficult. He was, moreover, favored in his undertaking by circumstances, since he had access not only to the data obtained in the Koninklijke/Shell-Laboratorium, Amsterdam, where he is engaged, but also to the results of research work carried out over a number of years in the laboratories of Shell Development Company (Emeryville, California), Shell Oil Company and Shell Chemical Corporation (Houston, Texas), and Shell Research Limited (Thornton, Cheshire, Great Britain). These results, together with the views of the specialists in the latter laboratories and in N.V.De Bataafsche Petroleum Maatschappij (The Hague) on matters of theory and equipment, play an important part in the present book.

In the text, use has been made of the principal publications on the subject of gas chromatography up to January 1st, 1956. The literature that has appeared since then could be referred to only in exceptional cases. In general, it has, for instance, not been possible to deal with the papers contributed to the symposia on gas chromatography held in Dallas, Texas, in April, and in London in May/June 1956, though some points of importance that came up in the latter meeting have been added as footnotes.

In arranging the subject matter it has been the aim to reconcile practical usefulness with theoretical soundness. In most normal analyses by gas chromatography excellent results can be obtained with little or no knowledge of the underlying theory. Once, however, the investigator leaves the field of routine separations and attacks more difficult applications, he will find that some familiarity with the fundamentals is essential. For these reasons the normal practice of gas-liquid chromatography is dealt with before theoretical matters are discussed.

Nevertheless, it was considered necessary to devote the opening chapter to a review of the whole field of chromatography and of related physical processes. There exists, even in today's literature, considerable confusion in the definition of chromatographic procedures, particularly as regards their relation to other methods of separation such as distillation and extraction. Chapter 1 contains a proposed definition of chromatography in general and a classification of its subdivisions. It should be realized, however, that this classification is not entirely rigid and that "hybrid" methods exist. (An example that may be quoted is gas-liquid chromatography employing a "molecular sieve" as support.) So far there has been very little unity in the names given to the various chromatographic techniques. The present book employs the simple and effective nomenclature recommended by a special subcommittee appointed for this purpose during the Symposium on Gas Chromatography, held by the Institute of Petroleum in London, May/June 1956.

Chapter 2 describes normal practical applications of gas-liquid chromatography (G.L.C.), while Chapter 3 discusses in detail the apparatus required, including the various forms of detectors and their characteristics. The theories underlying G.L.C. are discussed in Chapters 4, 5 and 6, and Chapter 7 shows how these principles can be utilized when dealing with difficult separations and nonanalytical applications. Chapter 8, finally, is devoted to gas-solid chromatography. Though it seemed until recently that this older form of separation had been largely superseded by G.L.C., some new developments suggest that there are still interesting possibilities in the process based on adsorption.

It is impossible for the author and editor to thank individually more than a few of those who kindly aided them in the realization of this book. In the first place they wish to mention Dr. A. J. P. Martin, one of the inventors of G.L.C., with whom the author had stimulating discussions on several occasions. Many thanks are also due to Imperial Chemical Industries Ltd. (Billingham and Nobel Divisions) for much valuable information, and to Messrs. J. Brooks and A. F. Williams of that company for the description of the glass-channel katharometer given in Appendix II. The author and editor further gratefully recognize their indebtedness to several members of the staff of N. V. De Bataafsche Petroleum Maatschappij: Dr. G. G. Baylé and Dr. A. Klinkenberg gave much valuable advice in matters of a theoretical nature; their views had a major influence on Chapters 1 and 4; much of the experimental work contained in the book is due to Mr. F. van de Craats and Dr. H. Boer, and to Messrs. A. Kwantes, Th. van Bavel, together with their enthusiastic team of workers. Their sincere thanks are also extended to the specialists on chromatography in the American and British Shell companies mentioned above, whose results have been so freely used and who submitted the manuscript to constructive criticism, and to the management of N. V. De Bataafsche Petroleum Maatschappij for permission to publish the subject matter.

It is hoped that this volume may assist and stimulate investigators in using the fascinating methods of separation that are described and in searching for the many undiscovered possibilities that they certainly still hold.

A. I. M. KEULEMANS
C. G. VERVER

Amsterdam, Holland
February 1957

LIST OF SYMBOLS

The pages on which the symbols are used are listed after each definition.

A — coefficient of the "eddy" term in the schematic van Deemter equation: 148, 152, 192, 193, 195, 196, 197
constant in Pierotti's building block equation: 174, 175, 176, 177

a — katharometer constant: 85, 89, 90
gas cross-section of column: 141, 142, 144, 145, 147

$a_i(i = 1, 2 \cdots)$ — amount of solute i per unit weight of adsorbent: 206, 208

B — coefficient of the diffusion term in the schematic van Deemter equation: 148, 152, 192, 193, 195, 196, 197
constant in Pierotti's building block equation: 175, 176, 177, 179
bottom liquid: 117, 118

B_0, B_1, B_2 — bottom liquid in stage zero, 1, 2: 117

C — coefficient of the mass transfer term in the schematic van Deemter equation: 148, 152, 192, 193, 196, 196, 197
constant in Pierotti's building block equation: 175, 176, 177, 179
a factor depending on shape of the particles in flow through a packed bed: 147

C_{gas} — solute concentration in gas phase: 134, 135
$C_{liq.}$ — concentration of solute in stationary liquid phase: 134, 135
C_l — concentration of solute in moving liquid phase: 113, 114, 115
C_s — concentration of solute in solid phase: 113, 114, 115
c — proportionality constant for conversion of distances on recorder chart: 123
$c_i(i = 1, 2 \cdots)$ — concentration of solute i per unit volume of column fluid: 205, 206, 207, 208
$c_{1.1}$ — concentration of solute 1 in first flat of curve: 207

D — constant in Pierotti's building block equation: 175, 176, 177
diffusivity: 134

$D_{eff.}$ — effective longitudinal diffusivity: 132, 134, 135
D_{gas} — molecular diffusivity in gas: 132, 133, 135, 139, 152, 156, 193
$D_{liq.}$ — molecular diffusivity in liquid: 133, 135, 136, 139, 157, 160, 192, 193
d — distance on recorder chart (IG in Figure 1.4.): 123, 138
d_F — distance on recorder chart (IB in Figure 1.4.): 123, 138
d_f — statistical average of liquid film thickness: 133, 135, 136, 139, 157, 159, 160, 192, 193
$d_{gas} \atop d_{liq.}$ — distances travelled by solute in voids and in the liquid contained in the pores: 132, 133
d_I — distance on recorder chart (IA in Figure 1.4.): 123, 138
d_p — particle diameter: 132, 135, 136, 139, 147, 156, 193

E — eddy diffusion coefficient: 131, 132
out-of-balance voltage of Wheatstone bridge: 86, 87

E_Y , E_Z extraction coefficient$\left(E_Y = K_Y \dfrac{V_T}{V_B} \right)$: 118, 119

F, F' constants in Pierotti's building block equation: 175, 176, 177, 179
F_{gas} volume fraction of gas and liquid in column: 134, 135, 136, 157, 158,
$F_{liq.}$ 160, 192, 193

f^0 fugacity of pure solute: 171, 183, 184, 185, 186

G_s grams of adsorbent per unit length of column: 113, 114

H H.E.T.P.: 135, 136, 137, 139, 148, 149, 151, 152, 156, 157, 158, 195, 197
$H_{min.}$ minimum value of H.E.T.P.: 152, 193
H.E.T.P.   height equivalent to a theoretical plate: 67, 68, 108, 124, 130, 134,
                       135, 136, 137, 138, 148, 151, 153, 156, 188, 192, 195, 197, 199
[H.E.T.P.]$_0$ limiting value of H.E.T.P. for sample size zero: 124

I total bridge current: 86, 87
i current katharometer wire: 85, 86

K permeability of packed column: 62, 141, 142, 144, 147, 148, 193
K, K' pooled constants in Pierotti's building block equation: 175, 177, 179
k partition (distribution) coefficient equals amount of solute per unit
                       volume of stationary liquid phase divided by amount of solute
                       per unit volume of moving phase: 107, 117, 118, 120, 121, 122, 123,
                       124, 125, 135, 136, 138, 157, 158, 170, 171, 172, 173, 177, 178, 179,
                       183, 189, 193, 194, 199
k^0 partition coefficient at infinite dilution: 173
k' $k\,\dfrac{F_{liq.}}{F_{gas}}$ (equivalent to the extraction coefficient): 135, 136, 139, 157,
                       158, 159, 160, 193, 194

L length of column: 138, 141, 142, 143, 144, 145, 147, 193
l length of katharometer wire: 89, 90
m_A , m_B moles of solute A, B in solute band: 126, 127, 128, 129
m_i moles of solute i: 126
Δm_i overlap of elution curves: 126

N_{gas} moles of gas per unit volume: 170, 171
$N_{liq.}$ moles of stationary liquid per unit volume: 170, 171, 172, 177, 178,
                       179, 183
n total number of plates: 122, 123, 124, 125, 127, 128, 138, 171, 172, 194,
                       199
n' number of CH_2 or CH_3 groups in solvent: 174, 175, 176, 177, 179, 186
P total pressure above solution: 162, 170, 171
p mole fraction of vapor in carrier gas: 86, 88
                    ordinal number of plate or stage: 118, 119, 120, 121, 126, 127, 138, 139
                    partial vapor pressure of solute above the solution: 162, 170
                    pressure of carrier gas: 141, 142, 143, 144, 145
p_i pressure of carrier gas at column inlet: 141, 142, 143, 144, 145, 146,
                       147, 150, 151, 193, 196, 198

p_o pressure of carrier gas at column outlet: 141, 142, 143, 144, 145, 146, 147, 150, 151, 193, 196, 198

$\bar{p}$ average column pressure: 144, 145, 146

p^0 vapor pressure of pure substance (solute): 162, 170, 171, 172, 173, 177, 179, 183, 184

Q ionization cross section: 81, 82
                      total solute content: 113, 114

R gas constant: 171, 174, 179, 183, 189

R, R' alkyl groups: 174, 175

R_F retardation factor: 114, 145, 146, 194

R_t resistance of katharometer wire at temperature t: 86

R_{t_w} resistance of katharometer wire at its mean temperature: 85, 86, 87, 89

R_0 resistance of katharometer wire at standard state: 86

ΔR change in resistance of katharometer wire brought about by a change in temperature Δt: 86

$R.V.$ short for retention volume used in a general sense: 16, 28, 38

r_c radius of channel of katharometer: 89, 90

r_w radius of sensing wire of katharometer: 89, 90

T absolute temperature: 28, 29, 38, 171, 173, 174, 179, 183, 189
                      top liquid: 117, 118

T_0, T_1, T_2 top liquid in stage zero, 1, 2: 117

t_c temperature of katharometer wall: 85, 86, 87

t_g residence time of an inert gas in the column: 145, 146, 150, 193, 194

t_m mean temperature of carrier gas in katharometer: 85

t_w mean temperature of katharometer wire: 85, 86, 87

u linear gas velocity: 132, 134, 135, 136, 139, 141, 142, 143, 145, 148, 149, 151, 152, 156, 157, 193, 195, 197

u_i linear gas velocity at column inlet: 150, 151

u_o linear gas velocity at column outlet: 142, 143, 145, 150, 151, 193

V volume of eluent that has passed through: 121

ΔV small volume of eluent: 114

V_B volume of bottom layer in extraction vessel: 118

$V_{\text{eff.}}$ $V_G + kV_L$ = effective plate capacity: 172, 194, 199

V_G volume of gas in extraction vessel: 120, 121, 122, 123, 124, 138, 171, 172, 194, 199

V_{gas} gas hold-up of column (distance IO in Figure 1.4.): 16, 138, 145, 146, 171, 183, 192

V_L volume of liquid in extraction vessel: 120, 121, 122, 123, 124, 138, 171, 172, 194, 199

V_l ml of liquid per unit length of column: 113, 114

$V_{\text{liq.}}$ liquid hold-up of column: 138, 171, 183, 192

V_R retention volume (distance IG in Figure 1.4.): 16, 26, 122, 123, 138, 145, 146, 171, 194

V'_R apparent retention volume (distance OG in Figure 1.4.): 16, 138

V_{RF} final retention volume (distance IB in Figure 1.4.): 16, 138

V'_{RF} apparent final retention volume (distance OB in Figure 1.4.): 16

V_{RI} initial retention volume (distance IA in Figure 1.4.): 16, 138

V'_{RI} apparent initial retention volume (distance OA in Figure 1.4.): 16

$V_R{}^0$ limiting value of V_R as $p_i \to p_o$: 146, 183

V_T volume of top layer in extraction vessel: 118

V_t volume of gas emerging from column in unit time: 141, 142, 144, 145, 146, 147, 150, 193

v $V/(V_G + kV_L)$; $V_G + kV_L$ = effective plate volume (dimensionless plate "volume"): 121, 122, 126, 127, 138, 139

v_R $V_R/(V_G + kV_L) = n$ (dimensionless retention "volume"): 122, 123, 138, 139

v_1, v_2 volume of gas passed through column at break-through: 206, 207

w peak width at base (AB in Figure 1.4.): 17, 121, 123, 138

w_A, w_B peak width at base for solute A, B: 125

w_b peak width at base (AB in Figure 1.4.): 17

w_h peak width at half height (EF in Figure 1.4.): 17

w_i peak width at inflection points (CD in Figure 1.4.): 17

X functional group: 174, 175

$X_{\text{G.p}}$ concentration of solute in gas phase of stage p: 120, 121

$X_{\text{L.p}}$ concentration of solute in liquid phase of stage p: 120, 121

x mole fraction of solute in solution: 162, 170

       distance from column inlet: 141, 142, 143, 144

x_p $\dfrac{X_{\text{G.p}}}{X_{G.o}}$: 121, 126, 127, 138

Δx length of small section of column: 114, 134, 135

Y functional group: 174, 175

y mole fraction of solute in gas phase: 170

α temperature coefficient of resistance of katharometer wire: 86, 90, 91

       mass transfer coefficient: 135

       polarizability in Table 6.3.: 166

       relative volatility: 125, 127, 128, 129, 172, 173

$\alpha_{A.B}$ relative volatility of two solutes A and B: $\alpha_{A.B} = k_A/k_B$: 125

β temperature coefficient of the thermal conductivity of the carrier gas: 86

γ ratio of resistances in Wheatstone bridge: 86

       tortuosity factor: 132, 135, 139, 152, 156, 193

       activity coefficient: 170, 171, 172, 173, 174, 176, 179, 182, 183, 187, 188, 189, 190

γ^0 activity coefficient at infinite dilution: 171, 172, 173, 174, 175, 176, 178, 179, 183, 184, 185, 186, 187, 188, 190

ϵ $\dfrac{\Delta\lambda}{\lambda}$ = relative change in thermal conductivity: 86, 87, 88, 89

       fractional void volume of packing: 147

       $v - p$: 127

η	absolute sensitivity of katharometer: 86, 87, 90
	dynamic viscosity of carrier gas: 141, 142, 144, 147, 193
η, η_A, η_B	fractional band impurities (overlap of elution curves): 126, 127, 128
η_A	$\dfrac{\Delta m_B}{m_A - \Delta m_A}$: 126
η_B	$\dfrac{\Delta m_A}{m_B - \Delta m_B}$: 126
$\eta_A \approx \eta_B$	$\dfrac{\Delta m_B}{m_A} = \dfrac{\Delta m_A}{m_B}$: 126
λ	measure of packing irregularities: 132, 135, 136, 139, 156, 193
	thermal conductivity of carrier gas: 86, 88, 89
λ_{air}	thermal conductivity of air: 89
λ_t	thermal conductivity of carrier gas at temperature t: 86
λ_{t_m}	thermal conductivity of carrier gas at its mean temperature: 85
λ_0	thermal conductivity of carrier gas at standard state: 86
λ'	effective thermal conductivity: 88, 89
μ	statistical mean: 133, 134
	dipole moment in Table 6.3: 166
ρ	specific resistance of the sensing wire material: 90, 91
σ	standard deviation: 121, 122, 133, 134
φ	fraction of solute in moving phase = probability for solute molecule to be in the moving phase: 112, 113
ψ	$e^{-\epsilon^2/2p}$: 127

CONTENTS

Chapter 1

THE CHROMATOGRAPHIC METHODS;
GAS CHROMATOGRAPHY

The main purpose of this book is to deal with the various forms of gas chromatography, a group of physical separating methods that have aroused wide-spread interest in the short time since their introduction. Gas chromatography is principally used as an analytical technique for the separation, identification and quantitative determination of volatile compounds (gases and liquids) having boiling points up to about 350°C or even 400°C.

The methods have striking advantages: they are sensitive, rapid and simple in execution and with due care furnish accurate quantitative information with extremely small amounts of sample.

GENERAL ASPECTS OF CHROMATOGRAPHY

For a good understanding of the scope of gas chromatography it will be necessary to consider its place among the chromatographic methods and the relation of the latter to other physical methods of separation.

The word "chromatography" is at present used as a collective term for a group of methods that at first sight may appear somewhat diverse. Nevertheless, these methods have a number of common features, as we shall show below. All the chromatographic separations, for instance, involve the transport of a sample of a mixture through a column (or a physical equivalent of a column*). The mixture may be a liquid or a gas (vapor). The column contains a substance—the *stationary phase*—which may consist either of a solid adsorbing agent or of a liquid partitioning agent. The transport of the constituents of the sample through the column is effected either by a gas or a liquid—the *moving phase*. Owing to the selective retardation exerted by the stationary phase, the components of the mixture move through the column at different effective rates. They thus tend to segregate into separate zones or "bands"; the chromatographic procedures are designed to detect, characterize (and if necessary isolate) these bands at some point, usually at the exit of the column.

The chromatographic methods are founded on the distribution of the components of the sample over two phases and on a subsequent separation of these two phases. For instance, in gas-liquid chromatography—the main

* In "paper chromatography" the equivalent of the column is a strip of filter paper.

subject of this book—the volatile components of the sample are distributed between an inert gas phase (the carrier gas) and a stationary liquid. Similarly, in adsorption chromatography, we bring about a distribution of the sample over the solid adsorbent and the moving fluid phase. Phase separation in both cases results from the fact that the fluid phase moves along the stationary phase.

However, the principle just described (the formation of a two-phase from a single-phase system by some means, and the subsequent separation of the two phases) is the foundation of nearly all physical methods of separation. In liquid-liquid extraction, for instance, the two-phase system is formed by adding to the original liquid mixture an appropriate selective solvent (or occasionally two solvents), whereby two liquid phases result which, after having been intimately contacted, are separated from each other. In distillation the formation of two phases, the liquid and the vapor phase, is effected by the introduction of heat. Progressive separation of these two phases takes place because the vapor phase moves upward by a pressure gradient and the liquid moves down by gravity.

In view of such resemblances, which might be extended even further, it is difficult to define the chromatographic methods of separation solely on the grounds of the physical principles involved. Another basis must therefore be sought. It can be found in a common feature, present in the execution of all the chromatographic separations, and is embodied in the following definition:

Chromatography is a physical method of separation, in which the components to be separated are distributed between two phases, one of these phases constituting a stationary bed of large surface area, the other being a fluid that percolates through or along the stationary bed.

This definition may need some explanation. Its keynote lies in the word "percolates." In considering separation processes, such as distillation, solvent extraction, adsorption, extractive distillation, the number of moving phases enables us to draw a distinction between percolation and the other forms of execution, such as countercurrent operation. Countercurrent processes and percolation both may be (and frequently are) carried out in columns. If, however, this is done in the case of distillation, extraction, etc., there will be two phases moving in opposite directions in the equipment, and we may speak of a "countercurrent" system. The distinction between countercurrent and percolation processes has an important practical consequence. Countercurrent forms of distillation, etc., can be executed in a truly continuous manner, percolation (and hence also chromatography) is intrinsically a batch process. The difference becomes evident when we remember that a continuous process, once it has been adjusted to a steady state, yields products of unvarying composition at certain points in the apparatus; in percolation, on the other hand, the properties of the effluent change from the beginning to the end of the operation, as in any batch procedure. It is suggested that only processes in which two phases move in opposite directions through the equipment shall be referred to as countercurrent processes.* This definition of the term "countercurrent," of course, does not necessarily imply that the procedure is continuous: a batch distillation with a fractionating column is evidently a countercurrent process.

The implications of the above definition may be illustrated by a few examples. We might visualize a process in which a stream of liquid or gas is made to pass up through a column, and a continuous stream of some adsorbing agent is admitted at its top, falls down through the fluid and is removed at the base of the column. This procedure, though bearing a superficial resemblance to a chromatographic method, should not be classed as such, but as a continuous countercurrent separation based on adsorption. An example of the opposite type can also be given. Suppose that in a series of vessels each vessel is half filled with a certain liquid. A liquid mixture of lower density, only partially miscible with the other, is admitted through a tube into the bottom of the first vessel; it percolates up through the heavier liquid, thereby undergoing certain changes; it overflows through a tube into the bottom of the second vessel, and continues in this manner through the series, finally emerging from the last vessel.† According to our definition this procedure, also employing a flow of one phase only, might be described as a chromatographic method, or considered as closely related to it, since the second phase is stationary in the apparatus.

In the foregoing it was pointed out that the physical methods of separation have many points of mutual resemblance or analogy. To one of these, in particular, attention should be drawn. It may be referred to as the "effect of repeating an elementary step."

If, to take the case of distillation first, we convert a liquid mixture into a vapor and a liquid by introducing heat, the vapor will generally contain a higher proportion of certain constituents—the more volatile—than the liquid in contact with it. The separation will, however, seldom be anything like quantitative unless one of the components differs greatly in volatility

* There is some confusion in the literature in the use of these various terms. The term "percolation," with the meaning given above, has been proposed before (see for instance Thiele[1] and Klinkenberg[2]).

† A fully automatic procedure operating much along these lines, but with intermittent operation of the stages, was developed by Craig and co-workers[3]. It is usually not classed as a chromatographic method, partly in view of its history. An argument against doing so is the absence of the "large surface area" referred to in the definition. For further details on similar types of apparatus the reader is referred to textbooks by Rauen and Stamm[4], by Hecker[5] and by Röck[30].

from the others. The effect of a single equilibrium step of the separation (one "elementary process") is therefore often unsatisfactory. The separation may, however, frequently be improved enormously by a procedure that intrinsically consists in repeating the elementary process on the primarily separated phases. A very efficient way of doing this in distillation or extraction is to perform the process in countercurrent with the aid of a column provided with plates or packing, or in equivalent apparatus, such as a series of mixers and settlers in extraction.

The elementary processes underlying the chromatographic separations* are usually also inefficient. Here also a vast improvement is effected by using a column for providing a repetition of elementary exchanges. Even though one of the phases in this case is stationary in the apparatus, various analogies to processes such as distillation can then be applied, as will be demonstrated more fully in Chapter 4. It is characteristic of certain types of chromatography that even columns of moderate length have a surprisingly high number of equilibrium steps. However, as will be shown later, the number of steps required to effect a separation in a chromatographic procedure is larger than that required in a countercurrent process. Furthermore, theories for these types of execution differ appreciably.

APPLICATIONS OF CHROMATOGRAPHIC SEPARATIONS

If the preceding definition is strictly applied, certain industrial processes might be classed as chromatographic separations. An example is the improvement in color of a liquid by percolating it through an adsorbent (for instance a lubricating oil through a bed of fuller's earth), or the removal of a constituent from a gas by passing it through a surface-active solid (e.g., the separation of gasoline from natural gas by means of active charcoal). These industrial batch processes are nearly always confined to cases in which the component to be removed is a very small fraction of the total mixture. For separations involving constituents in larger amounts a truly continuous procedure is generally preferred in industry.

Industrial separations will not be dealt with in this book.

In laboratory practice, continuous operation is seldom essential, since large quantities of material are rarely involved. For separating components by physical means on a small scale, distillation, solvent extraction, etc., carried out batchwise, were formerly the most widely used processes. These

---

* The elementary processes of the two groups of separating processes may be identical. Thus the equilibration of a liquid with a solvent, when shaken together and subsequently separated, is the elementary process underlying both countercurrent solvent extraction and chromatography with liquid moving and stationary phases. The elementary process of adsorption chromatography with a liquid moving phase would be realized by shaking the liquid and the adsorbing agent together in a vessel and separating.

methods still retain their value for dealing with mixtures in appreciable amounts. They are now, however, supplemented by the chromatographic procedures, which can separate samples efficiently in quantities far too small for the other methods. The chromatographic methods have the further advantages that the separating equipment itself is simpler, that the operation is easier to control and that it is often considerably less time-consuming.

The main uses of chromatography in the laboratory are:

(a) as *analytical methods* for identifying the constituents of a mixture qualitatively, for determining them quantitatively, or for both purposes;

(b) as *research methods* for determining certain physical quantities, such as partition coefficients and adsorption isotherms;

(c) as *preparative procedures* for isolating components (or, in complicated cases, groups of components) from mixtures.

The first-mentioned application, in particular, has aroused a wide interest in chromatography during recent years, on account of the advantages already mentioned and several others that will be referred to later.

Chromatography has most of the general advantages of the physical methods of separation. As a rule they are carried out in such a manner that no constituents of the mixture are lost and no new substances are formed by chemical reactions.* Consequently if a substance has been isolated by one of these methods, it is almost certainly present in the original sample.

THE SUBDIVISION AND HISTORY OF THE CHROMATOGRAPHIC SEPARATIONS

Subdivision According to Phases Employed

In chromatography, as has already been stated, the components of the mixture are distributed over two phases: a *stationary phase* and a *moving phase*.

The stationary phase may be: (I) A *solid* having adsorptive properties. We then may speak of adsorption chromatography. (II) A *liquid*. Methods of this type are sometimes referred to as "partition chromatography". The liquid stationary phase is generally distributed over an inert solid support in order to give it a large surface for exchange.

The moving phase can be: (1) A *liquid*; (2) A *gas* (or vapor).

We hence already have four possible basic systems of chromatography. The names given to these systems have not yet been universally standardized; the nomenclature that will be employed in this book is one founded

---

* Aluminum oxide, for instance, would preferably not be used as adsorbing agent in chromatography on mixtures containing acetone, since it converts this compound into diacetone alcohol.

simply on the states of aggregation of the moving and stationary phases, respectively.* The four systems will thus be termed as follows.

I. Solid stationary phase
$\Bigg\{$
1. Liquid moving phase—"Liquid-solid chromatography" (L.S.C.)
2. Gaseous moving phase—"Gas-solid chromatography" (G.S.C.)

II. Liquid stationary phase
$\Bigg\{$
1. Liquid moving phase—"Liquid-liquid chromatography" (L.L.C.)
2. Gaseous moving phase—"Gas-liquid chromatography" (G.L.C.)

Subdivision According to Techniques

A further subdivision must now be made owing to the fact that each of these four methods may (at any rate in theory) be carried out by three different techniques. They are termed:

(a) Elution development.
(b) Frontal analysis.
(c) Displacement development.

A short description of these techniques is given below. In order to avoid duplication and the use of alternatives, the description in each case will deal only with the case of L.S.C., i.e., of a liquid moving phase and a solid stationary phase, the type of chromatography to which they were first applied. The reader will, however, readily be able to supply the alternatives for a gaseous moving phase or a liquid stationary phase himself.

Elution Development (see Figure 1.1, a). A small sample of the liquid mixture is introduced into the top of a column of a solid adsorbent. For the sake of simplicity the mixture is assumed to contain only two components, A and B, the latter being a substance that is more powerfully adsorbed by the solid than A.

After the sample has been taken up by a small zone of the adsorbing agent, we introduce a slow current of a liquid (the *eluent*) that is not adsorbed by the solid, or at all events is less strongly adsorbed than either A or B, in order to wash down the components selectively. The zones occupied by A and B originally overlap, but they travel down the column at different speeds in accordance with the strength of adsorption of the components. If the difference in the latter property is sufficient, the process ultimately re-

---

* This nomenclature is that recommended during the Symposium on Gas (Vapor Phase) Chromatography (London, May–June 1956), organized by the Institute of Petroleum (see Inst. Petroleum Rev., 10, 217 (1956)). It should be noted that the term "liquid-liquid chromatography" was originally used by Martin and Synge in their classical publication[24] of 1941 (see Table 1.1).

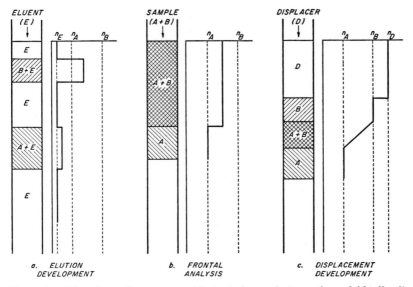

Figure 1.1. The three chromatographic techniques (schematic and idealized).

sults in an actual separation of A and B, in the form of "bands" of substance in eluent solution. The band of the solution of A is ahead of that of B and is separated from it by a zone of pure eluent. This state of affairs is illustrated to the right of Figure 1.1, a by a fictitious plot of the refractive index, which is here employed as parameter for characterizing the zones.

By admitting a further amount of eluent, the bands successively emerge from the column. If they are visible, as in the case of colored components or when using suitable indicators, the cut points may be determined by inspection. Otherwise some special method of detection is required; the determination of the refractive index might be used for this purpose here.

A drawback of the elution technique is that strongly retained components travel very slowly. This difficulty can be overcome by successively using eluents with an increasing affinity for the adsorbent or by "gradient" elution (Williams[6]).

Frontal Analysis (Figure 1.1, b). A liquid mixture is fed into a column of adsorbent, in this case during the whole course of the process, one of two components being again adsorbed in preference to the other. An adsorbate of the strongly adsorbed component will then be progressively built up in the column until the adsorptive capacity of the latter is saturated. In the meantime the other component passes through the column, and it continues to pass in a pure state until the strongly adsorbed constituent breaks through. From this moment on the mixture flows through in its original composition.

If more than one component of the mixture forms adsorbates, they break through in succession in an order depending on their adsorptivities, but with exception of the first component in impure form. The latter case will be discussed further in Chapter 8.

Tiselius[7, 8] and Claesson[9] have used this technique for analysis, by recording the changes in concentration as the fronts of material leave the column. The technique has hence been termed "frontal analysis." The impurity of all the bands after the first, however, detracts from its value as an analytical procedure. Its greatest usefulness lies in the possibility of segregating a powerfully adsorbed minor component from a bulk mixture.

The industrial processes referred to previously under the heading "Applications" are carried out according to this technique.

Displacement Development (Figure 1.1, c). As in method (a), a small sample $(A + B)$ is introduced into the column, and a current of liquid is subsequently admitted. Contrary to the liquid used in elution development, however, that employed here is more powerfully adsorbed than either A or B, so that it displaces these components and forces them down and, if desired, out of the column. The mutual displacement causes a segregation in the following manner, from bottom to top (see Figure 1.1, c):

(1) a band of relatively pure A, the least powerfully adsorbed substance;

(2) a small intermediate zone in which the composition changes from A to B;

(3) a band of relatively pure B;

(4) the displacer D.

The recovery of a part of both components in a fairly pure state is the feature distinguishing this technique from that of frontal analysis.

For analytical separations it possesses the disadvantage that the bands of constituents are not separated by bands of relatively pure displacing fluid as in elution development. Hence, if some property is plotted against the emerged volume we obtain a series of adjoining "steps,"* which may lie at different levels if the property observed differs in value, but sometimes do not and are then indistinguishable; in all cases, moreover, the boundaries between the steps are unsharp owing to the "overlap" zone.

The displacement technique is useful for preparative purposes, and for isolating a component in concentrated form from a mixture, with the object of submitting it to further analysis by the elution method.

The four basic forms of chromatography (L.S.C., G.S.C., L.L.C. and G.L.C.), together with the three techniques of execution (elution development, frontal analysis and displacement development), give rise to twelve possible ways of carrying out a chromatographic separation; some of these, however, exist only on paper or are of little interest.

* See, for instance, Figure 8. 6.

TABLE 1.1. CLASSIFICATION OF CHROMATOGRAPHIC METHODS
(Including names of investigators who have employed them)

Stationary phase	I. Solid		II. Liquid	
Moving phase	1. Liquid (L.S.C.)	2. Gas (G.S.C.)	1. Liquid (L.L.C.)	2. Gas (G.L.C.)
(a) Elution development	Tswett[12] (1906) Kuhn, Winterstein and Lederer[13] (1931)	Cremer[17] (1951)* Janák[14, 15] (1953/54) Patton, Lewis and Kaye[16] (1955)	Martin and Synge[24] (1941)	James and Martin[26, 27] (1952). Ray[28] (1954) Bradford, Harvey and Chalkley[29] (1955)
(b) Frontal analysis	Tiselius[7] (1940) Claesson[9, 10] (1946)	Phillips[19, 20, 21] (1953/54)	(Phillips[18]) (1952)	Phillips[21] (1954)
(c) Displacement development	Tiselius[8] (1943) Claesson[11] (1949)	Turner[22] (1943) Claesson[9, 10, 11] (1946/49) Turkel'taub[23] (1950) Phillips[19, 20, 21] (1953/54)	Levi[25] (1949)	

* First published by F. Prior as a thesis (Innsbruck, 1947).

These twelve possibilities are shown diagrammatically in Table 1.1, which includes the names of a number of investigators who have used the particular form of separation.

Though we shall be concerned only with a few of these possible forms, a brief history of chromatography in general may be useful at this stage, since the procedures to be discussed have been considerably affected by the others.

Chromatography was first employed by Tswett[12] in 1906, in the form denoted as "L.S.C., elution development," for separating components of plant pigments. Since he thus obtained discrete bands of colored material, he termed his method "chromatography" (literally: "color writing"). This name obviously became a misnomer when the methods were applied to colorless materials, but it is now so firmly established that it is irreplaceable. Tswett's procedure remained almost unnoticed for 25 years, and was actually rediscovered in almost the same form by Kuhn, Winterstein and Lederer[13], who used it to resolve plant carotene into its components. The further development of L.S.C. is largely due to the Swedish investigators

Tiselius[7, 8] and Claesson[9-11], who introduced both the frontal analysis and displacement techniques.

The adaptation of adsorption chromatography to mixtures in the form of gas or vapor (G.S.C.) is due to Cremer[17], Turner[22], Claesson[9] and a number of other workers from 1943 on and involved the use of all three techniques of operation. It will be more fully dealt with in Chapter 8.

"Partition" chromatography as a whole was introduced by Martin and Synge[24] in 1941 with the type using a liquid moving phase (L.L.C.), in a publication entitled "A new form of chromatogram employing two liquid phases." L.L.C. was further developed by Martin and his co-workers to a special form of the elution technique known as "paper chromatography," which has proved so fruitful in biological and medical research that Martin and Synge were awarded the Nobel Prize for this work in 1952.

The liquid stationary phase described by these investigators in their 1941 paper was supported in a column by a solid of large surface. (It was water-saturated silica gel.) In the same paper the authors announced the possibility of using a gaseous mobile phase with a similar stationary phase and specifically enumerated the advantages such a method would possess. A quotation from this part of the publication will clearly prove the insight and vision of these pioneers.

"The mobile phase need not be a liquid but may be a vapour. We show below that the efficiency of contact between the phases (theoretical plates per unit of length of column) is far greater in the chromatogram than in ordinary distillation or extraction columns. Very refined separations of volatile substances should therefore be possible in a column in which permanent gas is made to flow over gel impregnated with a non-volatile solvent in which the substances to be separated approximately obey Raoult's law. When differences in volatility are too small to permit of ready separation by these means, advantage may be taken in some cases of deviation from Raoult's law. . . ."

In spite of the clarity of this suggestion, other investigators were slow in following it up, a fact that may partly have been due to the prevailing war and the difficulties in the publication and circulation of scientific literature. The fact is all the more remarkable because G.S.C. was being actively investigated during this period, as will be seen from the dates given in Table 1.1.

Ultimately Martin, together with James, proceeded to elaborate his suggestion himself. The work was started in 1949, and the results were presented at the Oxford Congress for Analytical Chemistry in 1952[26]. This first application of G.L.C. dealt with "The Separation and Micro-estimation of Volatile Fatty Acids from Formic Acid to Dodecanoic Acid". The word "micro-estimation" stressed one of the characteristic features of the method: the very small size of sample employed.

Scope of the Book

We shall in this book discuss the two forms of chromatography using a gaseous moving phase: gas-liquid chromatography and gas-solid chromatography. Since G.L.C. has in general proved by far the more effective and versatile, and is preferable to G.S.C. except in certain special cases, it will be dealt with in considerably greater detail.

In the present chapter a preliminary outline of the two methods, their execution and some of their features will be given.

Gas-Liquid Chromatography

Gas-liquid chromatography has also been variously referred to as vapor-phase chromatography, gas-liquid partition chromatography, gas-partition chromatography, vapor fractometry and by several similar designations. The term G.L.C. will be retained in this book with a view to the classification developed in the preceding pages.

G.L.C. is almost always carried out by the technique of elution development.

The equipment normally used for G.L.C. is shown schematically in Figure 1.2. (Alternative arrangements are also possible.) It embodies a tube, which may be straight, U-shaped or coiled, generally containing a column of an inert solid, which merely acts as the support for the stationary phase, the latter being a liquid of low volatility at the temperature of the experiment. The stationary liquid can in some cases be a nonpolar

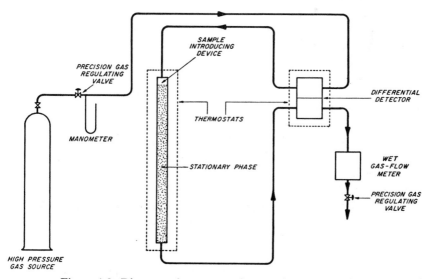

Figure 1.2. Diagram of apparatus for gas chromatography.

liquid, for instance a hydrocarbon oil, but in other cases a better separation of components is obtained by employing a polar liquid. Examples illustrating the choice of the stationary phase will be given in Chapter 2, while the fundamentals of its action will be considered in Chapter 6.

A small sample of the volatile mixture to be separated is introduced into the front end of the column by some device (shown diagrammatically in Figure 1.2). The column is maintained at a certain temperature and a constant current of an inert gas is passed through it. This gas is the eluent; it transports the components of the mixture in the form of vapor through the column, where they are retained by the stationary liquid to a different extent, so that their effective speeds of transport also differ, and they emerge from the column as individual "bands," separated by zones of the carrier gas. The composition of the effluent is "sensed" by a delicate detecting device, capable of indicating the presence of the components qualitatively and quantitatively.

The two main functions of the process and the equipment are: (a) the separation of the constituents of the sample, and (b) the detection and measurement of these constituents. The development of G.L.C. has been largely a matter of (a) discovering the most favorable operating conditions, stationary liquids and inert supports, and (b) developing adequate and sensitive detecting devices. Though these matters will be discussed fully in subsequent chapters, they may be briefly reviewed at this point.

The *separating* power of the column depends upon a number of factors, including the nature and amount of the stationary liquid, the particle size of the support, the uniformity of packing, the length and diameter of the column, the temperature, the nature, velocity and pressure distribution of the carrier gas, the properties of the components of the mixture to be separated in their solution in the solvent and the size of the sample. In analytical applications the latter is as a rule very small and varies between, say, 10 micrograms and 10 milligrams. The upper limit is determined by the dimensions of the column, among other factors. G.L.C. columns have high efficiencies, but the latter can only be effectively realized if the sample, after introduction, occupies only a small elementary section of the column. It is therefore of importance to employ small samples. The accurate introduction of very small samples gives rise to problems of its own. Liquid samples may be introduced by means of a micro-pipette, a capillary tube, by a hypodermic syringe through a serum cap or by crushing a sealed bulb; gases may be introduced by entrapping a measured volume and forcing it into the column with the carrier gas, and also with a hypodermic syringe.

The methods used for *detecting and measuring* the components in the effluent gas can be divided into two groups, which may be termed *integral types* and *differential types*, respectively. In the former some effect produced by a component in the effluent is registered additively; the elution curve (the graph showing the indication of the detector against the time or volume of effluent) in this case therefore shows a series of mounting steps, usually somewhat sigmoid in shape (Figure 1.3, a). A differential type of detector, on the other hand, registers some momentary property, usually physical, of the effluent gas. As the property reverts to that of the carrier gas between the bands of components, the elution curve in such cases shows a number of peaks on a horizontal base line. In G.L.C. these peaks are usually more or less symmetrical and approximate to Gaussian curves (Figure 1.3, b).

The integral detecting methods include the automatic titration of acid or basic constituents in the effluent, the volume of titrating fluid being recorded automatically. This system was employed by Martin and co-workers in their original work. Differential detection is at present more widely utilized. A detecting system that is very generally used is based on the measurement of thermal conductivity. Detection by thermal conductivity is usually carried out on a comparative basis. The detector then consists of two thermal conductivity cells—one for the effluent and one for the pure carrier gas (Figure 1.2)—the two forming arms of a Wheatstone bridge. This principle, which eliminates or minimizes certain fluctuations in operation, is also applied when using some of the other differential detecting systems to be described in Chapter 3.

The integral systems that have been employed allow the amount of the

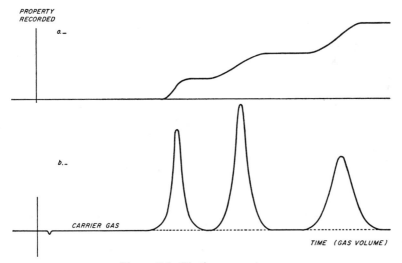

Figure 1.3. Elution curve types.

a.—Integral detection; *b.*—Differential detection (symmetrical curves).

components to be calculated directly. The majority of the differential systems, on the other hand, require calibration of their response for individual components, but when dealing with small samples are generally more suitable.

GAS-SOLID CHROMATOGRAPHY

The apparatus used for G.S.C. can in principle be almost identical to that employed for G.L.C., except for the fact that the column contains an active adsorbing agent instead of an inert solid impregnated with a liquid.

All three techniques—elution, displacement and frontal analysis—have been used in G.S.C. according to the object in view and the nature of the components.

Except in the case of components of very low boiling point, elution development in G.S.C. gives rise to peaks showing a marked asymmetry; they frequently have a fairly steep front, but a long, drawn-out "tail," a shape obviously unfavorable to sharp separation.* The reasons for this phenomenon will be given in Chapter 4. The asymmetry of the peaks is far less marked in the case of substances of low boiling point (e.g., hydrogen, nitrogen, oxygen, methane, carbon monoxide, etc.). Such mixtures are more readily analyzed by G.S.C., than by G.L.C., which is normally the more versatile method.

Displacement development, which is not easily realized in G.L.C. and frontal analysis, which is seldom employed in G.L.C., are both used in G.S.C. for the special purposes mentioned in describing these techniques.

ADVANTAGES AND LIMITATIONS OF G.L.C. AND G.S.C.

The phenomenal rise in favor of G.L.C. and G.S.C. since their introduction is due to their being rapid and reliable methods of separation, easily carried out with simple equipment, often only requiring milligram quantities of sample, and capable of identifying and measuring series of compounds that can frequently be separated only with the greatest difficulty by other methods.

A comparison of G.L.C. with G.S.C. and the other forms of chromatography shows the following points in favor of the first method.

(1) G.L.C. is at an advantage with respect to adsorption chromatographic methods because the elution bands are narrow and almost symmetrical, as opposed to the "tailed" bands characteristic of the adsorption methods.

(2) G.L.C. compares favorably with the chromatographic methods using a liquid moving phase because it allows of high flow rates and is hence

* See, for instance, Figure 8. 7, a.

rapid. High flow rates are possible because of the low viscosity of a gas, and permissible owing to the high rates of mass transfer from gas to liquid.

(3) There is a wide choice of stationary liquids for G.L.C. As was predicted by Martin, it is frequently possible to separate substances of equal boiling point by a proper choice of the stationary phase. G.L.C. shares this advantage with extractive distillation (as opposed to normal distillation).

An important feature of the methods of gas chromatography is that they can be converted to a considerable extent into automatic procedures. The design of reliable apparatus for this purpose involves a fair number of difficulties. Once these have been overcome, however, the procedures become so easy to operate that they are extremely suitable for routine purposes, even in the hands of personnel with limited training and skill.

Obviously G.L.C. also has its limitations. It is restricted to volatile substances. The vapor pressure of a component should exceed, say, 1 mm Hg at the temperature of the column, otherwise its rate of transport through the column will be too low for practical purposes. To increase the vapor pressure and rate of transport of components, the column may be operated at an elevated temperature. A limit to this temperature is set by (a) the volatility and stability of the stationary liquid and (b) the suitability of the detector for the temperature concerned (or the possibility of condensation if the detector is operated at a lower temperature). The upper limit imposed by the stationary liquid is at present about 300°C.

Although it has proved possible to separate individual components such as H_2, CH_4, C_2H_6, C_2H_4, etc., by G.L.C., this method is in general not suitable for the analysis of low-molecular weight gases, owing to the difficulty of finding a suitable solvent as stationary liquid. As a rule the vapor pressure of the pure components should not be much above approximately 1000 mm Hg at the temperature of operation. As already stated, the light gases constitute one of the few fields in which G.S.C. has an advantage over G.L.C.

DEFINITIONS AND NOMENCLATURE

Chapter 2 will discuss the use of G.L.C. in a number of typical, relatively simple cases where it is not necessary to go deeply into the theory of this process. As a preliminary to that and later chapters, a few frequently recurring terms will be defined at this stage.

Figure 1.4 schematically shows the *elution diagram* or *elution curve* obtained in G.L.C. for a single component (*solute*) by means of some differential method of detection. The horizontal axis is the *time axis*; at a constant gas rate it is also equivalent to the (gas) *volume axis*. The concentration of the solute in the effluent is plotted vertically; it is usually expressed in millivolts deflection of the recorder.

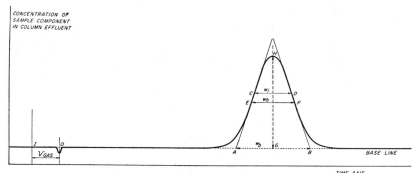

Figure 1.4. Quantities in elution diagram.

$$OG = V'_R \qquad IG = V_R$$
$$OA = V'_{RI} \qquad IA = V_{RI}$$
$$OB = V'_{RF} \qquad IB = V_{RF}$$

When no solute is emerging from the column, the recorder pen draws a straight line, termed the *base line*; the latter should be parallel to or coincide with the recorder's *zero line*.

At a certain point in time I (*zero time*) the substance is injected. A substance that is not absorbed by the stationary liquid breaks through the column at a moment 0. The interval $I - 0$, converted to a gas volume V_{gas} (and if necessary corrected for dead volume), is the *gas hold-up* of the column.

A component that diffuses into the stationary liquid and is partially retained by it travels more slowly than the unabsorbed carrier gas and emerges to give the more or less symmetrical peak shown. The length of time before its appearance, or the equivalent volume of gas, is the *retention time* or *retention volume* (*R.V.*). The latter is an important concept in chromatography. It can be expressed in various ways:

i) *Retention volumes*, referred to I.
  a) IG is the retention volume referred to the *peak maximum*, or center of the zone for a symmetric elution curve (V_R);
  b) IA is the initial retention volume (V_{RI});
  c) IB is the final retention volume (V_{RF}).
ii) *"Apparent" retention volumes*. These are measured from 0.
  a) OG is the apparent retention volume (V'_R) referred to the *peak maximum*, or center of the zone for a symmetric elution curve;
  b), c) OA and OB are the initial and final apparent retention volumes, respectively (V'_{RI} and V'_{RF});

Further important quantities are:

AB; the *peak width* at base (w_b or w);
CD; the *peak width at the inflection points* (w_i);
EF; the *peak width at half height* (w_h);
GH; the *peak height*.

These quantities are useful for comparing diagrams obtained under equal conditions. Factors, among others, on which they depend are the gas rate, the inlet and outlet pressures, the temperature, the nature and amount of the stationary liquid, and the gas hold-up of the column. Except for the peak height, hey are proportional in physical length to the chart speed.

In a great many cases distances and heights, as measured from the recorder chart, can be used for calculation instead of retention volumes (or times) and concentrations of solute in the column effluent, respectively.

REFERENCES

1. Thiele, E. W., *Ind. Eng. Chem.*, **38**, 646 (1946).
2. Klinkenberg, A., *Chem. Eng. Sci.*, **4**, 39 (1955).
3. Craig, L. C., and Post, O., *Anal. Chem.*, **21**, 500 (1949); Craig, L. C., Hausmann, W., Ahrens, E. H., Jr., and Harfenist, E. J., *Anal. Chem.*, **23**, 1236 (1951).
4. Rauen, H. M., and Stamm, W., Gegenstromverteilung, Berlin, 1953.
5. Hecker, E., Verteilungsverfahren im Laboratorium, Weinheim, 1955.
6. Williams, R. J. P., *Analyst*, **77**, 915 (1952).
7. Tiselius, A., *Arkiv Kemi, Mineral. Geol.*, **14B**, No. 22, 5 pp, (1940).
8. Tiselius, A., *ibid.* **16A**, No. 18, 11 pp, (1943).
9. Claesson, S., *ibid.* **23A**, No. 1, 133 pp, (1946).
10. Claesson, S., *ibid.* **24A**, No. 7, 7 pp, (1946).
11. Claesson, S., *Discussions Faraday Soc.*, No. 7, 34 (1949).
12. Tswett, M., *Ber. deut. botan. Ges.*, **24**, 316, 384 (1906).
13. Kuhn, R., Winterstein, A., and Lederer, E., *Hoppe-Seyler's Z. physiol. Chem.*, **197**, 141 (1931).
14. Janák, J., and Rusek, M., *Chem. Listy*, **47**, 1190 (1953).
15. Janák, J., and Rusek, M., *ibid.*, **48**, 207, 397 (1954).
16. Patton, H. W., Lewis, J. S., and Kaye, W. I., *Anal. Chem.*, **27**, 170 (1955).
17. Cremer, E., and Prior, F., *Z. Elektrochem.*, **55**, 66 (1951); Cremer, E., and Müller, R., *ibid.*, **55**, 217 (1951).
18. Griffiths, J., James, D., and Phillips, C., *Analyst*, **77**, 897 (1952).
19. James, D. H., and Phillips, C. S. G., *J. Chem. Soc.*, **1953**, 1600.
20. James, D. H., and Phillips, C. S. G., *ibid.*, **1954**, 1066.
21. Griffiths, J. H., and Phillips, C. S. G., *ibid.*, **1954**, 3446.
22. Turner, N. C., *Natl. Petroleum News*, **35**, R-234 (1943).
23. Turkel'taub, N. M., *Zhur. Anal. Khim.*, **5**, 200 (1950).
24. Martin, A. J. P., and Synge, R. L. M., *Biochem. J. (London)*, **35**, 1358 (1941).
25. Levi, A. A., *Discussions Faraday Soc.*, No. 7, 124 (1949).
26. James, A. T., and Martin, A. J. P., *Analyst*, **77**, 915 (1952).
27. James, A. T., and Martin, A. J. P., *Biochem. J. (London)*, **50**, 679 (1952).
28. Ray, N. H., *J. Appl. Chem. (London)*, **4**, 21, 82 (1954).
29. Bradford, B. W., Harvey, D., and Chalkley, D. E., *J. Inst. Petroleum*, **41**, 80 (1955).
30. Röck, H., Ausgewählte moderne Trennverfahren, Darmstadt, 1957.

Chapter 2

STRAIGHTFORWARD ANALYTICAL APPLICATIONS OF GAS-LIQUID CHROMATOGRAPHY

In a large proportion of the analyses encountered in practic , quite satisfactory results can be obtained in G.L.C. without considerir the fundamental theory. The majority of such analyses can be performeu adequately by applying a number of fairly simple rules and a certain amount of trial and error. The present chapter will deal with these straightforward applications.

Firstly, the factors affecting the procedure will be discussed generally. Some examples of actual separations will subsequently be quoted, in order to illustrate the measures adopted in solving individual problems.

There are, however, some non-analytical applications of G.L.C. and a few critical analyses for which a certain knowledge of chromatographic fundamentals is essential. The theory is treated in Chapters 4 to 6 and the "special" applications in Chapter 7.

A full description of the apparatus is given in Chapter 3. This subject is not discussed in detail in the present chapter, since the necessary equipment will often be available or may be purchased as a whole.

FACTORS CONCERNED IN G.L.C.

There are three main aspects to be considered in analysis by G.L.C.:

(1) The effective separation of the sample into its components;

(2) the identification of these components (qualitative analysis);

(3) the estimation of the amounts in which they are present (quantitative analysis).

These aspects will be discussed separately.

Factors Affecting the Separation

Column Dimensions. The internal *diameter* of analytical G.L.C. columns usually lies between 4 and 8 mm. The efficiency of columns having much larger diameters is lower per unit of length than that of columns within the above range. The diameter at which the adverse effect commences is believed to be about 12 mm; at all events the author has observed that the deterioration is noticeable at 20 mm I.D. and is considerable at 30 mm. Nevertheless, wide columns can, with certain precautions, be used successfully for preparative work or in separating fractions for further analysis[1a]. The efficiency of the column may then be restored by increasing its length or by other measures, which will be mentioned later.

The *length* of analytical columns may be anything between, say, 1 and 50 meters (3 and 150 ft). In very many cases a column of 2 meters (6 ft) will prove satisfactory. By increasing the length, the separating power of the column improves, but not necessarily to a proportional degree, because other operating variables (such as gas rates and pressures) are also affected. As will be shown later, we can express the efficiency of a chromatographic column in terms of "plate equivalents," as in the case of a distillation column. Doubling the length of a column need not produce a corresponding doubling in the number of plate equivalents.

All the same, an increase in length will result in an improvement, usually a substantial one, in separation.

The Inert Solid Support. The liquid stationary phase is supported in the column by an inert, size-graded solid which, when impregnated with the liquid, should not possess adsorptive properties towards the components of the sample.

The support originally used by James and Martin[1b] was "Celite", a diatomaceous earth; when graded as described by these authors it has an average particle diameter of about 40μ. Initially the same material (acid-washed and size-graded, or as such) was used by most investigators. For various reasons a very small particle size, as present in "Celite", may be expected to favor separating efficiency. It has, however, proved extremely difficult to pack a narrow column uniformly with impregnated "Celite". Investigations[2] have shown that it is permissible in many cases to employ a considerably coarser, narrow-grade solid; this has the further advantage of giving a much lower resistance to gas flow. Very good results are obtained by using narrow screen fractions prepared from ground fire-brick of suitable quality. Two types of fire-brick that have given satisfaction are Sterchamol No. 22 (a German make) and Johns-Manville fire-brick C22. The highest efficiency, viz., the best compromise between small particle size and absence of channeling, was obtained with 30/50 or 50/80 A.S.T.M. screen fractions of these materials. (Particle diameters: approximately 300–600 and 150–300 μ, respectively.)* A further narrowing of the screen fractions gives but a minor improvement.

The pretreatment of the support, its impregnation and the process of filling the column are described in detail in Chapter 3.

The Stationary Liquid. The stationary phase should be a liquid that is virtually nonvolatile at the column temperature. The liquid chosen depends on the composition of the sample. (As a rule the type of components likely to be present in the latter will be known before the analysis is started.)

* For certain limitations to the use of ground fire-brick see footnote on page 157.

There are two general requirements with which the stationary liquid must comply in order to function properly. It must firstly produce a differential partitioning of the components to be separated; secondly, it must have a sufficient solvent power for the vaporized components in question.* If the absolute solvent power for a particular component is low, the component will pass rapidly through the column and the separation may be poor unless the component differs widely in solubility from neighboring constituents and the sample is extremely small.

The second requirement, in particular, demands a certain compatibility between the stationary phase and the components. A useful practical rule is that, for an efficient, normal separation, the components of the mixture (the "solutes") and the stationary liquid (the "solvent") should preferably show some resemblance. For effecting separations according to boiling point in a homologous series we would therefore choose a non-polar solvent (say a paraffinic hydrocarbon) if the components are themselves little or not polar (e.g., paraffinic and olefinic hydrocarbons or ethers); an aromatic solvent such as benzyldiphenyl might be chosen for separating aromatics, a polar liquid such as polyethylene glycol for separating alcohols and amines, etc. Some solvents, however, have a wide range of applicability by virtue of their structure. The phthalic esters, for instance, can be used for separating a large variety of substances.

In Appendix I, a list is given of stationary liquids suitable for certain special purposes and of others that are more generally applicable. The list also contains some further indications that may prove useful, such as temperature limits within which the liquids can be used.

Departures from the above "rule of similarity" are frequently necessary if it is desired to separate components of about equal boiling points but of different chemical nature. A solvent must then be chosen that alters the position of a peak of one substance relative to that of another. As will be shown in several examples in this and subsequent chapters, the required effect can often be obtained by employing stationary liquids of different polarity. In the analysis of complex mixtures, giving rise to many peaks, interference is particularly liable to occur; it is therefore the rule rather than the exception that such mixtures are run over two or more different stationary phases.

A very marked shift in the order of emergence can sometimes be realized by using a stationary liquid containing a substance with which one of the

* The latter requirement may be illustrated by an analogy chosen from liquid-liquid extraction. For separating a mixture of a paraffinic hydrocarbon and an aromatic hydrocarbon, an excellent solvent on the basis of selectivity alone would be water, which shows a high preferential solvent power for the aromatic hydrocarbon. However, under normal conditions, the actual solvent power of water for these hydrocarbons is so low that impracticable volumes of liquid would be required.

solutes forms a loose adduct. An example of this type is found in a publication by Bradford, Harvey and Chalkley[3], who separated butene-1 from isobutene (boiling points -6.3 and $-6.9°C$, respectively) with a stationary phase containing silver nitrate. In this case butene-1 is selectively retarded by adduct formation.

The presence of *water* in a sample introduces complications in many cases.* Few stationary liquids are compatible with it; it is also frequently adsorbed to a certain extent by the support. Liquids such as a high-boiling hydrocarbon or ester have been found to be unsuitable for samples containing even small quantities of water. Diglycerol and certain polyethyleneglycols have, however, been used with success[4a]. In some cases it will be possible to remove the water prior to the analysis by some suitable treatment.

There are available numerous stationary liquids that can be used at column temperatures up to about 150°C. At present there exists a marked tendency to extend G.L.C., with all its advantages, to higher temperature ranges, say to 250 or even 300°C. This extension, even assuming thermal stability of the substances being separated, introduces a number of special difficulties.

(A) Practically all the normal organic solvents then become too volatile and/or unstable. (Instability is promoted by the catalytic influence of the support.) As far as the writer knows, certain silicones, Apiezon grease and bitumens are the only liquids suitable for temperatures above 250°C.

(B) In the case of polar liquids the selectivity for structural type decreases at high temperatures.

(C) In complex mixtures, such as petroleum fractions, the number of constituents increases enormously with the boiling point, and a resolution into individual compounds tends to become impossible.

For the last two reasons high-temperature G.L.C. will probably find less application as a self-supporting form of separation than that at lower temperatures, but will be used more as a means of providing fractions that are to be submitted to other methods of analysis, such as mass spectrometry. It is particularly in this field that wide columns, capable of dealing with samples up to a few grams and of furnishing fractions of appreciable size, will prove of value[4b].

The ratio of stationary liquid to inert support may in practice vary between about 15:100 and 50:100 parts by weight. "Celite" and the fire-brick fractions previously referred to can take up the latter quantity without becoming sticky. If the proportion of liquid is large, diffusion phenomena

---

* These complications appear to be less serious when employing radiological detection[14, 21] and other ionization methods, particularly the flame ionization detector (with which they are virtually absent); they are also circumvented in the procedures involving combustion to CO_2 or reduction to CH_4. (See the section on Detectors in Chapter 3.)

in the solvent tend to impair the separation, particularly at high rates of gas flow; at very low liquid ratios—say 5:100—the support may possess sufficient residual adsorptivity to cause tailing of the elution peaks. If large samples have to be separated it will generally be advisable to use a fairly high liquid ratio. For small samples (say up to 20 μl) the ratio can with advantage be reduced to 15:100. Under constant operating conditions the time of elution (or, more exactly, the distance *OG* in Figure 1.4) is proportional to the amount of stationary liquid. Furthermore, lower liquid ratios promote the establishment of equilibrium and hence allow higher gas rates to be employed. The use of a low liquid ratio, in conjunction with a small sample, therefore leads to a considerable saving in time, an important consideration in routine work. A small sample also has other advantages which will be mentioned later.

With proper precautions a column charge can be used for a very large number of analyses of volatile substances, often 2000 or more.* For a long life of the charge it is important that the column temperature should not exceed a value determined by its volatility and stability. Maximum temperatures are indicated in Appendix I for the various stationary liquids listed there. The need for change becomes evident by a decrease in the retention times of known compounds under standard conditions.

The Column Temperature. Changes in the temperature at which a separation is performed tend to affect the volatilities of sample constituents in the same sense. Small temperature changes give rise to but small alterations in the relative volatilities. A considerable increase in temperature, however, usually causes a definite lowering of volatility ratios. Though this effect is sometimes compensated by increased efficiency of the column with rising temperature, it is a general rule that separation is better at a low temperature.†

Usually the temperature is determined by a practical consideration: that is to say it is so chosen as to give a satisfactory time of analysis. As a rough guide it may be said that a temperature about equal to (or a few tens of degrees above) the average boiling point of the sample will be convenient and will result in an elution period between approximately 10 and 30 minutes.

For samples of very wide boiling range it may be desirable to increase the column temperature, either gradually or in steps, during the course of the

---

* See however Reference 10.

† This point may be illustrated by the following example. Vaughan[22] found the relative volatilities of *m*- and *p*-xylene to be 1.021 at 140°C and 1.035 at 60°C. In G.L.C. analysis a single peak was obtained for these two hydrocarbons at 140°C and one with a marked inflection at 60°C. Subsequent improvements in technique have made it possible to separate these isomers almost completely. (See Example G, this Chapter).

analysis. This procedure combines the advantage of a low temperature for the more volatile components, whereby a wider separation of their peaks is obtained, with that of a high temperature for the less volatile constituents, the latter measure resulting in (a) a shortening of the time of analysis and (b) a sharpening of the peaks (which broaden progressively with increasing elution time). If integral detection based on some property such as acidity, alkalinity or pressure increment is adopted, the temperature gradient may obviously be a gradual one. In the case where differential detection is employed, it will frequently be necessary to place the detector within the column thermostat to prevent condensation. The response of many forms of detector (including the katharometer) varies with temperature, and if an analysis is to be performed with an increment in temperature it is therefore essential to adhere to a fixed temperature profile and to calibrate under the same conditions. In practice two schemes for doing this have been followed. In the first, the temperature is increased abruptly to a predetermined higher level between two peaks by some suitable provision in the column thermostat. (When analyzing a full-range hydrocarbon gas containing methane to the C_5 hydrocarbons, for instance, the separation may be started at 0°C for the lower members, and raised to 60° for the elution of the C_5 components.) An alternative method, known as "two-stage chromatography"[29] consists in using two columns and detectors in series, the first being maintained at a higher temperature than the second. The lower components emerging from the first detector are also passed through the second column, where they undergo a better separation. The second scheme is to employ what is known as "programmed heating", by arranging for a definite, gradual profile of the time-temperature curve, for instance a linear course. The methods employed for establishing the stepped or gradual profiles in these two cases will be referred to in Chapter 3.

The stationary liquid and the column temperature together determine the relative volatilities of the components to be separated. The combined influence of the other variables is extremely complex and can be assessed to a sufficient degree only by considering the basic theory. Fortunately it is seldom critical within the limits so far suggested. The factors due to the carrier gas to be discussed below, however, are somewhat more important and need due attention.

The Nature of the Carrier Gas. The carrier gases most frequently used are nitrogen, hydrogen, helium and carbon dioxide.

From the aspect of separation in the column, nitrogen and carbon dioxide are slightly better than the two lighter gases, which enhance axial diffusion of the solutes, a factor lowering the efficiency. Considerations on detection and the quantitative interpretation of chromatograms, however, usually have a much greater weight in the choice of the carrier gas. Some systems of detection—including the widely used katharometer—are more sensitive with the lighter gases. In the United States, where helium is obtainable at low cost, this noninflammable gas has become very popular for G.L.C. Both hydrogen and helium simplify the quantitative interpretation of katharometer diagrams to a certain extent. In spite of its slight disadvantages in these respects, nitrogen is, however, still widely used.

Carbon dioxide finds its main application in integral detection systems involving a removal of the carrier gas by alkali. Hydrogen is used in detectors of the flame type.

The Gas Rate. In accordance with the usual practice, flow rates of the carrier gas will be expressed here in terms of the volumetric rate at the column outlet, measured at the pressure prevailing there and at the temperature of the surrounding air.

As will be shown in Chapter 5, the column efficiency depends upon the linear gas velocity, which itself is not uniform along the column. For a certain set of operational conditions there is an optimum linear gas velocity, but the optimum is very flat and the gas rate is consequently not a highly critical parameter.

The volumetric gas rate to be used depends on the column diameter, among other factors. The gas rates reported in literature as having been employed for columns of 6 mm I.D. range from about 10 to 400 ml/min. Very low and very high gas rates both adversely affect the efficiency of separation. A value of 100 ml/min. will in general be satisfactory in practice for columns of this diameter, but in certain circumstances a higher rate provides an effective means of accelerating elution.

For columns of different widths the volumetric gas rate should be varied in proportion to the squares of the diameters, so as to maintain the average linear rate at approximately the same figure.

Column Pressures. The required gas rate is obtained by applying a pressure difference between column inlet and outlet. The pressure at one of these points can be chosen at will. Frequently either the inlet or the outlet is allowed to ride at the prevailing atmospheric pressure; sometimes both pressures are controlled.

Good reasons exist for avoiding the use of very low outlet pressures. It is frequently believed that it must be possible in G.L.C., as in distillation, to transport a component of low volatility more rapidly at a low than at a high column pressure. This belief is in the main erroneous. As will be seen later, the rate of transport is roughly proportional to the pressure difference over the column, and only to a minor extent dependent on the absolute value of the pressures. For instance, the time of elution for a component, at atmospheric inlet pressure and an outlet pressure of 0.2 atm., will not differ much from the elution time at 1.8 and 1 atm. inlet and outlet pressures, respectively. Since the product of pressure and gas velocity is virtually constant along the column, the gas velocity will be more uniform at a low than at a high inlet-to-outlet pressure ratio (1.8 versus 5 in the above example) and it will be possible to operate the whole column closer to the linear gas velocity corresponding to optimum efficiency. Though it is not impossible to run a column efficiently at a pressure ratio of 10 or even more (see Chapter 5), the operating variables—notably the gas rate—become much more critical.

It is a virtue of the coarse-grained supports (mentioned on p. 19) that they produce low pressure gradients and low pressure ratios. With a support of this type, columns up to 20 meters long may be operated at a pressure drop of at most 1 atm. The best arrangement is then to employ atmospheric outlet pressure and 2 atm. inlet pressure. A pressure ratio below, say, 3 should at all events be aimed at. In the case of very long columns and columns containing a fine support this figure may be attainable only by using elevated pressures both at the inlet and outlet. In this manner Scott was able to operate columns with 30000 theoretical plates and more (see Chapter 7).

Columns with a low resistance can be operated without disadvantage at somewhat reduced pressures if desired. It has been claimed that the introduction of the sample by syringe becomes somewhat more reproducible at an inlet pressure below atmospheric. A low outlet pressure may, for instance when using thermal conductivity, also tend to improve the sensitivity of the detector.

Introduction of the Sample and its Size. The various techniques of sample introduction are dealt with in Chapter 3. For liquid samples the most commonly used method is by micro-syringe with a needle through a rubber serum cap. Another procedure consists in crushing a sealed ampoule in a chamber in the carrier gas supply; when introducing the ampoule the chamber is temporarily by-passed. The syringe method is extremely rapid and convenient; though it has been criticized on the score of being subject to systematic errors, it is capable, with experience, of dispensing minute samples with surprising reproducibility. For gaseous samples the usual technique is the displacement of a known volume from a calibrated chamber by the carrier gas.

If the narrowest elution peaks are to be obtained the method of introduction should be designed to bring the sample into the column in the most concentrated form, viz., into the shortest possible column section. The syringe method is very satisfactory in this respect.

Theory shows that the efficiency of separation in a gas-chromatographic column improves as the size of the sample is reduced. Together with the advantages stated (p. 22) this fact provides important motives for using very small samples. With a normal analytical column of 4–8 mm I.D. a liquid sample of 2 to 20 microliters (μl) and a gas sample of $\frac{1}{2}$ to 5 milliliters (ml), measured at atmospheric pressure, is generally satisfactory.

Exceptions do, however, occur. It may sometimes be necessary to estimate components present only in traces, for which purpose G.L.C. is extremely suitable. In such cases the use of a larger sample (say up to 200 μl of liquid) may be essential in order to obtain a sufficient response from the detector for the trace component. The resulting reduction in column efficiency may then cause a partial masking of small peaks by larger ones, and should then if necessary be compensated for by resorting to a longer column. As will be shown in Chapter 4, the size of the sample may be increased in proportion to the square root of the column length, so that doubling the sample would entail a fourfold increase in length. Other measures besides the latter that may be used, either alone or in combination, for dealing with large samples are increasing the column diameter and increasing the proportion of stationary phase to support (see pp. 21–22). The former of these two measures does not result in a higher concentration of the constituent, since it involves raising the gas rate in the same ratio. An increase in the amount of stationary liquid is therefore probably one of the best ways of dealing with the large amounts of sample necessary for the detection of trace components.

The Identification of Components

Under a definite set of operational conditions the retention volume* or retention time is characteristic of a certain component.

In many cases—particularly in routine work—the components present in the mixture to be analyzed will be known with fair certainty, and so long as conditions remain unaltered† the constituents can then be identified by a simple comparison of their retention volumes with those found in some previous analysis. The time axis of a constant-speed recorder chart can obviously be used for this purpose instead of a volume axis.

If there is less precise information on the constituents of the mixture, various methods may be used as aids in their identification. At present the

---

* In the case of small samples that are introduced virtually instantaneously into the column the correct parameter for use is V_R (i.e., the distance IG in Figure 1.4). Small variations in the size of the sample, in the manner of introducing it and a considerable deviation in the ideality of the solute-solvent system may cause slight fluctuations in this parameter. Often, however, the initial or final retention volumes (IA or IB) then prove to be constant. It will frequently repay the trouble to settle this point by a few experiments for a given set of conditions.

† As will be shown in Chapter 7, retention volumes can be converted to a quantity (the partition coefficient) that is dependent only on temperature. See also Littlewood, Phillips and Price[5].

principal of these methods are: (a) the method of adding a supposed component, (b) the method of logarithmic plotting, (c) the use of two detectors giving a different response, (d) running the effluent in the "Time-Of-Flight" mass spectrometer, (e) isolation and separate identification.

The Addition of a Supposed Constituent. If the sample is mixed with a pure compound that is suspected of corresponding to a certain peak, and a new chromatogram is run, the height of the peak will be increased if the supposition is correct, while a new peak (or break in the old peak) will usually be found if the two compounds are not identical. There remains, of course, the possibility that the substance added has the same retention volume as another compound already present, and thus gives a single peak with it. If any doubt remains in this respect, recourse may be had to experiments with stationary liquids of differing polarity; one or more of these will generally resolve the peak into two, or cause a break, if the compounds are not the same.

Special Plots of Retention Volumes. James and Martin[1b] showed in their original publication that for normal and iso fatty acids a plot of the logarithm of the retention volume (corresponding to the distance *OG* in Figure 1.4) against the number of carbon atoms yields an almost straight line, at all events above a certain chain length, in this case above about 4 C atoms (see Figure 2.1). As shown in Figures 2.2 and 2.3, Ray[6] and others have since then shown that similar relationships exist for several other

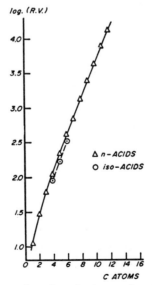

Figure 2.1. log (retention volume) against no. of carbon atoms. Column liquid: silicone/stearic acid; 137°C. (After James and Martin).

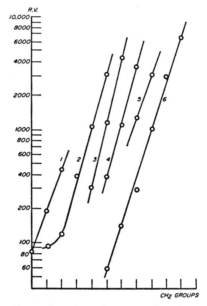

Figure 2.2. log (retention volume) against no. of carbon atoms. Column liquid: dinonyl phthalate. (After Ray).

1. Paraffins (n-C_5H_{12}—n-C_7H_{16})
2. Alcohols (normal) (CH_3OH—n-$C_5H_{11}OH$)
3. Formates ($H \cdot CO_2C_2H_5$—$H \cdot CO_2C_4H_9$)
4. Acetates ($CH_3 \cdot CO_2CH_3$—$CH_3 \cdot CO_2C_3H_7$)
5. Propionates ($C_2H_5 \cdot CO_2CH_3$—$C_2H_5 \cdot CO_2C_2H_5$)
6. Methyl ketones ($CH_3 \cdot CHO$—n-$C_5H_{11}CO \cdot CH_3$)

homologous series of organic compounds as solutes and a variety of stationary liquids.

Plots of this type hold for one set of conditions only. For conversion to another temperature use may be made of a linear relationship between log $R.V.$ and the reciprocal of the absolute temperature*, a relation equivalent to the well-known linearity of log (vapor pressure) against $1/T$. This holds satisfactorily for temperature ranges of 100°C or even more. A few of such plots, due to Phillips *et al.*[5], are shown in Figure 2.4.

Another very valuable form of graphic representation, also first employed by Martin[7] and co-workers, consists in plotting the retention volumes for one stationary phase against those for another. If proportional scales are used for both retention volumes, as was done by these authors, straight lines through the origin are obtained for homologous series of solutes (see

* Or, more correctly, between log $\dfrac{R.V.}{T}$ and $\dfrac{1}{T}$.

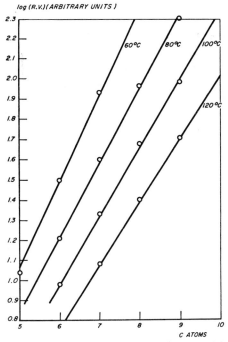

Figure 2.3. log (retention volume) of α-olefins against no. of carbon atoms. Column liquid: dinonyl phthalate.

Figure 2.5); the slopes of the lines are characteristic of the functional grouping. By plotting both scales logarithmically, as was done by Pierotti *et al.*[8], the resulting graph shows a series of almost parallel straight lines (Figure 2.6) and the intercepts are characteristic of the functional grouping.

The usefulness of such identification plots is limited by the fact that retention volumes change with the operational variables employed. A method of overcoming this difficulty is to express retention volumes as ratios with respect to those of certain standard compounds under the same conditions; for this purpose a number of convenient standard values determined under definite circumstances is required. The procedure eliminates the operational variables, except the temperature, which may be dealt with by the $1/T$ method already indicated. A sounder procedure consists in eliminating the experimental parameters fully by a complete correction of retention volumes[5] or partition coefficients[9], but such a calculation is somewhat laborious and will seldom be necessary in the cases considered in this chapter.

The Use of two Detectors giving a different Response. The relations between the signals given by the detector for compounds in the effluent gas depend, *inter alia*, on the principle of the detector used. If, under

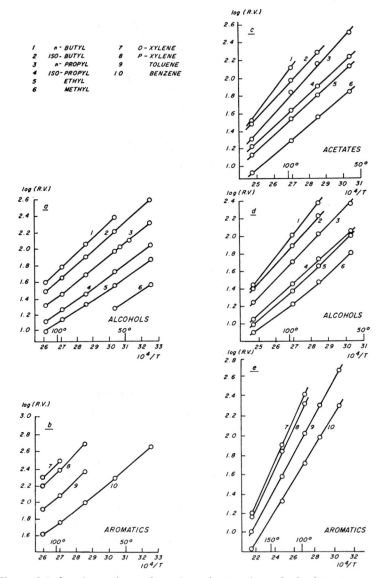

1	n - BUTYL	7	O - XYLENE
2	ISO- BUTYL	8	P - XYLENE
3	n - PROPYL	9	TOLUENE
4	ISO- PROPYL	10	BENZENE
5	ETHYL		
6	METHYL		

Figure 2.4. log (retention volumes) against reciprocal absolute temperatures. Column liquid for *a* and *b*, silicone 702. Column liquid for *c*, *d* and *e*, tritolyl phosphate. (After Phillips.)

otherwise identical conditions, two different detectors are employed, the elution diagrams may therefore show differences in the relative heights of the peaks. If the relationship between the responses of the two detectors in question is previously established by means of experiments with mixtures of pure substances, they may be utilized for purposes of identification. Grant[23] has shown that this procedure may be followed for mixtures of aromatic, paraffinic and naphthenic hydrocarbons, by comparing the chromatograms obtained with his flame emissivity detector (see Chapter 3) and a katharometer.

The Use of the "Time-of-Flight" Mass Spectrometer. If the effluent is run through the "Time-of-Flight" mass spectrometer, the mass

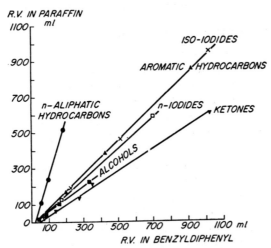

Figure 2.5. Retention volumes in benzyldiphenyl against retention volumes in paraffin. (After Martin.)

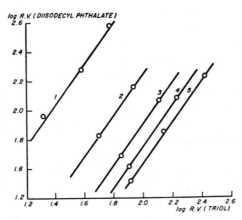

Figure 2.6. log (retention volumes) in triol against log (retention volumes) in diisodecyl phthalate. (After Pierotti *et al.*)

1. *n*-Alkanes; 2. Alkanones; 3. Tertiary alkanols; 4. Secondary alkanols; 5. 1-Alkanols.

spectrum of a component can be directly observed on the cathode screen and thus provides strong evidence for the identity of the component in question. The method will be more fully referred to in Example I at the end of this chapter.

Isolation and Separate Identification. Another method consists in condensing the relevant fraction by a cold trap and submitting it to identification by mass spectrometry; alternatively, the condensed fraction might be analyzed by other physical or chemical means, but in such cases it would be necessary to use a large column and a sample of appreciable size.

Quantitative Determination of Components

When the components of a sample have been identified it will usually be required to determine the amounts in which they are present.

With the integral detection systems so far used, an "absolute" property is registered; no calibration of the detector is then necessary and the amounts of each constituent can be calculated directly. This is the case when an automatic titrating device is used, as was done by James and Martin[1b, 7] for the estimation of organic acids and bases, and by Boer[10] for the determination of acids, bases, aldehydes and ketones, or when the constituents of a gas are collected over alkali, using CO_2 as carrier gas, and are determined either by volume at constant pressure (Janák[11]) or by pressure increments at constant volume (Van de Craats[12]).

With the more generally employed detectors of the differential type the methods of quantitative interpretation depend upon the system of detection used (see Chapter 3). In many of these systems the response of the detector will vary with the component to be sensed; in some of the others the response is stated to be either independent, within limits, of the nature of the components or predictable from their structure. An instance of the latter type is detection by β-ray ionization[14, 21].

We shall here mainly consider the use of the katharometer (thermal conductivity cell), at present probably the most widely used sensing device. This detector belongs to the first category mentioned above: its response varies not only with the amount, but as a rule also with the type of compound that is sensed. A quantitative interpretation of a chromatogram obtained with a katharometer therefore as a rule requires a procedure of calibration and hence usually involves the determination of chromatograms with pure components of the sample, either singly or as mixtures. For insuring results of the highest accuracy, calibration is always essential with the katharometer, on account of all sorts of non-linearities in its response. It is true that calibration can sometimes be dispensed with if the very highest precision is not required. With hydrogen or helium as carrier gas, the response of the thermal conductivity detector is much less dependent upon the nature of the components than with nitrogen. If these constituents do not vary too much in type, we can therefore sometimes omit calibration when using one of the two light gases. Calibration may also be omitted when using nitrogen with high molecular weight substances of similar type (for instance fatty acids).

The necessity of calibrating is not a serious disadvantage in dealing with regularly-recurring samples of more or less constant type. On the other hand, it involves a loss in time with incidental samples. Fortunately in such cases calibration can often be simplified considerably by the use of the "bracketing" technique, which will be described later.

The actual quantitative interpretation of a differential gas chromatogram is based either on the peak height or the peak area. The latter is fundamentally the more correct parameter. The height is very sensitive to variations in the operating conditions, particularly in the temperature; the area is mainly sensitive to changes in the gas flow rate.

The areas of peaks may be determined: (a) by cutting them out from the chart and weighing them, (b) by means of a planimeter, (c) by employing some automatic integrating device in the recording equipment (e.g., an integrator motor or a ball-and-disc integrator), (d) by one of several methods of geometric approximation. Among the latter methods one frequently used consists in multiplying the peak height by the width at half height ($HG \times EF$ in Figure 1.4). For various reasons the writer prefers (half) the product of peak height and the width given by the inflection tangents at the base ($HG \times AB$).

When analyzing gas mixtures, using the katharometer as detector, it is best to carry out the calibration with the pure components. This case has been discussed by Van de Craats[30]. Small quantities of gas—as opposed to small liquid samples—can be measured off with great accuracy (see page 67 and fig. 3.9). The use of mixtures for calibration is here not advisable, since it has proved difficult to prepare standard gas mixtures without introducing errors in composition. However, when employing the pure gaseous components, certain factors liable to cause discrepancies have also to be taken into account. These factors are:

(a) deviations from the ideal gas conditions of the (undiluted) gas sample;

(b) the so-called "surge" effect, consisting in an increase in the true flow rate due to the sudden transfer of the component from the dissolved state to the gaseous state at the end of the column, and resulting in a peak area smaller than that corresponding to the measured flow rate;

(c) differences between the viscosities of the carrier gas and the gaseous component, causing a departure from the normal rate of flow at the existing adjustment of the gas pressures or restrictions employed.

In the publication just cited a nomogram is given for correcting to the ideal gas state in the case of CO_2 and the hydrocarbons above methane. (The permanent gases and methane need no correction). Van de Craats further shows how the surge effect may be corrected for by calculation, and discusses the best method of regulating the gas flow rate for minimizing the viscosity effect*.

Sometimes calibration can be extremely simple. A case that is frequently encountered is the determination of a minor component—say an impurity—in a material. If it is possible to introduce a sample of sufficiently accurate size, calibration may be performed by preparing a few mixtures of the basic material with various amounts of the minor constituent (or by simply adding a known amount of the trace impurity above that already present) and analyzing these mixtures under the same conditions as the sample. The peak height or area can then be taken as a direct measure of the amount of the trace constituent.

Frequently, however, a quantitative evaluation cannot be done on an absolute basis, because it may be difficult or inconvenient to measure off the sample with sufficient absolute accuracy. (This is often the case when using the syringe technique for very small samples.) Two methods are then available for eliminating the amount of the sample: (a) the "marker" technique and (b) the "method of internal normalization."

The Marker Method. This method consists in adding to the sample an accurately known amount of a suitable pure substance (the "marker"); usually this is a compound not present in the sample. To simplify the explanation let us suppose that the sample originally contains two components A and B. For calibration we should then run chromatograms on synthetic mixtures of pure component A and the marker in several accurately known proportions, the latter being chosen in the neighborhood of the proportion that is to exist in the case of the actual sample. The ratios of the areas of the peaks for the marker and for A are now plotted against the ratios of the amounts actually present; this plot will frequently be a straight line over the restricted range in question. The same procedure will be repeated with pure component B. (In none of these runs need the size of the sample be exactly known.) The actual analysis, also with a known amount of marker in the sample, is then performed and the ratios of marker to component peaks are again determined. The composition of the sample can then be calculated. (The tacit assumption that the ratios do not change by the presence of more than one component is closely satisfied.)

The peak of the substance employed as marker should be situated near

---

* It should be noted that these three factors need not be taken into account in the methods of calibration with standard mixtures to be described in the following paragraphs, effect (a) being, of course, absent, while the results of (b) and (c) form a part of the calibration factors determined.

those of the components to be estimated, but should not overlap them. For reasons of accuracy the height of the marker peak should also not differ too much from that of the component of interest. Consequently, each component to be determined may require its own marker, though one marker may be used in favorable circumstances for two or even three constituents. The use of a marker for a preponderating component has the disadvantage that it causes an appreciable dilution of the sample and thus impairs the over-all accuracy.

For these reasons the marker technique should preferably be restricted to the determination of a few constituents only, occurring in amounts up to, say, 10 per cent in mixtures of not too complex a nature.

The Method of Internal Normalization. Let us first assume that the area under each peak is directly proportional to the amount of the component to which it belongs and is independent of its nature. We could then calculate the composition by adding together all the peak areas and finding the proportion of each area to this total. If hydrogen or helium is used as carrier gas this procedure may actually be adopted, provided a small range of closely similar compounds is involved and the highest accuracy is not essential. In other cases the peak areas cannot be used directly for calculating the composition, but must first be multiplied by factors depending on the components concerned, before they are added and proportioned. The factors must be determined by the preparation and analysis of a suitable number of synthetic blends made up of the pure substances in question.

Within moderate variations in operational circumstances and sample composition* the calibration factors may be taken as constant. Their determination, however, obviously requires considerable time and is mainly necessary where samples of similar type have to be analyzed repeatedly. For incidental analyses the procedure can be considerably simplified by using the so-called *bracketing technique*. In this technique an approximate composition of the sample is first calculated from its chromatogram by the total peak area method without applying calibration factors. Next, a synthetic mixture of this composition is prepared and analyzed under the same conditions. The peak areas are compared with those obtained for the original sample and the figures for the analysis are adjusted accordingly. If necessary, a second synthetic mixture is made and the final composition if determined by "bracketing" (inter- or extrapolation).

Modifications or combinations of the above-mentioned quantitative methods are often used in practice.

---

* The calibration factor depends upon the concentration of the component in the carrier gas, hence, for a large range of concentrations the calibration factor cannot be a constant (see also Chapter 3).

Examples of Analyses by G.L.C.

The examples of separations given in the remaining part of this chapter were taken from literature or from experimental material collected by the author and his colleagues in Europe and the United States. It should be noted that in most cases the results do not correspond to the attainable optimum; the experimental conditions adopted were usually just a convenient set that gave the desired separation. Many of the examples were chosen from the petroleum and petrochemical industries. Since the mixtures encountered in this field are among the most complex and difficult to resolve, this choice of examples probably covers a wide field of applications.

Example A—Separation of Ammonia and the Methylamines

This example is of classical interest, because it was one of the first problems attacked by James and Martin[15]. The analytical separation of ammonia from the methylamines is of great importance in biochemistry and formerly constituted a difficult task.

James and Martin employed various stationary liquids on kieselguhr, and made use of automatic titration with $0.04N$ H_2SO_4 and methyl red solution as the indicator. Figure 2.7 shows the results obtained with three stationary liquids. Two of these are mixtures in different proportions of the polar liquid hendecanol (5-ethylnonan-2-ol) and liquid paraffin (non-polar). These separations were carried out in a 4-ft column of 4 mm I.D.; other experimental conditions stated in the paper are shown in the Figure. The third stationary liquid was the highly polar substance glycerol.

Curve B was derived from curve A and shows how an integral trace may be converted into a differential one by plotting the tangents of the slopes*.

The three figures form a very good illustration of how the order of elution in G.L.C. may be modified by the polarity of the stationary phase. Eighty-five per cent hendecanol-15 per cent liquid paraffin, a mixture of relatively low polarity, gives an elution, with negligible overlap, in the order of boiling points, viz.: ammonia (b.p. $-33.4°C$), monomethylamine (b.p. $-6.5°C$), trimethylamine (b.p. $+3.5°C$), dimethylamine (b.p. $+7.4°C$). With the less polar 50–50 mixture of the two liquids as stationary phase the tri- and dimethylamines coincide, while with glycerol the order becomes trimethylamine— (dimethylamine + ammonia) —monomethylamine.

James and Martin in their paper give an interpretation of these changes

---

* It will be observed that the somewhat diffuse steps for the methylamines in the integral curve, observed experimentally, do not allow of a very close quantitative estimation. The peaks of the derived differential curve, however, appear fairly definite. This fact strengthens the view that direct differential detection allows of a more precise quantitative determination than integral detection in cases where the separation of components is not perfect.

in order of elution, which repays reading. As the theory of solution behavior
—dealt with more fully in Chapter 6—seldom allows of a fully quantitative
treatment, Martin's interpretation is of a qualitative nature.

Eighty-five per cent hendecanol-15 per cent liquid paraffin thus gives a

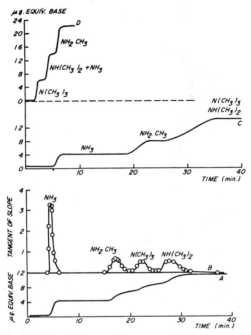

Figure 2.7. Separation of Ammonia, mono-, tri- and dimethyl amines.

A.: Experimental. Column liquid: hendecanol—15% liquid paraffin (v/v); column
length, 4 ft.; column temp., 78.6°C; nitrogen flowrate, 5 ml/min.; nitrogen pressure,
65 mm Hg.

B. Obtained by differentiation of *A*.

C. Column liquid: hendecanol—liquid paraffin 50–50 v/v; temp. 78.6°C; carrier
gas N₂ , 3.6 ml/min.

D. Column liquid: glycerol; temp. 100°C; 4.0 ml N₂/min. (After James *et al.*)

TABLE 2.1. SEPARATION OF NITROGEN BASES ACCORDING TO JAMES AND MARTIN

For Samples Containing the Following Components				Suitable Stationary Phase
NH₃	CH₃ NH₂	(CH₃)₂NH	(CH₃)₃N	
×	×	×		50% Hendecanol-50% liq. par.
×	×	×	×	85% " -15% " "
×	×		×	Hendecanol
	×	×	×	Glycerol

reasonable, if somewhat critical separation of the four nitrogen bases. The results of the authors demonstrate that a better spacing of the steps may be obtained, in cases where only three of the components are present, by the stationary liquids indicated in Table 2.1.

More cases in which the order of elution is influenced by the nature of the stationary phase will be mentioned in this book. (See also Adlard[4a] and Keulemans[16].)

Example B—Determination of High-boiling Material in a Volatile Product

This example firstly deals with the analysis of a hydrocarbon mixture consisting mainly of C_6 to C_8 α-olefins, intended as base material for syntheses in the petrochemical industry. The mixture was made by a cracking process, a refining treatment and a final fractional distillation. The C_6 to C_8 olefins boil between 55 and 120°C; an important clause in the specification was that the finished product should contain less than 0.5 per cent of material boiling above 140°C, constituted by heavy fractions passing over in the final distillation, and primarily consisting of C_9-olefins.

Previously the determination of "heavy ends" had been carried out by distillation. The bulk of the low-boiling hydrocarbons was removed by a reversed distillation and the high-boiling contaminants by sharp rectification of the residue to 140°C. This operation was laborious and lengthy; it was therefore decided to replace it by G.L.C. analysis.

Figure 2.8 is an elution diagram obtained on a particular sample of the material. It shows three main peaks and two smaller ones for contaminants. The three large peaks could be assumed to correspond to hexene-1, heptene-1 and octene-1; the correctness of this assumption was confirmed in several ways. A plot of log $(R.V.)$ against the number of carbon atoms gave a straight line and at the same time indicated that peaks A and E corresponded to pentene-1 and nonene-1. Further confirmation was obtained by running a number of synthetic blends at various temperatures; plots of the logarithm of retention volumes against carbon numbers and values of $1/T$ for these runs are shown in Figures 2.3 and 2.9, respectively.

The main interest was centered in the nonene fraction. By running a sample to which 1 per cent of nonene-1 had been added, it was found that the new nonene peak became 1.7 times as high as before (as shown by the full line in Figure 2.8); the heights of the other peaks remained the same. By simple proportionality, the original sample must have contained 1.4 per cent of nonene-1.

This result was in disagreement with that of distillation analysis, which repeatedly gave a figure of 0.6 per cent for the heavy ends. By submitting the two fractions removed in this distillation to G.L.C. it could be shown that more than half of the nonene was entrained by the distillate, so that the earlier form of analysis was quite unreliable. The total of nonene in the three distillation fractions corresponded accurately to the value of 1.4 per cent found for the whole.

Analysis by G.L.C. has now been adopted for routine purposes in this

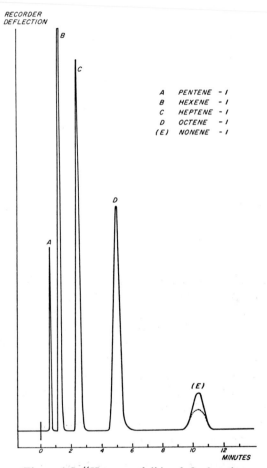

Figure 2.8. "Heavy ends" in olefin fraction.

Column: 1800 mm x 6 mm diam. coiled copper tubing; 50.1 ml; column material: 24.4 grams dinonyl phthalate on 30/50 mesh (ASTM) ground fire-brick (30/100 wt/wt). d fire-brick = 2.17, d 20/4 DNP = 0.969; carrier gas: nitrogen; pressures: 787 mm Hg at column inlet, 655 mm Hg at column outlet; gas rate: 30 ml in 24.6 sec. (measured with wet gasmeter at 24°C); column temp. (oil thermostat): 100°C; detection: thermal conductivity, 100 mA total bridge current; chart speed: 12″/h; recorder: 2.5 mV full scale deflection.

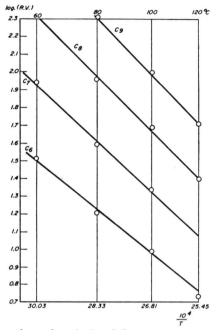

Figure 2.9. log (retention volume) of α-olefins against reciprocal absolute temperatures.

application. A sample of standard size (100 μl) is employed. The elution curve is compared to curves obtained under the same conditions with standard mixtures containing 0 to 5 per cent of nonene; the latter show a perfectly straight line for peak heights against concentration. A G.L.C. run takes 20 minutes, as against 10 hours for the distillation analysis.

Analysis by G.L.C. has proved to be applicable to several similar "heavy end" problems encountered in the petrochemical industry. Two such cases are: (1) The determination of trichloroethane and tetrachloroethanes present as contaminants in dichloroethane. (2) The determination of C_9 aromatics in xylenes. These two analyses could be carried out by a method essentially the same as that used in the first case.

Example C—Separation of C_1–C_7 saturated hydrocarbons.

In the petroleum industry various catalytic reforming processes are used to improve the octane rating of low-quality gasolines by converting straight-chain paraffins and saturated cyclic hydrocarbons into olefins, branched paraffins and aromatics. In the analysis of these reformates it has proved to be convenient to determine aromatics and olefins by displacement liquid-adsorption chromatography over silica gel. The analysis of the remain-

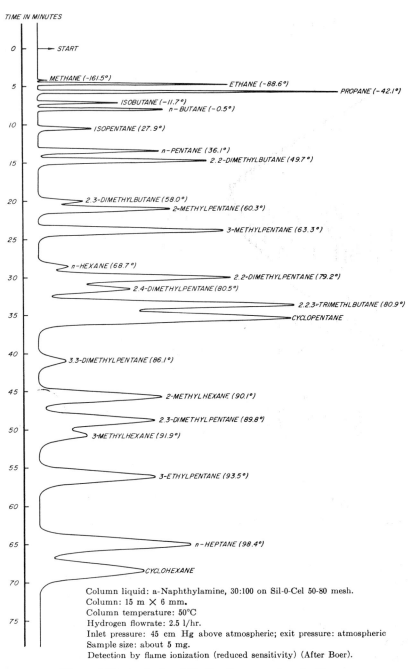

Figure 2.10. Analysis of C_1-C_7 alkanes and cycloalkanes.

ing saturates, particularly that of the branched chain paraffins, was formerly cumbersome. Only with the aid of very sharp analytical rectification, combined with analysis by infra-red spectroscopy, could satisfactory results be obtained. For this purpose the chromatographic removal of aromatics and olefins had to be carried out on a considerable scale in order to obtain a sufficiently large fraction of saturates for the analytical rectification.

Fig. 2.10 shows how the advent of G.L.C. has changed the situation completely. The chromatogram in question was obtained by Boer[24] on a synthetic mixture of practically all saturated hydrocarbons from C_1 to C_7. Although we are today perhaps no longer impressed by the possibility of separating such a mixture, it is certainly remarkable that it can be carried out in so short a time on a product covering a boiling range of about 250°C. The success is largely due to the choice of α-naphtylamine as the column liquid. The solubility of saturated hydrocarbons in this solvent is low and good separations will therefore usually require the use of small samples. Fortunately the development of very sensitive gas detectors no longer prevents the use of samples even in the microgram range. The low retention times of the higher-boiling paraffins should further be noted as well as the relatively high retention of the cycloparaffins; cyclopentane is retained even longer than the C_7 alkane 2.2.3-trimethylbutane.

As might be expected, the use of a single column temperature (50°C) considerably above the boiling point of the lowest component causes a certain crowding of the most volatile constituents. This is, however, to some extent compensated by the wide difference in the boiling points of these light components. For the purpose in view, the accuracy with which the latter could be determined was amply sufficient.

In this analysis the flame-ionization detector (Chapter 3) was used. The extremely high sensitivity of this detector had to be considerably reduced because the presence of very volatile substances made it difficult to introduce small enough samples. In Chapter 7 the problem of introducing samples of microgram size into hyper-efficient columns will be discussed.

Example D—Analysis of Oxidation Products of Hydrocarbons

The analysis was required of a product obtained in the petrochemical industry by the oxidation of propene. It was known to contain oxygenated compounds ranging in boiling point from acetaldehyde (b.p. 20.2°C) to allyl alcohol (b.p. 97.1°C). In order that these strongly polar substances should be eluted approximately in the order of boiling points, a highly polar stationary liquid was selected, namely, triethylene glycol; the support was "Celite."

Figure 2.11 shows the curve obtained on two samples with a column temperature of 99°C, whereby elution up to allyl alcohol was completed within

		b.p. °C	FULL LINE % wt	DOTTED LINE % wt
A	ACETALDEHYDE	20.2	4.5	9.7
B	ACROLEIN	52.4	37.7	48.8
C	ISOPROPYL ALCOHOL	82.4	3.7	6.1
D	ALLYL ALCOHOL	97.1	46.5	26.4

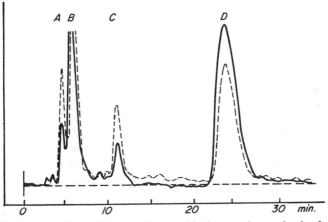

Figure 2.11. Separation of hydrocarbon oxidation products obtained under two sets of reaction conditions. Column liquid: triethylene glycol; column temp.: 99°C; nitrogen flow: ca. 35 ml/min.

30 minutes. The peaks for the major components (acetaldehyde, acrolein, isopropyl alcohol and allyl alcohol) are wholly or partly resolved, but there are evidently a number of minor constituents present.

As the relatively high temperature maintained in this run impaired the resolution of the low-boiling components, and the identification of the main trace constituents in this range was desired, the front end of the separation was repeated at a temperature of 43°C with the same stationary phase. In this experiment a larger sample was taken in order to obtain a higher absolute response for the isolated lower peaks. The resulting elution curve is reproduced in Figure 2.12. The small peaks occurring before acetaldehyde proved to belong to a number of C_4 to C_7 unsaturated hydrocarbons, which had been displaced to the front end of the elution curve by reason of their large difference in polarity with respect to the stationary liquid.

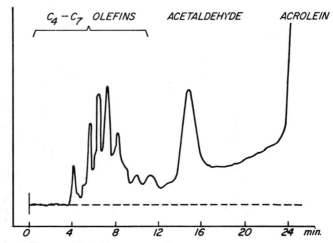

Figure 2.12. Front end of Figure 2.11. Column liquid: triethylene glycol; column temp.: 43°C; nitrogen flow: ca. 12 ml/min.

A direct identification of these peaks—by efflux times or the addition of pure components—would have been difficult or impossible. By condensing fractions before and between the major peaks in a liquid nitrogen trap and submitting these fractions to mass-spectrometric analysis, it was possible to identify about fifteen trace constituents. More might undoubtedly have been recognized, if necessary, by collecting narrower bands for analysis, or by using various stationary phases of different polarity for separating (and possibly refractionating) the components.

Example E—The Combination of a Chemical Reactor with Analytical Apparatus

Kokes, Tobin and Emmett[17] have described an ingenious combination of a reactor with analytical equipment, which they employed for studying catalytic processes. The reactor was connected to the top of a chromatographic column; a small amount of a reaction mixture was injected into a current of carrier gas, which transported it through the reaction vessel and into the column. (For the study of hydrocarbon cracking reactions the latter contained dioctyl phthalate on "Celite.") By placing a flow-type Geiger counter in series with the chromatographic column and thermal conductivity detector the apparatus was also made suitable for experiments with radioactive tracers.

Figure 2.13 gives an example of the results. It shows the trace obtained from the G.L.C. detector (dotted line) together with the radioactive record (full line) on passing a 50/50 mixture of radioactive ethene and inactive propene in a current of hydrogen over a cracking catalyst at 400°C. The record clearly indicates that some of the radioactive ethene had entered into the formation of C_4, C_5 and C_9 polymerization products.

As the authors point out, numerous applications of such a microtechnique are possible. The catalyst chamber may be replaced by an empty tube for thermal reactions or reactions in the presence of radiation. The apparatus could be adapted to high-pressure experiments. It may therefore prove very valuable for fundamental work on reaction mechanisms of various types.

An important feature of the combination is that it opens up possibilities for getting information about substances which, owing to their low volatility, cannot be run directly on the gas chromatograph, but can if they are cracked beforehand. The information will be much like that obtained with the mass spectrograph, which, after all, examines a somewhat different cracking pattern. The combination of reactor and chromatograph was used by Keulemans and Voge[25] for the analysis of naphthenes in the gasoline range. In this case the micro-reactor was charged with a "platforming" catalyst (a gasoline cracking and conversion catalyst containing platinum). At a temperature of 300°C cyclohexanes are converted into the corresponding aromatics; the conversion is practically complete, whereas the cyclopentane derivatives do not react under these conditions. By the appropriate choice of a column liquid the aromatics are so much retarded with respect to the

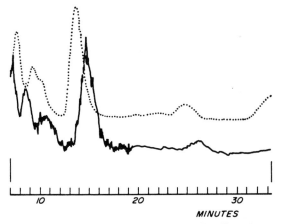

MINUTES

Figure 2.13. Part of chromatogram (dashed line) and radioactive record (solid line) of the products formed when a mixture of 8 cc of radioactive ethylene and 8 cc of non-radioactive propylene was injected into a stream of hydrogen carrying gas and passed over 1 cc of cracking catalyst at about 400°C. The peaks corresponding to the various products and reactants are displaced to as much as 1 minute longer time than the peaks on the dashed line because of several details of operation. (After Kokes, Tobin and Emmett.)

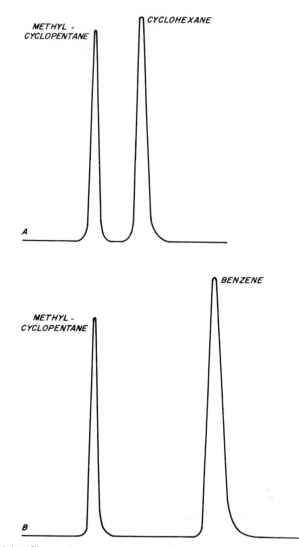

Figure 2.14. Chromatograms of methylcyclopentane-cyclohexane mixture: A. Without reactor. B. After passage over catalyst. (Stationary phase: Octoil S; temperature 80°C.)

naphthenes that a complete separation between these two classes of substances results. Fig. 2.14 shows the principle of this analysis by giving corresponding chromatograms for a mixture of methylcyclopentane and cyclohexane A) as such, and B) after passage over the catalyst. In the same study it is shown how the combination can be used to obtain a rapid survey of reaction kinetics.

Example F—Analysis of Lacquer Solvents

Whitham[18] chose the field of solvent analysis for illustrating how G.L.C. saves time in the technical laboratory and allows previously insoluble problems to be dealt with. The determinations of the main components of a lacquer solvent might require anything up to four months with the conventional techniques of distillation, organic group analysis and spectroscopy, and the reliability would be lower than with G.L.C. Minor constituents might perhaps not be determinable by the conventional techniques.

A lacquer solvent could consist of a blend of hydrocarbons, alcohols, ketones and other oxygenated compounds. In the case of a completely unknown sample the procedure described by Whitham is commenced by carrying out a few routine tests, such as those for distillation range, acid, saponification and carbonyl values, active hydrogen and any other properties deemed necessary. Next, a type separation by liquid-solid chromatography, using the fluorescent indicator adsorption analysis technique (F.I.A.) developed by Ellis and Le Tourneau[9], is performed. This procedure consists in displacing a 0.5–1 ml sample down a narrow column packed with silica gel, employing for instance *n*-butylamine as displacer, whereby the material separates into paraffins, (olefins), aromatics and oxygenated components (plus compounds of similar adsorptive affinity). By adding a trace of a dye mixture to the sample the various zones become visible when irradiated with ultraviolet light. Quantitative estimation to approximately 1 per cent of the original sample is possible by measuring the lengths of the various zones.

For cases in which the amount of sample was limited, Whitham modified the analytical F.I.A. column in such a way that the various zones could be collected, the small overlaps being rejected. Better results were obtained with larger samples in proportionally enlarged F.I.A. columns.

The fractions obtained by L.S.C. were now further analyzed by G.L.C. Two G.L.C. units were used, one on the normal analytical scale (6 mm I.D.) taking samples of 5 to 40 μl, and a second of 12–15 mm I.D. for dealing with samples of 0.1 to 2 ml. The latter unit was provided with a manifold trap system for isolating constituents to be identified. Quantitative estimation was performed by one of the techniques already described, i.e., component addition (which also provides identification), marker addition or normalization of peak areas, or by a combination of these methods.

Figures 2.15 a, b and c/d show the G.L.C. traces for the paraffinic, aromatic and oxygen-containing fractions of the F.I.A. separation, respectively. The paraffin fraction was run over dinonyl phthalate as stationary phase. The trace corresponds to that of the saturated portion of a petroleum distillate boiling between 65 and 95°C. The curve for aromatics revealed the presence of benzene, toluene and a trace of xylene. Most of the oxy-

	a	b	c	d
COLUMN TEMP., °C	80	140	100	100
STATIONARY LIQUID	DINONYL PHTHALATE	DINONYL PHTHALATE	PARAFFIN	POLYETHYLENE GLYCOL
NITROGEN FLOW, AT INLET, l/h	1.0	1.0	1.0	1.0

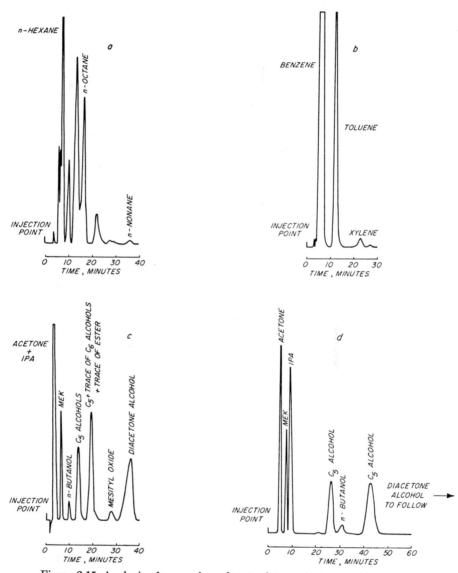

Figure 2.15. Analysis of a complex solvent mixture. (After B. T. Whitham.)

TABLE 2.2. COMPOSITION OF A COMPLEX SOLVENT MIXTURE DETERMINED
WITH THE AID OF G.L.C., ACCORDING TO WHITHAM[18]

Component	Per cent by volume
Petroleum spirit, aromatic-free	16
Benzene	13
Toluene	2
Acetone	10
Methylethyl ketone	5
Isopropyl alcohol	14
Technical amyl alcohol	17
Mesityl oxide	1
Diacetone alcohol	18
n-Butyl alcohol	1
Minor components (water, esters, etc.)	3

genated compounds were identified by running over liquid paraffin (non-polar) and polyethylene glycol (polar) stationary phases (c and d). The C_5 alcohols were identified by condensing the relevant fractions from the G.L.C. column and analyzing them in a mass spectrometer. The over-all composition of this sample is given in Table 2.2.

Example G—The Separation of Meta- and Paraxylene

In the early days of G.L.C. meta- and paraxylene could barely be separated by this technique or not at all, owing to the fact that the ratio of volatilities lies very close to unity (see footnote on page 22). A satisfactory separation has recently been effected in two ways.

(a) A stationary phase can be employed that forms loose adducts with

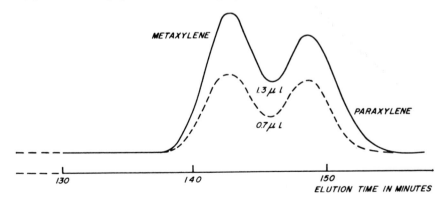

Figure 2.16. Separation of *m*- and *p*-xylene over methyl-propyl tetrachlorophthalate (after Langer, Zahn and Pantazoplos) with samples of 0.7 and 1.3 µl (Column: 27 ft, 4.5 mm ID, narrow mesh fraction firebrick coated with 20 per cent w/w stationary liquid; temperature 110°C; exit pressure 1 atm., Δp = 929 mm Hg. Number of theoretical plates of column: 6000).

aromatic compounds, the adducts of the two xylenes causing more favourable relative volatilities. (It should be noted that an improvement of even
a few hundredths in this figure may greatly facilitate separation; see Fig.
4.16). Langer, Zahn and Pantazoplos[26] investigated the use of various
tetrahalophthalates for this purpose. Figure 2.16 shows the separation obtained by these authors with samples of two sizes on a column containing
methyl-propyl tetrachlorophthalate as stationary phase.

(b) A column of extremely high efficiency can be used. Scott[27], who has developed columns with upwards of 30000 theoretical plates, reports that
they allow m- and p-xylene to be separated, even with stationary liquids
that formerly gave poor resolution.

Example H—Analyses of (Hydrocarbon) Gases

In considering the analysis of gases by chromatography we can distinguish
two types of samples:

(a) Mixtures of gases uncondensable in liquid air or liquid nitrogen,
such as H_2, N_2, O_2 and CO. (Mixtures containing large amounts of methane
also fall into this category.) As has already been stated, G.L.C. is not suitable for dealing with such cases, owing to the low solubility of the components. Excellent results may, however, be obtained on such mixtures by
adsorption chromatography, as will be shown in Chapter 8.

(b) Mixtures containing small amounts of methane, acetylene, ethene,
ethane and other hydrocarbons up to C_5.

For the latter category G.L.C is eminently suitable. In this field it has,
however, to compete with other established types of gas-analysis. Low-
temperature fractional distillation (Podbielniak, etc.) is accurate, but time-
consuming. Mass spectrometry is extremely rapid, but it is only moderately
accurate and requires costly equipment. G.L.C., which is both rapid and
low in outlay, can hence replace these methods if carried out in a form known
to give precise data.

The hydrocarbon gas mixtures that can be analyzed by G.L.C. may again
be divided into two categories: (a) mixtures of narrow range, consisting
mainly of compounds with the same number (or two successive numbers)
of carbon atoms; (b) wide-range mixtures.

Narrow-range mixtures of gaseous hydrocarbons may be analyzed by
G.L.C. at a single definite column temperature with a differential detector.
Fredericks and Brooks[19] describe a series of experiments on a number of hy-
drocarbon mixtures of known composition marketed by the Phillips Petro-
leum Company*. Figure 2.17 shows the results of a run on Phillips mixture
No. 35, using a 6-ft, $\frac{3}{8}$ in. I.D. column containing diisodecyl phthalate on
"Celite" 545 (40:100 wt), temperature 35°C, helium as carrier gas. The

* Phillips Petroleum Company, Special Products Division, Bartlesville, Oklahoma.

components are separated according to boiling point, so that paraffins and olefins of approximately the same boiling points coincide.

A more polar stationary liquid, dimethylsulfolane, retarded the olefins selectively, even to such an extent that they overlapped the paraffins of next higher carbon number. Excellent results were obtained by employing

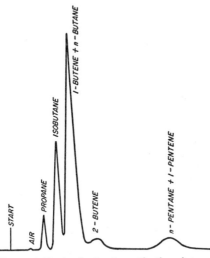

Figure 2.17. Analysis of synthetic mixture.

Column liquid: diisodecyl phthalate; column length: 6 feet; column temp.: 35°C; helium flowrate (exit): 45 ml/min; exit pressure: 1 atm. (After Fredericks and Brooks.)

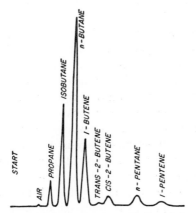

Figure 2.18. Analysis of synthetic mixture.

Column liquid: diisodecyl phthalate–dimethylsulfolane; column length: 6 feet–16 feet; column temp.: 35°C; helium flowrate (exit): 45 ml/min; exit pressure: 1 atm. (After Fredericks and Brooks.)

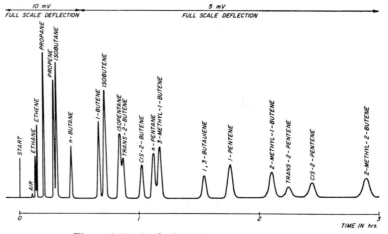

Figure 2.19. Analysis of 19-component mixture.

Column liquid: dimethylsulfolane; column length: 50 feet; column temp.: 0°C; helium flowrate (exit): 110 ml/min; exit pressure: 1 atm. (After Fredericks and Brooks.)

in series a 6-ft column containing diisodecyl phthalate and a 16-ft column of dimethylsulfolane (see Figure 2.18). The first column then gave a separation according to Figure 2.17, the second retarded the olefins sufficiently to separate them from closely adjacent paraffins.

In analyses of wide-range hydrocarbon gas mixtures one is confronted by the difficulty that components of widely different volatilities are involved. If differential detection is employed and the mixture is complex. it may not be convenient to increase the temperature abruptly between two peaks. If the analysis is now carried out at a high temperature, so as to elute the high-boiling components in a reasonable time, the resolution in the lower range becomes unsatisfactory; a low temperature gives a better over-all resolution, but a very long time of analysis. Figures 2.19 and 2.20 show the elution curves of two multi-component gas mixtures, also given in the publication of Fredericks and Brooks. The former was recorded at 15°C with the same two-stage diisodecyl phthalate-dimethylsulfolane columns as used for the preceding analysis. For the analysis of Figure 2.20 a 50-ft column with dimethylsulfolane at 0°C was employed in order to obtain a better resolution of certain peaks, such as 1-butene and isobutene. As a column of this length, if packed with "Celite", produces a very large pressure drop, this support was replaced by a 35/80 mesh fraction of Johns-Manville C-22 fire-brick. The total time of elution necessary for the former analysis was 3 hours.

For quantitative determination Fredericks and Brooks applied the

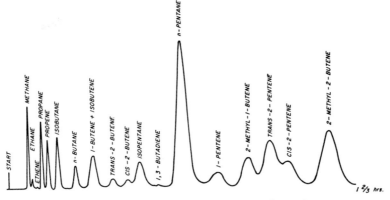

Figure 2.20. Analysis of complex hydrocarbon mixture.

Column liquid: diisodecyl phthalate-dimethylsulfolane; column length: 6 feet–16 feet; column temp.: 15°C; helium flowrate (exit): 45 ml/min; exit pressure: 1 atm. (After Fredericks and Brooks.)

method of proportional peak areas (determined by planimeter), without applying calibration factors. In the case of partially overlapping peaks, areas were partitioned by drawing a vertical line from the lowest point to the base-line. The quantitative data so found for the 19-component mixture of Figure 2.20 are compared with the known composition in Table 2.3.

The agreement is reasonable considering the difference in thermal conduc-

TABLE 2.3. QUANTITATIVE DATA (WT %) FOR A 19-COMPONENT HYDROCARBON GAS MIXTURE ANALYZED BY G.L.C. ON A DIMETHYLSULFOLANE COLUMN

	Known Composition	G.L.C. Data
Ethane	1.3	1.5
Ethene	2.0	2.7
Propane	7.4	8.3
Propene	7.4	8.1
Isobutane	11.5	11.8
n-Butane	5.0	5.3
1-Butene	5.3	5.5
Isobutene	8.3	8.4
trans-2-Butene	} 6.3	3.1 } 6.7
cis-2-Butene		3.6
1.3-Butadiene	3.4	3.4
Isopentane	6.5	6.0
n-Pentane	5.7	5.1
1-Pentene	5.8	5.4
3-Methyl-1-butene	6.7	6.2
2-Methyl-1-butene	5.7	5.2
trans-2-Pentene	} 5.9	1.9 } 5.2
cis-2-Pentene		3.3
2-Methyl-2-butene	5.7	5.2

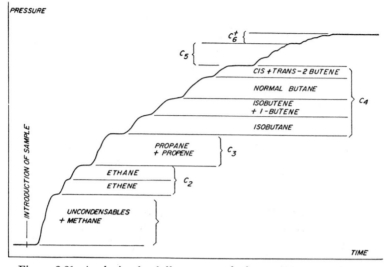

Figure 2.21. Analysis of a full-range cracked gas. (After v.d. Craats.)

tivity of the various hydrocarbons, and supports the view that the correction of areas for response is not always strictly necessary when using hydrogen or helium as carrier gas. It should, however, be observed that for samples containing constituents in largely different concentration, calibration may become essential.

The difficulties in analyzing long-range mixtures, due to the use of differential detection with a single column temperature, may be circumvented by adopting some "absolute" (usually integral) type of detection. The column temperature may then be increased progressively from start to finish at any convenient rate. Such a procedure was employed by Van de Craats[12], who, like Janák, used CO_2 as carrier gas and absorbed the latter in caustic potash after the column, but determined the constituents by registering the pressure increments in a vessel of known volume with an automatic pressure recorder*. Figure 2.21 shows the elution curve so found for a full-range gas from a cracking process. The column was 6 m long and contained liquid paraffin on fire-brick; the temperature was gradually increased from 20 to 60°C during the analysis. An integral type of detection does not allow minor constituents to be estimated accurately.

Example I—Use of G.L.C. in Combination with the Mass Spectrometer for the Structural Investigation of High-boiling Petroleum Fractions

G.L.C. may constitute a valuable aid in investigating the structure of components in complicated organic mixtures. Whitham[20] used it in analyz-

* See Figure 3.13 for the apparatus.

ing a petroleum fraction of 170 to 260°C boiling range. The material was first separated into an "aromatic" and a "paraffinic" fraction by displacement L.S.C. Samples of these fractions were then further split up in a large G.L.C. column (830 cm long, 12.7 mm I.D.) over Silicone MS 550 as stationary liquid. Figures 2.22a and 2.22b reproduce the chromatograms of the two fractions. At certain points, indicated in the diagrams, samples were taken in a cold trap. These samples were then analyzed in a mass spectrometer. The data so collected enabled the investigator to draw certain qualitative and semi-quantitative conclusions as to the structure of the hydrocarbons. These conclusions are summarized in Table 2.4.

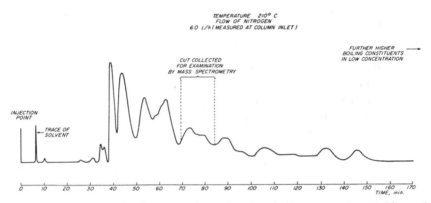

Figure 2.22a. Aromatics from petroleum fraction, boiling range 170–260°C. 1 ml. Large-scale analytical G.L.C. unit. 830-cm column. Silicone M.S. 550 stationary phase on 44–52 Sterchamol brick. (After Whitham.)

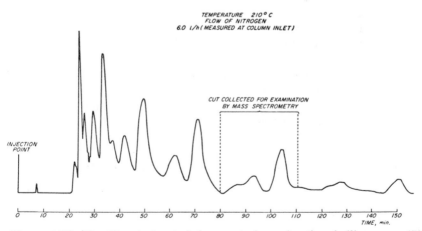

Figure 2.22b. Paraffins (saturates) from petroleum fraction, boiling range 170–260°C. 1 ml. Large-scale analytical G.L.C. unit. 830-cm column. Silicone M.S. 550 stationary phase on 44–52 Sterchamol brick. (After Whitham.)

TABLE 2.4. COMPOSITION OF NARROW CUTS FROM A PETROLEUM DISTILLATE
(B.P. 170–260°C) OBTAINED BY G.S.C. AND G.L.C. AND ANALYZED
BY MASS SPECTROMETER

"Aromatic" Cut	% Vol. Approx.	"Paraffinic" Cut (no quantitative data)
Major constituents		*Major constituents*
Alkylbenzenes, C_{11}	20	Isoparaffins, C_{13}
do. , C_{12}	22	do. , C_{14}
Indanes and tetralins, C_{10}	14	Monocyclic naphthenes, C_{13}
do. , C_{11}	27	do. , C_{14}
do. , C_{12}	9	Dicyclic naphthenes, C_{12}
Minor constituents		do. , C_{13}
Alkylbenzenes, C_{10}		*Minor constituents*
Indanes and tetralins, C_9		Monocyclic naphthenes, C_{12}
do. , C_{13}		Dicyclic naphthenes, C_{14}
Naphthalene		

In the investigation by Whitham, and in similar studies where use has been made of the mass spectrometer for the identification of the column effluent, the latter was trapped in a sample tube, the contents of which were then transferred to the sample inlet system of the spectrometer. Gohlke, at the 1957 A.C.S Meeting in New York City, reported on the combination of the gas chromatograph with a new type of mass spectrograph that can be used continuously, and directly monitors the effluent gas from the column. The instrument produces 2000 spectra per second, which can be observed on an oscilloscope screen The pattern is usually observed visually, but if a permanent record is desired it may be photographed.

The instrument uses the "Time-Of-Flight" principle[28] for scanning the spectrum and the mass resolution is such that complete separation of adjacent mass units is realized to a mass of about 180, whilst usable resolution is claimed to be obtained to a mass of at least 400. Like all mass spectrometers it employs a minute amount of sample. It is evident that the combination of the gas chromatograph with the T.O.F. mass spectrograph, which directly provides a "fingerprint" of the components separated in the column, is a useful tool for research work. For quantitative routine analyses the use of the conventional mass spectrometer with a small time constant will be preferable for its higher sensitivity.

REFERENCES

1a. Evans, D. E. M., and Tatlow, J. C., *J. Chem. Soc.*, **1955,** 1184.
1b. James, A. T., and Martin, A. J. P., *Biochem. J.* (*London*), **50,** 679 (1952).
2. Keulemans, A. I. M., and Kwantes, A., Vapour Phase Chromatography, Desty, D. H. (ed.), London, 1957 (Proc. of London Symposium on V.Ph. Chr., May/June 1956), p. 15.
3. Bradford, B. W., Harvey, D., and Chalkley, D. E., *J. Inst. Petroleum*, **41,** 80 (1955).

4a. Adlard, E. R., Vapour Phase Chromatography, Desty, D. H. (ed.), London, 1957 (Proc. of London Symposium on V. Ph. Chr., May/June 1956), p. 98.
4b. Ambrose, D., and Collerson, R. R., *Nature*, **177**, 84 (1956).
5. Littlewood, A. B., Phillips, C. S. G., and Price, D. T., *J. Chem. Soc.*, **1955**, 1480.
6. Ray, N. H., *J. Appl. Chem. (London)*, **4**, 21 (1954).
7. James, A. T., Martin, A. J. P., and Smith, G. H., *Biochem. J. (London)*, **52**, 238 (1952).
8. Pierotti, G. J., Deal, C. H., Derr, E. L., and Porter, P. E., *J. Am. Chem. Soc.*, **78**, 2989 (1956).
9. Ellis, W. H., and Le Tourneau, R. L., *Anal. Chem.*, **25**, 1269 (1953).
10. Boer, H., "The Use of Ozonolysis in Oil Constitution Research," World Petroleum Congr., Proc. 4th Congr., Rome, 1955.
11. Janák, J., and Rusek, M., *Chem. Listy*, **47**, 1190 (1953).
12. Craats, F. van de, *Anal. Chim. Acta*, **14**, 136 (1956).
13. Martin, A. E., and Smart, J., *Nature*, **175**, 422 (1955).
14. Deal, C. H., Otvos, J. W., Smith, V. N., and Zucco, P. S., "A Radiological Detector for Gas-Liquid Partition Chromatography," Dallas Symposium on Vapour Phase Chromatography, American Chemical Society, April 1956.
15. James, A. T., and Martin, A. J. P., *Brit. Med. Bull.*, **10**, 170 (1954).
16. Keulemans, A. I. M., Kwantes, A., and Zaal, P., *Anal. Chim. Acta*, **13**, 357 (1955).
17. Kokes, R. J., Tobin Jr., H., and Emmett, P. H., *J. Am. Chem. Soc.*, **77**, 5860 (1955).
18. Whitham, B. T., Vapour Phase Chromatography, Desty, D. H. (ed.), London, 1957 (Proc. of London Symposium on V. Ph. Chr., May/June 1956), p. 395.
19. Fredericks, E. M., and Brooks, F. R., *Anal. Chem.*, **28**, 297 (1956).
20. Whitham, B. T., Vapour Phase Chromatography, Desty, D. H. (ed.), London, 1957 (Proc. of London Symposium on V. Ph. Chr., May/June 1956), p. 194.
21. Boer, H., *ibid.*, p. 169.
22. Vaughan, G. A., *Analyst*, **81**, 55 (1956).
23. Grant, D. W., Gas Chromatography 1958, Desty, D. H. (ed.), London (Proc. of 2nd Symposium on Gas Chr., Amsterdam, May 1958), p. 153.
24. Boer, H., private communication.
25. Keulemans, À. I. M. and Voge, H. H., A.C.S. Meeting, San Francisco, 1958.
26. Langer, S. H., Zahn, C., and Pantazoplos, G., *Chem. & Ind. (London)*, (1958) 1145.
27. Scott, R. P. W., private communication.
28. *See, for instance*, Wiley, W. C. and McLaren, I. H., *Rev. Sci. Instruments* **26**, 1150 (1955).
29. *See, for instance*, Harrison, G. F., Knight, P., Kelley, R. P. and Heath, M. T., Gas Chromatography 1958, Desty, D. H. (ed.), London (Proc. of 2nd Symposium on Gas Chr., Amsterdam May 1958), p. 216.
30. Van de Craats, F., *ibid.*, p. 248.

Chapter 3

THE APPARATUS FOR GAS-LIQUID CHROMATOGRAPHY IN PRACTICE

INTRODUCTION

The general set-up of the apparatus required for gas chromatography has been outlined in Chapter 1, but its details have, with a few exceptions, not yet been considered.

In a simple case, a separation by G.L.C. could conceivably be carried out with very simple equipment. The column might be maintained at room temperature, the carrier gas could be regulated manually, fractions of the effluent vapors might be analyzed "by hand" with the aid of normal laboratory methods. It will be evident, however, that such a procedure would impose severe limitations. The analysis would be suitable only for components with boiling points up to, say, 60°C. The composition of the effluent, which undergoes rapid changes, would be registered in crude steps. The analysis would be clumsy, difficult and time-consuming. Though efficient separations have actually been performed with quite simple apparatus[1], the adoption of more elaborate automatic facilities is in general amply justified.

In this chapter the main elements of the apparatus used for G.L.C. will be considered individually. This procedure will enable those wishing to construct their own equipment to combine components giving satisfactory performance in the case in view. It will be found that the choice involves a number of compromises, since the separation by G.L.C., itself, is usually a matter of effecting compromises between optimum values for the various individual factors concerned.

THE MAIN COMPONENTS OF THE APPARATUS

The apparatus can be divided into four sections:
(1) Equipment for providing a controlled flow of carrier gas;
(2) The column and its thermostat;
(3) The system employed for dispensing and introducing the sample;
(4) The apparatus used for detecting the components in the effluent.
These four items will be considered separately.

Apparatus for Supplying and Measuring the Carrier Gas

The separation of components by G.L.C. does not intrinsically require a precise control of the flow of carrier gas, since fluctuations in flow affect all components in the column to about the same extent. The identification of components by their retention volumes or efflux times requires a better regulation of the gas current. For quantitative analysis it is necessary for the flow to be substantially constant, in order that all components recorded on the time axis may be sensed on the same volumetric basis.

In general it is not essential for the flow to be accurately reproducible in successive separations. All that is required—particularly in quantitative analyses using an internal standard—is that it is constant, accurately known and of approximately the right value during the period required for stripping all components from the column.

Since the permeability of the column does not alter during operation if it has been properly packed, the flow of gas at a certain temperature can be controlled by a precise regulation of the inlet and outlet pressures with suitable instruments. If either of these pressures is atmospheric, only one pressure regulator is necessary, but the versatility of the apparatus is then lower than if two are provided.

Accurate pressure regulators are commercially available. James and Martin[2], and James and Phillips[3] describe mercury-glass regulators that can be constructed in the laboratory; satisfactory service can also be obtained from a mercury manometer provided with an external metal strip and a proximity switch feeding magnetically operated valves.

The rate of gas flow can be measured by means of a rotameter, an orifice meter or a soap-film flow meter. Rotameters are good indicators, but less suitable for measuring gas flow with the accuracy required in G.L.C. Both the rotameter and the orifice meter depend on the viscosity of the gas and therefore may require thermostatting; sometimes it is possible to place them inside the thermostat regulating the temperature of the column and/or the sensing instrument.

The soap-film meter (Figure 3.1) is a very simple device in which the rate of travel of a soap-film in a vertical calibrated tube is timed with a stopwatch. It is extremely accurate and gives virtually no back pressure; errors appreciably below 1 per cent can be realized over a wide range. Unlike the rotameter and orifice meter it does not give continuous readings. The writer usually employs a set-up containing both a rotameter and a soap-film meter (Figure 3.2); readings with the latter are only carried out at the beginning and end of a run. The flow rates determined with the soap-film meter should be converted from the prevailing temperature to that in the column and corrected for the vapor pressure of water. (Saturation in the meter is always practically complete.)

The gas—nitrogen, carbon dioxide, hydrogen or helium—is obtained from high-pressure cylinders through suitable reducing valves. The use of dry gas is essential, since water is a component that is far from inert. Though the gas as compressed by the supplier is usually free from moisture, it is advisable to pass it through a drying agent such as silica gel. The most effective method is to place a high-pressure drying tower immediately after the cylinder and before the reducing valve.

The Column and its Temperature Regulation

The Column. The importance of uniform packing of the column with the moistened support was stressed in Chapter 2, and it was pointed out that uniformity is more easily achieved with a relatively coarse-grained material such as a 30/50 or 50/80 mesh refractory brick fraction than with a fine material such as diatomaceous earth ("Celite"). Packing a column with the latter material, especially if it is impregnated with stationary liquid, requires great care, but does not present insuperable difficulties in the case of straight columns of glass. Long columns may then be built up from units of suitable length by connecting them by return bends. Aggregate columns of this type are generally placed in a constant-temperature vapor jacket or an air thermostat.

Very satisfactory units can be built by *coiling* the tubing. Coiled columns may be made of glass, but then must be filled by a special technique, which

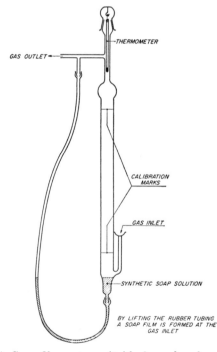

Figure 3.1. Soap-film meter suitable for reduced gas pressures.

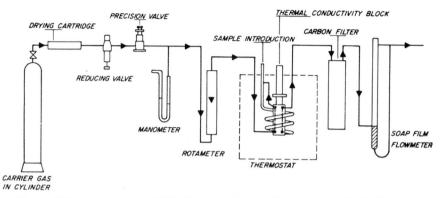

Figure 3.2. Arrangement of G.L.C. apparatus for the analysis of volatile organic liquids, using a katharometer as detector (with other types of detector, modifications may be necessary).

again is more easily carried out with coarse-grained than with fine-grained material. The use of tube coils of metal (particularly of a soft metal such as copper or aluminum) presents great advantages if they can be employed*. A coarse-grained support here, however, is essential; it has been found very difficult to fill a metal column, even when straight, reproducibly with impregnated "Celite". With any support, a metal column should be filled first and coiled afterward.

The great advantage of a coiled column is its compactness and the consequent small size of the thermostat. Metal coils are superior to glass in heat transfer and constancy of temperature. Coiled columns tend to have a slightly lower efficiency per unit of length than straight ones, but with the dimensions used for analysis (tubing of 4 to 8 mm I.D., coiled to say 6 to 8 in. diameter) the difference is negligible†.

The writer will describe the method of column preparation which has now become more or less standard practice in the laboratories with which he is associated.

The column, which according to circumstances may have any length from a few feet to, say, 60, is made of $\frac{1}{4}$ in. I.D. copper tubing and is provided with a male union joint at each end for connection in the apparatus. The tubing is first softened by heating it to 500–600°C in a flame and allowing it to cool.

---

* Cases exist in which the use of metal columns is excluded, e.g., because of interaction or catalytic decomposition.

† The effect is noticeable with columns of, say, 20 mm I.D., and the same coil diameter. Wide columns are, however, not used for analysis. Accurate temperature regulation is then seldom essential and it is usually possible to employ straight tubes with some simple form of heating.

The support employed is a 30/50 or 50/80 mesh screen fraction of ground C 22 Sterchamol fire-brick*, which has been freed from adhering dust by elutriation with some liquid (e.g., water, pentane or acetone) compatible with the subsequent solution. The wet support is then made into a slurry in a flask with the calculated amount of the selected stationary liquid dissolved in a suitable volatile solvent. The solvent is removed on a steam bath at a somewhat reduced pressure, with shaking, agitation being gentle so as not to crush the soft granules. The resultant impregnated support appears quite dry and can be readily poured if the amount of stationary liquid does not exceed 35 to 40 per cent weight on dry support.

The straight softened copper tube is clamped in a vertical position; the bottom is plugged loosely with $\frac{1}{2}$ in. of glass wool and the packing is poured in through a funnel. The packing is gently tamped from time to time with a piece of rubber vacuum tubing. The column is filled to within $\frac{1}{2}$ in. of the top and a second plug of glass wool is inserted.

As a check on proper packing the bulk density may be calculated from the weight of the packing and the volume of the tube, but a better specification is based on a certain value of the permeability K (see p. 141), as deduced from the flow of gas at known inlet and outlet pressures.

The packed column is now coiled around a mandrel of suitable diameter (6–8 in.). If the tubing has been properly annealed it will be quite soft, but will become rigid on shaping. The distance between the coils is not critical. If sensing is by thermal conductivity and the cell is placed in the same thermostat as the column, the height of the coil will be made about equal to that of the katharometer, which is mounted in its center (Figure 3.3).

The Column Thermostat. The column temperature is an important operating variable. As in the case of pressure, it is not necessary for good separation to control the temperature accurately; close temperature regulation is, however, essential for quantitative analysis with differential detection, particularly if the height of the peak is used as the parameter for calibration.

As stated previously, the detecting device—which usually also requires temperature control—can for convenience be placed in the same thermostat as the column. (The same may apply to a rotameter or orifice meter.) A drawback to the inclusion of a thermal conductivity cell is that its response then alters with a change in column temperature. Though this is not always a serious drawback, separate thermostatting may sometimes be preferable. However, care must then be taken that there can be no condensation of components or stationary liquid in or before the cell. The detector can in practice only be maintained at a lower temperature if the stationary liquid is extremely low in volatility. The dead space between

* Manufactured by Sterchamol Werke G.m.b.H., Dortmund, Germany. An alternative and even better material is Johns-Manville C 22 fire-brick.

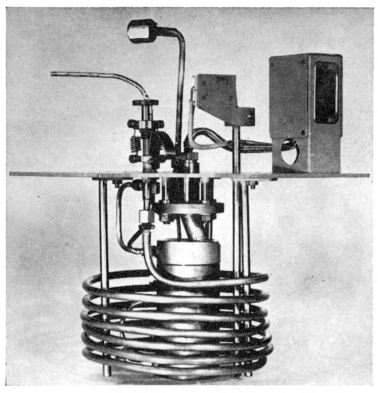

Figure 3.3. Assembly of column and thermal conductivity cells.

the column and detector should be reduced to a minimum by the use of capillary tubing.

Various types of thermostats can be employed. For accurate analysis at a constant temperature throughout the run the writer advocates a good oil thermostat with a temperature constancy of, say, ±0.05°C, a figure readily obtainable with conventional equipment. A bath oil of the lowest viscosity compatible with lack of volatility at the operating temperature should be used. The customary measures as regards circulation of the bath, arrangement and shielding of temperature sensing elements and the maximum and minimum values of the heat input should be adopted in order to minimize irregularities in temperature.

As was stated on page 22, the wide range in volatility of a sample may sometimes render it desirable to increase the temperature during the course of an analysis, in which case two procedures may be adopted: (1) changing the temperature abruptly to a higher level between two peaks, or (2) employing a predetermined, gradual time-temperature profile.

(1) For rapidly increasing the temperature, an oil bath is less suitable

because of its high heat capacity. In this case one of the following devices may be used:

(a) A vapor bath containing a liquid boiling at a controlled pressure (below, at, or above atmospheric). Satisfactory liquids of good thermal stability are:

acetone,	suitable for a temperature range of					30 to	50°C
benzene,	"	" "	"	"	"	50 "	80°C
toluene,	"	" "	"	"	"	80 "	110°C
p-xylene,	"	" "	"	"	"	110 "	140°C

(b) An air thermostat with a sufficient gas velocity.

It has been found that this method can be developed to permit rapid changes in temperature (up to 20°C per minute). An air thermostat having the required properties, namely, rapid adjustability to a new temperature level and temperature constancy over the whole length of the column, has been described by Ashbury, Davies and Drinkwater[4]. The requirements were met by applying forced air circulation within a vacuum jacket.

The chromatographic column is located in a vertical tube, down which air is drawn at about 50 ft/sec. by a high-speed radial fan. The air issuing from the fan flows past a non-inductively wound heater coil arranged concentrically around the fan. The maximum working temperature is about 350°C. At 300°C the constancy within the working space is about ±1°C.

(2) For establishing a definite, gradual temperature profile a mechanical arrangement of servo-motors linked to potentiometers and controlled by a resistance thermometer can be devised. Such an arrangement for "programmed heating", with which for instance a linear time-temperature curve can be established, has been described by Harrison and collaborators[25].

Methods of Introducing the Sample

The manner in which the sample is introduced into the chromatographic column is of the utmost importance owing to its influence on the shape of the elution peaks. These should preferably be as narrow as possible.

The sample, however small, occupies a certain volume in the form of gas or vapor. If, as in some methods for introducing liquids, the sample is first vaporized to a definite volume in the carrier gas, this initial volume of course becomes larger. There are now in theory two limiting ways in which the above-mentioned volume of vapor may reach the first plate of the column:

(1) the vapor arrives as a "plug," without (further) dilution by carrier gas; the latter follows it with a sharp interface;

(2) owing to complete mixing of the vapor with the carrier gas following

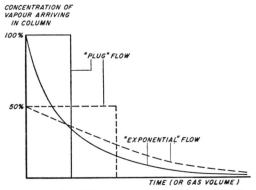

Figure 3.4. Limiting cases of sample introduction.

it into the initial space, the first trace of vapor arrives without dilution, but the concentration tails off exponentially with time to a value of zero.

These two limiting cases, which will be referred to as "plug" flow and "exponential" flow, respectively, are shown diagrammatically in Figure 3.4, the full lines referring to a sample at 100 per cent concentration in the vapor phase and the dotted lines to a sample diluted with carrier gas to 50 per cent concentration. Since the size of the samples was equal, the areas below the curves must be the same in all four cases.

In practice, the various methods of sample introduction will presumably follow some course lying between these two extremes. Precise data on this subject are at present scarce, but it is possible to estimate the approximate position for each method of introduction.

The two limiting cases of "plug" flow and "exponential" flow have been dealt with mathematically by Porter, Deal and Stross[5], who have derived equations from which the respective shapes of the elution peaks may be calculated. Figure 3.5 shows the resulting type of curves calculated for "plug" flow; the various curves refer to samples of increasing size introduced at the same concentration. It will be seen that the downward slope of the curves is substantially parallel; a very large sample gives rise to a flat top, since an appreciable part of the column is occupied before the charging step is complete. Figure 3.6 shows the corresponding curves for "exponential" mixing; the three curves refer to the same amount of a component, charged during different periods, viz., evaporated in preliminary chambers of different volumes. Here the average width of the peaks is roughly the same, but the bases vary and become considerably extended by larger initial dilution (longer charging periods).

In their experiments Porter *et al.* employed the method of evaporation in a preliminary chamber and they demonstrated that the elution curves

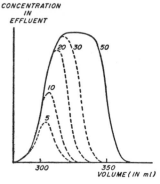

Figure 3.5. Plug flow.
Calculated elution curves for variable sample (5, 10, 20, 30, 50 ml) at constant concentration. (After Porter *et al.*)

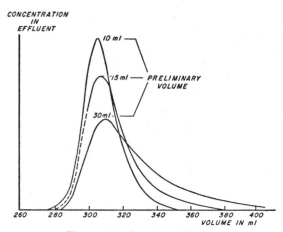

Figure 3.6. Complete Mixing.
Calculated elution curves for variable charging periods; constant amount of solute. (After Porter *et al.*)

actually obtained approximated closely to ideal exponential mixing (Figure 3.7). They were thus able to apply corrections to the observed curves. It is evident from Figure 3.6 that with closely adjacent peaks the separation is critically affected by the charging period.

A fundamental study on the influence of the concentration in the carrier gas at which the sample is introduced and of the size of the sample was also carried out by van Deemter, Zuiderweg and Klinkenberg[6]. Theory shows that for a given amount of solute the column efficiency increases with rising concentration and drops with increasing size of the sample. These results were confirmed experimentally by van de Craats[7], who determined the height of one effective plate as a function of the sample size for butane

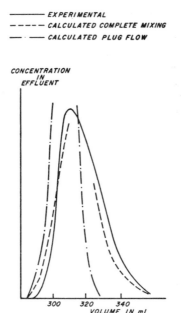

——————— *EXPERIMENTAL*
— — — — *CALCULATED COMPLETE MIXING*
— · —— *CALCULATED PLUG FLOW*

Figure 3.7. Elution curves. (After Porter *et al.*)

and ethane, the samples being introduced in the pure form and as 5 per cent dilutions in nitrogen. Figure 3.8 demonstrates the increase in H.E.T.P.* with dilution and size of sample; the two effects were, however, far larger in the case of ethane than of butane.

From the foregoing it follows that the narrowest bands (and therefore the sharpest separations) are obtained by introducing a small sample in a high concentration as a "plug".

The methods of sample introduction employed in practice will be described below.

Gaseous Samples. Samples of gases are usually introduced by trapping a definite volume of the gas in a tube between two stopcocks and forcing it into the column by the carrier gas. This form of volumetric measurement is very accurate. The arrangement employed by van de Craats[8] is shown in Figure 3.9, and is so designed that the current of carrier gas need not be interrupted during sampling.

If the dead gas space in the top of the column is sufficiently small and the sample tube is narrow in bore this method presumably approaches "plug" flow. The micro-syringe (see below) has also been successfully used for taking and introducing samples of gas.

* Height equivalent to a theoretical plate; see Chapter 4. A low H.E.T.P. corresponds to a high column efficiency per unit of length.

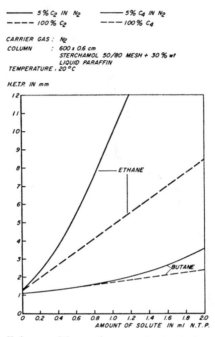

Figure 3.8. Column efficiency with varying sample size in 5 and 100% concentration.

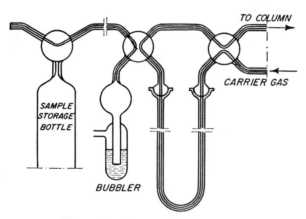

Figure 3.9. Gas sample inlet system.

Liquid Samples. *Introduction by Syringe.* The method that is probably most widely used at present consists in injecting the sample of liquid with a small needle syringe through a self-sealing serum cap closing the front end of the column (Figure 3.10). If care is taken that the point of the needle is level with the top of the column packing, the sample immediately

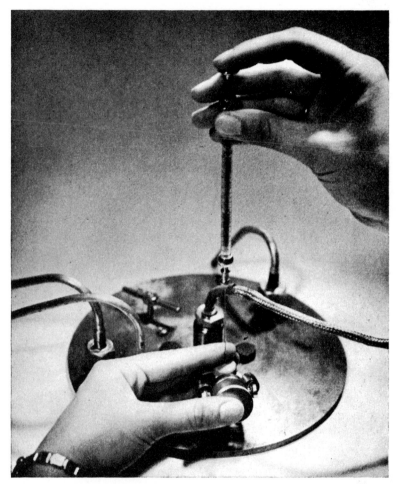

Figure 3.10. Sample introduction by syringe.

dissolves in the stationary liquid and the method probably constitutes the closest possible approach to "plug" introduction. For this reason the procedure is extremely suitable for obtaining maximum separation. If the liquid is injected into a vapor space above the packing, the introduction will be somewhat less ideally of the "plug" type and separation will tend to be impaired.

Commercial rubber caps intended for the sterile withdrawal of serum from ampoules are used for this purpose. They may be used repeatedly, say up to 30 times.

A disadvantage of the normal type of micro-syringe is that the absolute size of the sample injected is subject to small systematic errors, due for instance to creeping of liquid, expansion of the needle etc. In the hands of an experienced operator, however, it gives a good reproducibility. As was stated in Chapter 2, it is usually not essential to know the absolute size of the sample accurately.

An improved design of micro-syringe, especially intended for chromatographic work, has been published by Carle[26]. It has a volume of 0.06 ml; fractions of this amount may be injected by using stops arresting the plunger travel. Needle end effects are stated to have been practically eliminated. The reproducibility for a 15 μl sample is of the order of ± 0.2 per cent.

Sample Introduction under Pressure. Scott[27] has described a device for introducing samples at a high inlet gas pressure (an essential feature of the ultra-high-efficiency chromatographic columns developed by this investigator; see also Chapter 5). A slight modification of Scott's design is shown in figure 3.11.

It consists of a brass tube into which a piece of thick-walled rubber tubing fits; the latter can be squeezed shut by a screw- or cam-operated plunger. The brass tube, which is cooled at its lower end by a water-jacket, has a screw cap; this cap carries a narrower brass tube, closed at its upper end, for holding the sampling pipette prior to injection. The pipette is a brass or glass rod with a steel upper section; at its lower end the actual sampling tube is attached to it. This is a piece of fine-bored metal capillary, which is filled with the sample by capillary action.

The charged pipette is placed in the upper brass tube and held there by a solenoid fitting around it, after which the cap is screwed onto the lower section. The screw or cam compressing the rubber tubing is opened and by interrupting the solenoid the pipette is allowed to fall into the column, where the sample is taken up by the column support. The pipette is finally withdrawn with the solenoid and the rubber tubing is again closed. The latter automatically forms a good seal with the outer shell by the pressure in the column.

Introduction by Crushing a Glass Bulb. In this technique a suitable amount of the sample is introduced into a weighed, thin-walled glass bulb; the latter is sealed and reweighed. The bulb is placed in a specially designed chamber capable of being heated and provided with an arrangement whereby the bulb may be crushed; the chamber is filled with the carrier gas, the bulb is crushed in the heated chamber and the vapor mixture is forced into the column by the carrier gas. A diagram of a chamber designed for this purpose is shown in Figure 3.12.

The method will generally approximate to the introduction of the sample by "exponential" flow in a relatively dilute form, so that some broadening

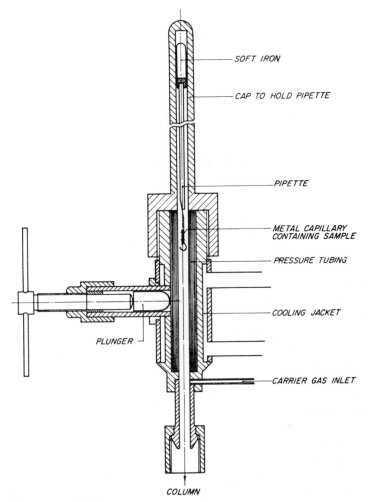

SOFT IRON

CAP TO HOLD PIPETTE

PIPETTE

METAL CAPILLARY
CONTAINING SAMPLE

PRESSURE TUBING

COOLING JACKET

PLUNGER

CARRIER GAS INLET

COLUMN

Figure 3.11. High-pressure sampling device. (After Scott, modified)

of the peak bases is to be expected; for a vaporizing chamber not exceeding, say, 10 ml the effect is, however, quite small.

The procedure is obviously more laborious than the syringe technique, but is still often used in cases where it is necessary to know the absolute size of the sample accurately.

Techniques for Introducing the Sample in Special Cases. Occasionally the nature of the sample renders it necessary to adopt a technique different from the normal procedures.

Boer[9], for instance, in analyzing fatty acids, introduced the sodium salts

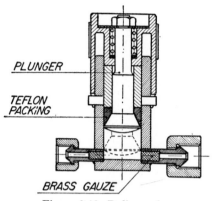

PLUNGER

TEFLON
PACKING

BRASS GAUZE

Figure 3.12. Bulb crusher.

into a separate chamber partly filled with "Celite", where the acids were liberated with phosphoric acid and from which they were distilled with a current of carrier gas into the cold column. The column was then rapidly heated by means of a vapor jacket and the separation was carried out. A similar technique would be suitable in various cases where volatile components are present in a high dilution in an inert gas. Examples are the analysis of tobacco smoke, the estimation of unburnt organic material in exhaust gases, etc. For very volatile substances the first part of the column may have to be chilled while they are being collected.

The opposite case may also occur. If it is necessary to separate a volatile component from a mixture of which the bulk is relatively nonvolatile, and if it is desired for convenience in routine work to keep the column uncontaminated by the latter fractions, the following procedure offers a practical solution[10]. A small separate "guard" section of impregnated packing is placed in the top of the column in such a manner that it can be readily removed. The sample is brought into the top of the guard section. After the volatile component has passed into the main part of the column, the guard section is taken out and the analysis is continued in the normal manner. This method has been used for estimating small amounts of isopropyl nitrate in diesel fuels. It has also been applied to the analysis of samples containing water, the guard section in this case being impregnated with glycerol, which retains water very selectively.

Descriptions of various types of equipment for sample introduction will be found in the publications indicated by references 2, 8, 9, 11, 12 and 16 at the end of this chapter.

Detection Devices

The detector, which has to sense and measure the amounts of components present in the effluent gas, may be termed the brain of the apparatus. Its main properties should be a rapid response and a high sensitivity combined with a good stability, as it has often to indicate extremely small and rapidly varying concentrations or amounts of substance.

It may be remarked here that it is not a simple matter to give a good definition of the "sensitivity" of a detector for gas chromatography; this subject is at present still being actively considered by various standardizing organisations. With modern electronic equipment it is, of course, easy to amplify a signal to almost any extent and thus make the instrument give a large response. Obviously, however, amplification will be useless unless long-term instability of the detector ("base-line drift") and short-term instability ("noise") are absent to a sufficient degree. The difficulty is that these instabilities are usually not due only to inherent shortcomings in the principle of the detector, but also to more or less fortuitous circumstances, such as deficiencies in its mechanical design, lack of constancy in operational parameters (temperature, gas rate etc.) and other factors. Since the subject is so complex, no attempt will as a rule be made in this book to express detector sensitivity in a figure (though proposals for such expressions have already been published); the term "sensitivity" in the subsequent descriptions will be based rather on a general impression of the instrument's performance, as gathered from published data and personal experience.

The methods of detection described in the literature or otherwise known to the author are listed below. They are subdivided into "integral" and "differential" methods (see pp. 12–13).

Integral methods

(1) Automatic titration of acids and bases.
(2) Detection by the conductivity of a collecting solution.
(3) Determination of volatile components by volume or pressure increments in a vessel.

Differential methods

It will be convenient to divide the differential detection methods again into two classes on the basis of their practical significance. The first class contains the methods that were proposed for use, and partly employed, up to about the beginning of the year 1957. They are procedures of moderate to good sensitivity, suitable for concentrations of components in the effluent down to, say, 1 molecule in 50000 of carrier gas; some of them (for instance detection by katharometer) are still widely used and are very satisfactory for the majority of normal analyses.

The second class contains a number of hypersensitive detectors that have recently been developed. They are capable of revealing components in the effluent in far smaller amounts than the foregoing class (down to 1 molecule in 10^9 of carrier gas), so that they bring the size of the sample required from the milligram into the microgram range with a gain in signal. Not only is this fact of importance in itself; it also has the consequence that a high efficiency becomes much more readily attainable in a chromatographic column, since the optimum efficiency can be approached only if the sample occupies a very small height of the column (see page 124). The less sensitive devices will, however, doubtlessly retain their place in routine applications.

The methods to be considered in the two classes are: *Differential detection methods of moderate sensitivity for general purposes.*

(1) Detection by the flow of gas through a restriction.

(2) Surface potential method.

(3) Detection by dielectric constant.

(4) Detection of organic compounds by complete combustion or hydrogenation and determination of CO_2 or CH_4 .

(5) Detection by Martin's density comparator.

(6) Detection by a thermocouple above a hydrogen flame.

(7) Radiological detection, involving the measurement of ionization of the total column effluent by β-rays.

(8) Detection by the light-emissitivity of a flame.

(9) Detection by differences in thermal conductivity.

Hypersensitive differential detection methods

(10) The low-pressure electric discharge detector.

(11) The argon β-ray detector.

(12) The flame ionization detector.

A description of the various systems of detection is given in the following pages.

Integral Methods. *Automatic Titration of Acids and Bases.* This was the method described in James and Martin's first publication[2] on G.L.C., where a full account of the apparatus employed will be found. In short, the procedure consisted in collecting the acid or basic components in a vessel containing an aqueous solution of an indicator, the color intensity of which was measured photoelectrically. The photoelectric cell steered a valve for the admission of standard alkali or acid, the volume of the latter being registered on a chart by recording the position of a plunger.

Determination by measuring the conductivity of a solution. Boer[9] described a simple procedure in which organic acids in the effluent were collected in an alkaline solution, the composition of which was measured conductometrically and recorded. An analogous procedure was employed for bases, aldehydes and ketones, the absorbing liquid then being standard acid or hydroxylamine hydrochloride solution, respectively.

Methods (1) and (2) are evidently limited to reactive compounds.

Determination of volatile compounds by volume or pressure increments in a vessel. If a gaseous mixture is to be analyzed and carbon dioxide is used as carrier gas, the latter can be removed by solution in an alkali and the components may be measured directly.

Janák[11] used a graduated vessel filled with caustic potash solution and measured the gaseous components visually at constant pressure. The same procedure was followed by Ray[12]. The method is excellent for hydrocarbons of low molecular weight; the higher members of some series (notably the olefins) are, however, to some extent lost by solution.

The method was improved and made self-recording by van de Craats[8], who employed a constant-volume technique, because pressures are more easily recorded automatically than gas volumes. His apparatus is illustrated in Figure 3.13. Its most interesting part is the CO_2 scrubber, which was designed to remove the carrier gas completely with a minimum amount of solution and virtually no back pressure. It consisted of a stainless steel tube (500 by 5 mm), containing a loose coil for increasing the path travelled by the KOH solution, and kept in vibration electromagnetically. At an inlet gas pressure of 80 mm Hg, a current of carbon dioxide, corresponding to 6 l/h at 760 mm, was quantitatively absorbed by 2 ml per minute of KOH solution (30 per cent), which entered the tube at 30°C and was heated by the absorption of CO_2 to 60°C. At the latter temperature its solvent power for hydrocarbons is negligible. The amount of alkaline solution in the receiving space was kept constant by a level controller and the pressure was measured and recorded by means of an electrodynamic precision meter. The accuracy of the method is estimated at ±0.3 per cent on the total sample.

In this form of detection it is essential to use CO_2 not containing more

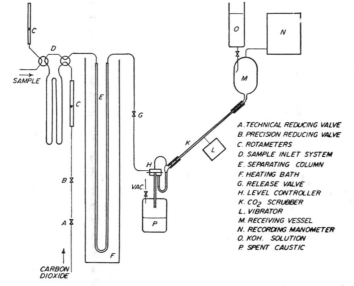

A. TECHNICAL REDUCING VALVE
B. PRECISION REDUCING VALVE
C. ROTAMETERS
D. SAMPLE INLET SYSTEM
E. SEPARATING COLUMN
F. HEATING BATH
G. RELEASE VALVE
H. LEVEL CONTROLLER
K. CO_2 SCRUBBER
L. VIBRATOR
M. RECEIVING VESSEL
N. RECORDING MANOMETER
O. KOH. SOLUTION
P. SPENT CAUSTIC

Figure 3.13. Gas analysis apparatus with pressure recording. (After van de Craats.)

than, say, 0.001 per cent of air. A convenient method of purifying commercial CO_2 for this purpose is described in Appendix II.

The procedure was employed for analyzing wide-range mixtures of gases (hydrogen and hydrocarbons from methane up to the pentanes); an integral method is valuable for such a purpose, since the wide range in volatility makes it necessary to increase the temperature during the analysis. The result of such an analysis is illustrated in Figure 2.21.

Differential Methods.

General-purpose detectors of moderate sensitivity. Methods (1), (2) and (3) were suggested by Griffiths, James and Phillips[13].

Detection by Impedance of Gas Flow. The pressure differential developed across a restriction through which the carrier gas flows at constant rate changes if the gas carries volatile admixtures. If the restriction is an orifice, the pressure differential is closely related to the density of the gas, if it is a capillary, to the viscosity. The former property is the more sensitive and has the advantage of being related to a simple molecular parameter.

The inventors believed the sensitivity of the method to equal that of thermal conductivity measurement, but it is doubtful whether this comparison can still be upheld today, since the sensitivity of thermal conductivity cells has recently been greatly improved.

Surface Potential Method[13]. If a d.c. potential is applied across two parallel plates of different metals, one of which is kept in vibration, an oscillating condenser is formed and an alternating e.m.f. is set up. This e.m.f. is dependent on the gas between the plates. Griffiths *et al.* further found that differences due to gas composition are greatly enhanced if one of the plates is coated with a fatty acid or collodion.

The system is highly sensitive and appears to show large differences for certain types of compounds. Thus nitrogen, saturated at 0°C with ethanol and cyclohexane, respectively, gave potential changes of +40 and −5 mV with respect to the carrier gas, while they gave the same differential by thermal conductivity.

The method, however, suffers badly from slow response and retardation effects.

Detection by Dielectric Constant[13]. Griffiths *et al.* passed the effluent through a small condenser packed with charcoal, the capacity forming part of an oscillating circuit. Changes in capacity are thus converted into frequency modulations, which are then detected by a discriminator, and are further amplified and recorded.

The measurement of small changes in capacity requires considerable precautions and the method is not so simple as thermal conductivity.

Detection of Organic Compounds after Chemical Conversion. (1) Combustion to CO_2. Martin and Smart[14] described a method for detecting organic compounds in the effluent, based on employing nitrogen as the carrier gas, passing the effluent through a tube containing copper oxide heated to dull redness, and measuring the resulting carbon dioxide in the gas stream by means of an infrared analyzer-recorder. Instruments of the latter type are highly sensitive and give a full-scale deflection with 0.01 per cent of CO_2 in N_2 when using a 30 cm cell. It is not necessary to cool the gas emerging from the CuO tube; natural cooling is sufficient. The bulk of water formed should preferably be removed by a drying agent to prevent loss of CO_2 in the condensing water, but the analyzer does not respond to water vapor. The large volume of the 30 cm cell will be a drawback in many cases. Martin and Smart considered the method superior from various aspects to detection by thermal conductivity.

(2) Hydrogenation to Methane. Zlatkis and Ridgway[28] successfully converted a number of organic compounds, including the C_1–C_{12} paraffins, C_5–C_8 naphthenes and C_2–C_5 aldehydes, alcohols and ketones to methane (and water, when oxygen is present) by using hydrogen as carrier gas and passing the column effluent over a nickel catalyst at 350–450°C; water, if present, was removed by a drying agent before the detector (a katharometer).

In the writer's opinion the main points in favor of these methods of conversion are that they yield CO_2 or CH_4 in proportion to the number of carbon atoms in the molecule of the component, so that calculation is facilitated; furthermore, that only one compound (CO_2 or CH_4) has to be detected, whereby calibration problems are largely circumvented. The methods are evidently not limited to the detectors used by the authors, but to any type suitable for carbon dioxide or methane.

Detection by Martin's Density Meter (Gas Density Balance)[15]. This ingenious device*, developed by Martin, provides a highly sensitive method of comparing the densities of the pure carrier gas and the column effluent.

The body of the instrument consists of a copper block (6" x 2" x 2") in which a number of passages have been drilled, as shown in Figure 3.14. The instrument is first balanced out while pure carrier gas is passing into its two inlets. Balancing is done by adjusting the position of rods B, C, D and E (which are comparable to the four resistances of a Wheatstone bridge) until the points X and Y are at exactly the same pressure. The indicator employed for this purpose is an anemometer (A), which reveals minute currents of gas from X to Y or vice versa. The anemometer is shown diagrammatically in Figure 3.15. In the center of the passage XY it contains an

* Patent application filed by National Research Development Council, London. The Martin Density Comparator forms part of a complete apparatus for G.L.C. manufactured by Casella Electronics Ltd., London.

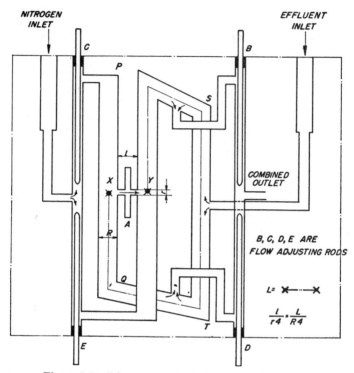

Figure 3.14. Diagram of Martin's gas density balance.

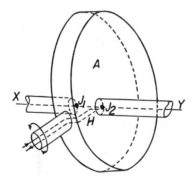

Figure 3.15. Anemometer in Martin's gas density balance.

electric conductor consisting of two sections of copper wire XJ_1 and J_2Y, joined by a short length of constantan wire J_1J_2, so as to form two thermo-junctions J_1 and J_2.

Below J_1J_2 a hairpin heater H, entering the anemometer through a side tube, is situated. By rotating the anemometer, the temperatures of J_1 and

J_2 can be equalized exactly. The smallest current of gas passing through XY will then be revealed by a difference in temperature of the two junctions.

If the carrier gas entering the right-hand inlet contains a volatile component, the density of the gas in bore ST will have a different value and the balance of the U-tube $PQTS$ (Figure 3.14) will be upset, so that a current of gas will flow through the anemometer. As a result of the design, this current is always pure carrier gas. The amount of heat conducted away from the anemometer hence does not depend upon the heat conductivity of the component sensed; true density differences are thus measured.

The density comparator is stated to be at least as sensitive as the thermal conductivity cell. The relationship of the signal to a simple molecular parameter is claimed as a further advantage.

Munday and Primavesi[29] have discussed the analogy between the Martin gas density balance and an electric bridge circuit, the degree of linearity between its response and the density difference of the gas, and the effect of modifications on its performance.

Detection by a Hydrogen Flame and Thermocouple. This method of detection, developed by Scott[30], originally consisted in employing hydrogen, or a mixture of hydrogen and nitrogen, as carrier gas and burning the effluent from the column at a fine jet placed a short distance below a thermocouple. The appearance of an organic compound in the effluent results in a lengthening and rise in temperature of the flame and an increase in voltage of the thermocouple. The normal output of the latter is balanced by a potentiometer network, differences in voltage being fed to a recorder. According to its inventor the peak areas obtained for hydrocarbons having approximately the same heats of combustion are linearly related (within 2 %) to the weight of substance present and independent of the hydrocarbon; with hydrocarbons or other organic compounds differing in heat of combustion, quantitative analysis can also be based on peak area, if the latter is corrected for the heat of combustion.

Wirth[31] found that the use of hydrogen as carrier gas gave a poor base line stability owing to the low viscosity of this gas, and modified the method by employing nitrogen as eluent, injecting the effluent into a constant stream of hydrogen, which is burnt. Wirth's method has further been studied by Henderson and Knox[32] and Primavesi et al.[33].

This detector possesses the advantage of being extremely easy to construct and sensitive, although for full utilization of its sensitivity the ancillary equipment (temperature and flow control) may have to be carefully constructed and accurately regulated.

Detection involving ionization by β-rays, with hydrogen or nitrogen as carrier gas. Within the last few years there have been developed several methods of detection involving an ionization of the effluent gas.

A gas can be ionized by various means, among which those of present
interest are: a) ionization by bombardment with high-speed particles, b)
ionization by the direct application of a sufficiently high electric potential,
and c) ionization in a flame. In all these cases a system of detection can be
founded on the measurement of the current passing through the ionized gas
between two electrodes across which an electric potential is applied, since
this current will be different in the case of the pure carrier gas and of the
carrier gas containing a component of the sample.

Under a separate heading we shall later describe three recently developed
detection systems of extremely high sensitivity, based on the three methods
of ionization mentioned above. The first ionization detector to be published,
which was developed in the laboratories of the Royal/Dutch Shell Group
of Companies[17, 18], can to some extent be regarded as a fore-runner of
these "hypersensitive" methods; it must now be classed as having a moderate to good sensitivity, comparable to (or somewhat better than) that
of a katharometer or the gas density comparator. In this system of detection the carrier gas is hydrogen—nitrogen can also be used, but the results
are then not so easy to interpret—and the gas is bombarded with β-rays
(high-speed electrons) produced by a radio-active element, ^{90}Sr. The saturation current passing through the ionized gas between two electrodes, under
a constant D.C. potential, is measured. A differential technique is followed
One form of apparatus that is employed consists of a cell containing two
chambers, through the first of which the column effluent passes, whilst pure
carrier gas flows through the second. The electric circuit, shown diagrammatically in Figure 3.16, is so arranged that the two ionization currents are
opposed, the differential current being measured by passing it through a
high load resistance. The resulting potential is determined by means of an

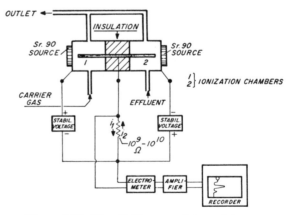

Figure 3.16. Circuit diagram of β-ray detector.

electrometer (for instance a vibrating reed electrometer), which in turn feeds an amplifier and recorder. The voltages applied to the chambers must be well above those producing current saturation and generally lie in the range of 100 to 300 volts.

Figure 3.17 shows details of the double ionization cell employed by Boer[18].

According to theory the ionization current produced should be proportional to a quantity Q, known as the ionization cross section of the molecule. In the case of hydrocarbons, Q is again approximately proportional to the molecular weight, and since the proportionality factor for converting peak areas i the diagram to weight fractions is given by

$$\text{factor} = \frac{Q(\text{component}) - Q(\text{carrier gas})}{\text{mol. weight of component}}$$

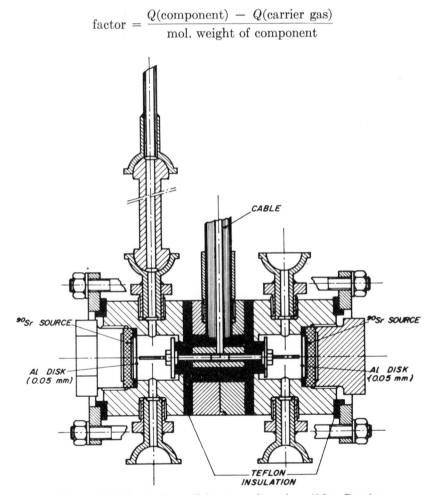

Figure 3-17. Ionization cell for β-ray detection. (After Boer)

and Q (carrier gas) has a small value, it follows that the fractions by weight of the various hydrocarbons can be derived by normalizing the peak areas directly. It is found in practice that this holds with satisfactory accuracy when the carrier gas is hydrogen; with nitrogen discrepancies occur and empirical correction factors must be applied.

The ionization current is insensitive to changes in the rate of flow of the gas, but sensitive to changes in pressure and temperature. An advantage of the double-cell arrangement is that the sensitivity both to pressure and temperature may be compensated for by joining the exits of the two chambers, as shown in Figure 3.16 (the flow of pure reference gas being reduced to a minimum), so that any pressure or temperature fluctuations that occur are nearly identical in both compartments.

The method described is a convenient one, particularly for hydrocarbons, but the ancillary apparatus required is slightly more complicated than that needed for katharometer detection. [90]Sr sources are obtainable in various convenient forms, which with proper precautions in handling are relatively safe to use.

As an example of a record obtained with β-ray ionization and hydrogen as carrier gas, a curve published by Boer[18] is reproduced in Figure 3.18. It was obtained on a synthetic mixture of aromatic hydrocarbons with a column containing mellitic ester as stationary phase. The peak areas were determined automatically by using a low-inertia electromotor with counter. The figures obtained in this analysis are compared with the known composition of the sample in Table 3.1.

The method of detection developed by Lovelock, to be described on page 100, is also based on ionization by irradiation from a [90]Sr β-ray source. The main factor rendering Lovelock's detector very much more sensitive than that just described is the use of argon or helium instead of hydrogen or nitrogen as carrier gas. As will be explained, the mechanism of ionization in the former two gases is different to that in the two last mentioned. The extreme sensitivity of the argon detector is, of course, not always essential nor even desirable, and the β-ray-hydrogen method therefore still constitutes a useful form of detection.

Detection by the Light-Emissivity of a Flame. Grant[34] described a detector consisting of a small flame of purified coal gas into which the effluent of the column is injected (the carrier gas employed is nitrogen). A reflector and lens concentrate the light of the flame onto a selenium photo-cell; organic components in the effluent cause the emissivity of the flame to increase. The photo-cell is placed in a suitable electric circuit whereby the differential voltages produced are fed to an amplifying recorder. Precautions are taken to prevent condensation in the effluent.

It would seem that the method, which appears to be sensitive, is capable of being developed further, possibly with the use of spectroscopic criteria.

One of the features of this detector is that it frequently gives a response differing markedly from that of a katharometer, a fact that could be of value for purposes of identification. It is suitable for high-temperature analyses.

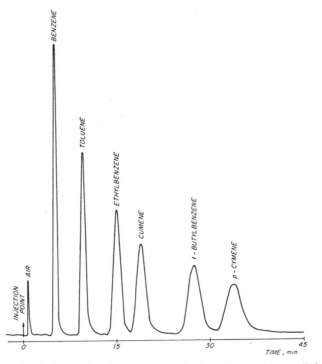

Figure 3.18. Analysis of mixture of aromatic hydrocarbons, using radiological detection.

Column packing: 40 parts mellitic ester on 100 parts "Sterchamol" 40–100 mesh; column length: 180 cm; column temp.: 122°C; hydrogen flow: 2.5 l/h; sample size: 5 mg; detector: β-ray unit; integrator: low inertia motor and counter ("Electro Methods Ltd"). (After Boer.)

TABLE 3.1. ANALYSIS OF A SYNTHETIC MIXTURE OF AROMATIC HYDROCARBONS;
RADIOLOGICAL DETECTION

Component	Composition Calculated from Peak Areas (% wt)	Actual Composition (% wt)
Benzene	16.3	16.5
Toluene	17.2	17.0
Ethylbenzene	17.0	17.1
Cumene	16.2	16.2
tert.-Butylbenzene*	17.2 ⎫ 33.3	17.4 ⎫ 33.1
p-Cymene*	16.1 ⎭	15.7 ⎭

* Slight overlap.

Detection Based on Thermal Conductivity

The principle of the method is that heat is conducted away from a hot body, situated in a gas, at a rate depending on the nature of the gas, other factors being constant. The variation in the amount of heat thus removed is considerable; Freon, for instance, has only about one-fifth of the heat conductivity of air, while hydrogen has approximately seven times its conductivity.

Detection instruments based on this property are known as thermal conductivity cells or katharometers. The latter word, which was introduced by Shakespear[19] will be adopted in this book. Katharometers usually contain a wire (or wires) of some metal, preferably having a high temperature coefficient of resistance, mounted axially in a space containing the gas. The wire is heated by a constant electric current. The conductivity of the surrounding gas is a factor determining the temperature of the wire and consequently also its resistance; the latter property is measured. If the presence of a foreign substance in the gas is to be detected by this means, it is obviously essential that this substance shall have a thermal conductivity differing from that of the pure gas. For quantitative determination, the thermal conductivity of the mixture should preferably be approximately a linear function of its composition in the range concerned; this condition is, with but few exceptions, fulfilled fairly closely by the dilute mixtures involved in G.L.C.

Since absolute measurements of thermal conductivity are difficult, a differential procedure is generally adopted. This is done by employing two gas channels and wires that are as nearly as possible identical. Pure carrier gas flows through the first channel, and the same (or an equal) current of gas, which has passed through the column, through the second. Any differences in resistance of the two wires due to the effects of volatile components in the effluent are then recorded. This may conveniently be done by means of a Wheatstone bridge circuit (Figure 3.19) containing the two heated wires C_1 and C_2 and two equal resistances R_3 and R_4. If the bridge is first balanced with pure carrier gas surrounding both C_1 and C_2, and the effluent subsequently becomes admixed with a component having a different thermal conductivity, the result will be an out-of-balance potential between A and B, which can be amplified and recorded on a chart.

It should be noted that heat does not leave the wire only as the result of conduction by the gas, but also by convection (viz., by heating the flowing gas), by radiation and by secondary effects, e.g., conduction through the electric leads, etc. In a properly designed cell these quantities are small compared with the heat lost by conduction. In a symmetrical double cell they are largely balanced out. The various effects of asymmetry occurring in a differential katharometer are, however, important and will be considered later.

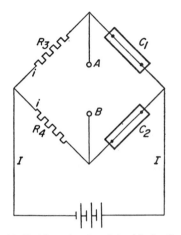

Figure 3.19. Bridge circuit of double katharometer.

Factors Determining the Sensitivity of a Katharometer

The sensitivity of a katharometer largely depends upon its design, that is to say on the geometry of the cell. There are also several other factors that must be considered in developing such an instrument, for instance its sensitivity to small fluctuations in gas rate and pressure, and its speed of response; these will be referred to later. A few basic factors affecting the sensitivity of katharometers will, however, be discussed briefly. For a more detailed account of the instrument and the underlying theory, the reader is referred to the literature [20, 21, 22].

A strict mathematical treatment of the thermal conductivity cell, taking into account all subsidiary effects (radiation, convection, etc.) is complicated. For the purpose in view it will be permissible to assume that heat is transported only as a result of conduction by the surrounding gas.

Then, if an electrically heated wire is placed in the axis of a cylindrical space filled with gas, the heat transported by the gas from the wire to the walls of the cylinder, at equilibrium, is equal to the heat generated by the current in the wire, i.e.

$$i^2 R_{t_w} = a\lambda_{t_m} \cdot (t_w - t_c) \tag{1}$$

in which

i = the current in the wire

R_{t_w} = the resistance of the wire at its own mean temperature, t_w

t_c = the temperature of the cylinder wall

λ_{t_m} = the thermal conductivity of the gas at a mean temperature t_m ; for practical purposes t_m may be approximated by $t_m \approx \frac{1}{2}(t_w + t_c)$

a = an instrument constant.

The temperature dependence of resistance of the wire and of the thermal conductivity of the gas are given by

$$R_t = R_0(1 + \alpha t) \tag{2}$$

and

$$\lambda_t = \lambda_0(1 + \beta t) \tag{3}$$

(the subscript zero refers to some standard state).

Let us assume, for an approximate calculation, that β is negligibly small and that the value of λ_{t_m} changes to the extent of $\Delta\lambda$, owing to a small amount of a component as vapor in the gas. The result will be a change in t_w by Δt. If the total energy $i^2 R_{t_w}$ is kept constant it follows from Eq. (1) that

$$\lambda_{t_m}(t_w - t_c) = (\lambda_{t_m} + \Delta\lambda)(t_w + \Delta t - t_c) \tag{4}$$

or (neglecting second order infinitesimals):

$$\Delta t = \epsilon(t_w - t_c) \tag{4a}$$

where $\epsilon(= \Delta\lambda/\lambda)$ is the relative change in thermal conductivity. The change in temperature Δt causes a change ΔR in the resistance of the wire given by

$$\Delta R = \alpha R_0 \Delta t = \frac{\alpha}{1 + \alpha t_w} \cdot R_{t_w} \cdot \epsilon \cdot (t_w - t_c) \tag{5}$$

If now (see Figure 3.19) $R_3 = R_4 = \gamma C_1$, and the total bridge current is I, the out-of-balance voltage E of the bridge, between A and B, is given by a well-known formula as:

$$E = \frac{\Delta R}{4} \cdot I \cdot \frac{2\gamma}{1 + \gamma} \tag{6}$$

($\gamma = 1$ would signify that the fixed resistors and the wires have equal resistances).

By substituting from Eq. (5):

$$E = \tfrac{1}{4} I \cdot R_{t_w} \cdot \frac{\alpha(t_w - t_c)}{1 + \alpha t_w} \cdot \epsilon \cdot \frac{2\gamma}{1 + \gamma} \tag{7}$$

We will now define the absolute sensitivty η. If ϵ, the relative change in thermal conductivity due to a mole fraction p of vapor in the gas, is a linear function of p (as can usually be assumed for the small percentages involved), E will also be a linear function of p and hence

$$E = \eta \cdot p \quad \text{or} \quad \eta = \frac{E}{p} \tag{8}$$

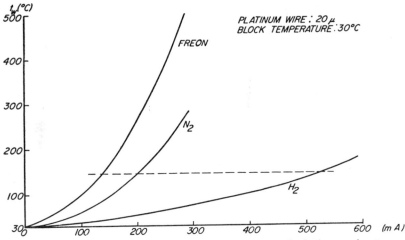

Figure 3.20. Relation between total bridge current and platinum wire temperature, t_w, for Freon 12 ($\lambda = 0.337$), N_2 ($\lambda = 1.000$) and H_2 ($\lambda = 7.160$) as the surrounding gas.

Means of influencing η through the various parameters occurring in Equation (7) can now be considered.

Effect of Changing the Current (and Temperature) of the Wires. An increase in the current affects E; it results in a higher wire temperature (see Figure 3.20) i.e., in an increase in $t_w - t_c$, and (since the wires as a rule have a positive temperature coefficient) in an increased value of R_{t_w}. As a rule ϵ falls somewhat, since thermal conductivities tend to converge at higher temperatures, but the net result in Equation (7) is a considerably larger value of E, and consequently also of the sensitivity η.

As a practical illustration it may be stated that, with butane in nitrogen, a twofold increase in I results in roughly a fivefold increase in η.

The conclusion therefore is: *a higher current (a higher heater temperature) greatly increases sensitivity*. The stability of the base-line, however, thereby becomes correspondingly lower, and this fact sets a practical limit to the sensitivity attainable in practice by increasing t_w.

Effect of Thermal Conductivity of the Carrier Gas. If the carrier gas is changed to another having a different thermal conductivity, the amount of heat conducted away will be different, and, if the current in the wire remains the same, its temperature will be established at another value. Figure 3.20 shows the relationship, experimentally determined, for a particular type of cell, between the current and the average temperature of the platinum wire, as calculated from its resistance. It gives curves for hydrogen, nitrogen and Freon 12, respectively. It will be seen that for maintaining a wire temperature of 150°C, about 130 mA was required with Freon 12, about 200 mA with nitrogen and about 530 mA with hydrogen, the latter gas having the highest heat conductivity of the three.

A discussion of the effect of λ can best be based on conditions of constant wire temperature (and appropriate values of I). Let us consider a change-over from nitrogen to hydrogen as carrier gas.

Most organic components (the lower hydrocarbons in particular) have thermal conductivities far closer to that of nitrogen than of hydrogen. Thus, with hydrogen, the quantity $\Delta\lambda$ becomes greater, and consequently also ϵ.

Hence, *for most organic compounds the sensitivity with hydrogen is considerably greater than with nitrogen.*

The use of hydrogen, however, has its drawbacks. Catalytic reactions of organic compounds with hydrogen in the presence of the platinum wire have been experienced and have resulted in a complete upsetting of the signal by the heat effects involved. The use of helium, which also has a high value of λ, would avoid this difficulty, but is expensive in some countries. A practical drawback to using hydrogen in cells designed for nitrogen is that the higher current necessitates larger storage batteries, but this may be overcome by employing voltage-stabilized rectifiers instead. Both hydrogen and helium have been successfully employed for several purposes. A further advantage of hydrogen is that the ratio ϵ/p becomes much less sensitive to the nature of the component sensed, a fact considerably facilitating calibration of the detector, particularly for components of similar type.

Table 3.2, in which the thermal conductivities of the usual carrier gases and of frequently occurring types of components are listed, may be a useful guide in the selection of a carrier gas for a particular analysis.

Thermal Conductivity of Mixtures of Gases. It should be noted, however, that the values of λ given in Table 3.2 refer to the pure substances only, and that the thermal conductivity of a mixture of two gases is in general not a linear function of composition (see, for instance, Lindsay and Bromley[22]). On the other hand, at the very high dilutions generally prevailing in G.L.C., the interpolation is usually linear* if an "effective" value of λ is assumed for the minor component. This fact is illustrated in Figure 3.21, which shows the measured values of λ for mixtures of nitrogen and carbon dioxide, and nitrogen and isobutane. In mixtures containing a very low proportion of CO_2 or i-C_4H_{10} the thermal conductivity behaves as though the admixture had a value of $\lambda'(CO_2)$ or $\lambda'(i$-$C_4)$, respectively. The close adjacency of the true thermal conductivities $\lambda(CO_2)$ and $\lambda(i$-$C_4)$ and the

---

* Sometimes even a restricted linearity cannot be postulated. Thus the curve for acetylene in nitrogen shows a maximum in λ at about 4 per cent C_2H_2. The elution peaks for C_2H_2 in N_2 consequently may appear to stand in depressions on the baseline.

TABLE 3.2. THERMAL CONDUCTIVITY (λ)* OF GASES AND VAPORS[20]

	$\lambda \times 10^5$ (0°C)	λ/λ_{air} (0°C)	λ/λ_{air} (100°C)
Air	5.83	1.00	1.00
Nitrogen	5.81	0.996	0.996
Hydrogen	41.60	7.15	7.10
Carbon dioxide	3.52	0.605	0.700
Helium	34.80	5.97	5.53
Freon 12	1.96	0.344	—
Ammonia	5.22	0.897	1.04
Water	—	—	0.775
Methane	7.21	1.25	1.45
Ethane	4.36	0.750	0.970
Propane	3.58	0.615	0.832
n-Butane	3.22	0.552	0.744
n-Pentane	3.12	0.535	0.702
n-Hexane	2.96	0.508	0.662
Cyclohexane	—	—	0.576
Benzene	—	0.370	0.583
Ethene	4.19	0.720	0.980
Acetylene	4.53	0.777	0.900
Chloroform	1.58	0.269	0.328
Methyl chloride	2.20	0.377	0.530
Methanol	3.45	0.592	0.727
Ethanol	—	—	0.700
Acetone	2.37	0.406	0.557
Ethyl ether	—	—	0.747
Methyl acetate	1.61	0.421	—

* In cals./cm. sec.°C

wide discrepancy between the effective values (λ') also indicates that in extreme cases the order may even be reversed: a component of a lower thermal conductivity than another may, in some cases, produce a greater change in λ at the same high dilution in the carrier gas.

Influence of the Block Temperature. If, with a constant current, the temperature of the katharometer block is reduced, more heat will be conducted away and the temperature of the wire becomes lower; R_{t_w} therefore decreases. ϵ, however, tends to increase, owing to the divergence of thermal conductivities at low temperature levels. The result is that *sensitivity increases with a reduction in wall temperature.*

Obviously, however, the katharometer must be operated at a temperature sufficient to prevent condensation of components.

The Katharometer Constant. It has been shown that for a straight cylindrical wire the instrument constant (a) may be expressed in terms of the length of the wire l and the radii r_c and r_w of the channel and wire,

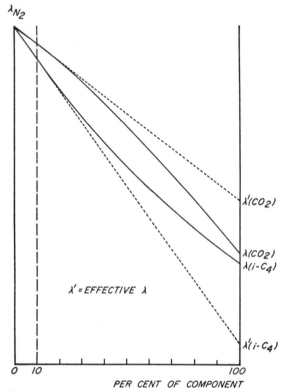

Figure 3.21. Thermal conductivity of two gas mixtures, one with a positive and one with a negative deviation from ideality.

respectively:

$$a = 2\pi l / \ln \frac{r_c}{r_w} \qquad (9)$$

From Eqs. (1), (7) and (9) it follows that the sensitivity rises with an increasing value of l and a decreasing value of r_c. The influence of r_w is less easily derived, but it can be shown that η also increases markedly with decreasing wire diameter.

Considerations of a constructional nature set limits to the length of wire, the smallness of the bore and the fineness of wire that can be chosen. The length of the wire can be increased by coiling it. (A modified formula for a is then obtained; see Daynes[20].) Platinum wires less than 20 μ in diameter have insufficient strength. Tungsten (which has somewhat different values for α and for ρ, the specific resistance) can be employed in thinner wires than platinum. Experiments with a cell of a form to be described later (see

TABLE 3.3

Metal	Resistivity ρ $\mu\Omega/cm^3$ (20°C)	Temp. Coeff. α (20°C)	$\alpha \sqrt{\rho}$ ($\times 10^3$)
Silver	1.62	3.61 $\times$ 10^{-3}	4.58
Copper	1.72	3.93 "	5.15
Aluminum	2.82	4.21 "	7.07
Tungsten	5.75	4.54 "	10.89
Nickel	7.24	4.91 "	13.21
Iron	9.78	6.34 "	19.82
Platinum	10.6	3.69 "	12.03
Invar	75	2.0 "	17.32
Antimony	41.7	3.6 "	23.26
Bismuth	120	4.0 "	43.82

p. 94), in which the 20 μ (27 Ω) platinum wires were replaced by 10 μ (80 Ω) tungsten wires, gave an increase in sensitivity by approximately a factor 3, mainly as the result of reduced wire diameter. Such an instrument also consumes less current. Some disadvantages experienced by the writer with tungsten-wire katharometers (which are still in an experimental stage) are the more serious permanent drift that occurs, and the increased difficulty of construction with respect to platinum.

Wires of other metals might be considered. A useful criterion for their suitability is the product $\alpha\sqrt{\rho}$, to which the sensitivity η proves to be roughly proportional, other conditions being equal. The values of ρ, α and $\alpha\sqrt{\rho}$ for a number of metals are collected in Table 3.3. As already stated, however, the choice of metal also depends upon secondary considerations. Thus antimony and bismuth, with their high values of $\alpha\sqrt{\rho}$, are ruled out because they cannot be drawn into wires.

The use of semi-conducting layers (thermistors) instead of simple conductors in katharometers appears to offer considerable promise. Thermistors have far higher values of $\alpha\sqrt{\rho}$ than the metals normally used. The selection of matched pairs of thermistors and their reproducibility in the long run still seem to involve difficulties. The main application of thermistors is in the range of low and moderate temperatures.

Katharometers in Their Practical Form

Geometry of the Filament. As already stated, the sensitive element may be a heated straight or coiled wire or a thermistor; unless there is a danger of chemical attack the body is preferably a metal block for reasons of temperature uniformity, though other constructions have also been employed (see below).

A point of importance is the location of the sensing element in the gas. Figure 3.22 shows three alternatives[16]. The location most frequently adopted is in a channel through which the whole gas current passes (Fig. 3.22a).

a
RAPID RESPONSE
SENSITIVE TO FLOW FLUCTUATIONS

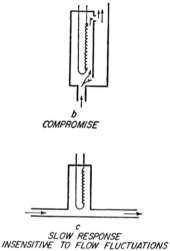

b
COMPROMISE

c
SLOW RESPONSE
INSENSITIVE TO FLOW FLUCTUATIONS

Figure 3.22. Locations of sensing wire in katharometers. (After Dimbat, Porter and Stross.)

A cell of this design has a rapid response but is sensitive to fluctuations in flow. (This effect, and methods of minimizing it, will be discussed later). Figure 3.22 (c) shows the location of the filament in a side-chamber off the gas stream; this construction reduces the influence of fluctuations in flow but causes slow response. Figure 3.22 (b) illustrates a compromise between Fig. 3.22 (a) and Fig. 3.22 (c).

Examples of Katharometers. Reference will now be made to some katharometers employed in practice. Katharometers are obtainable in commerce, or may be constructed by the investigator to his own design*.

Phillips[23], in his earlier work, used a single cell. Later, this was developed into a double cell constructed of glass which is depicted in Figure 3.23. In this instrument the "block" is formed by a mercury jacket containing the two channels C and D. The mercury jacket is maintained at a constant temperature by a part of the vapor bath that is used for thermo-

* Katharometers are marketed by the Gow-Mac Instrument Co., 100 King's Road, Madison, New Jersey, who also supply coiled wire elements in matched pairs for those intending to make their own instrument.

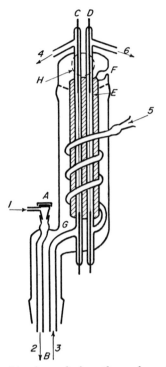

Figure 3.23. Double channel glass thermal-conductivity cells.
Gas path indicated by arrows 1 to 6. Sample injected at A, column sealed on at B, channel for measuring vapour concentration C, compensating channel D, mercury jacket E, mercury expansion bulb F, vapor jacket G, condenser connection H. (After Phillips.)

statting the column. An instrument with glass channels has also been described by Brooks, Murray and Williams[44]. In this katharometer the two channels are encased in a brass block which again is heated by the same vapors of a boiling solvent that maintain the column at a uniform temperature.

Katharometers with glass channels, which are still occasionally used, are relatively cheap and easy to construct and in the author's opinion may give good service if the highest constancy is not essential. Experience has shown, however, that glass-channeled cells tend to give poor base-line stabilities at elevated temperatures (e.g., 150°C). This fact is probably due to the difference in expansion of glass and metal, with consequent slackening of the wires and sensitivity to variations in flow.

Metal-housed katharometers, in simple or more complicated constructions according to the performance required, are at present in general use. Instruments of the filament type have maintained their place alongside those with thermistors. The latter are the more sensitive, but their construction is slightly more delicate and the maximum temperature of operation is lower, especially if the instrument is used in a reducing atmosphere. Taylor[35] has, however, employed thermistors up to 200°C. Some improvement with respect to attack by gases at higher temperatures has been obtained by providing the thermistor with a glass coating. A definite advantage of the thermistor is that it is point-shaped, so that the construction of a detector with a very small dead volume is possible.

Katharometers of the hot-wire type can if desired be made from simple commercial components. Felton[36], for instance, used model airplane glow plugs as sensing elements in an instrument capable of being used at temperatures in excess of 550°C. Stuve[37] made a katharometer with toy train electric light bulbs, from which the glass envelopes had been removed. A much more sensitive and delicate instrument that can be employed up to about 300°C has been described by Davies and Johnson[24]. The data on the characteristics of katharometer cells that are given in the next sections were obtained in the author's laboratory with a metal-housed instrument that has found considerable use in the Royal/Dutch Shell Group of Companies for research work and refinery control. It is of the double-channel type and consists of a copper body with brass end-pieces. The platinum wires (resistance about 27 Ω) are stretched in their channels by beryllium copper springs, metal-in-glass seals being used for insulation.

Characteristics of Katharometers

Symmetry of the Cells. It is found in practice that double-channel katharometers can show a very appreciable asymmetry between the two units. Even with great care in the selection of wires, in mounting them axially, etc., a complete identity between the two channels must not be relied upon. Asymmetry inherent in the instrument can manifest itself in various ways:

(1) Asymmetry on varying the wall temperature of both cells. If the cells, with the same gas in the two channels, are balanced at one wall temperature, the balance may prove to be upset at another wall temperature. Figure 3.24, a and b show the magnitude of such discrepancies found with carefully constructed cells; in each case two double cells were balanced at 30 and 120°C, respectively, and the wall temperature was then varied.

(2) Asymmetry on varying the current (wire temperature). Figure 3.24, c shows similar out-of-balance voltages produced in two double cells on varying the current passing through the two wires after the bridge had been balanced at 200 mA.

(3) Asymmetry on varying the rate of gas flow equally in both channels. This effect is illustrated in a corresponding manner for two double cells in

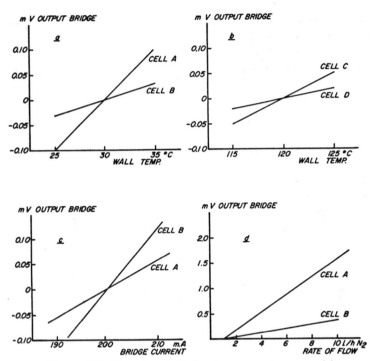

Figure 3.24. Base line drift due to asymmetry, caused by:
a and b, changes in wall temperature; c, changes in current (wire temperature); d, changes in gas rate (same flow in both channels).

Figure 3.24, d. The latter phenomenon (due to cell asymmetry) must not be confused with the discrepancies caused by varying the gas flow in one channel with respect to that in the other.

The conclusions to be drawn from these observations are self-evident: the parameters in question must be kept sufficiently constant, viz., *the katharometer must be thermostatted, the heater current carefully controlled and the gas rate kept at the same value.*

The effects of cell asymmetry just referred to are, of course, accidental and will vary from instrument to instrument. For accurate work it will frequently repay the trouble of determining the magnitude of these effects by special experiments in which the parameter in question is varied, all others being kept constant. It then becomes possible to state the precision with which the particular operating variable must be controlled in order to insure that the base line drift, due to this cause, shall not exceed a permissible fraction (say 0.2 per cent) of the full-scale deflection of the recorder. As an example, the case of katharometer A in Figure 3.24 may be considered. This instrument produces a bridge output varying by 0.02 mV per degree variation of wall temperature. If a recorder with a maximum deflection corresponding to 2.5 mV is used, the permissible base line drift may be taken to be 0.2 per cent of 2.5 mV or 0.005 mV. The latter figure corresponds to an alteration of 0.25°C in wall temperature; the katharometer should therefore be thermostatted to within ±0.125°C.

Gas Flow Effects—Location of the Filament. The manner in which changes in gas flow can affect the katharometer system as a whole depends upon the arrangement of the flow through the two channels. Three such arrangements, shown diagrammatically in Figure 3.25, a, b and c, are encountered in practice.

(a) The gas passes in series through (1) the chromatographic column, (2) the first channel, (3) a cold trap for removing components of the sample, (4) the second channel.

(b) In this arrangement we have flow in parallel through (1) the column

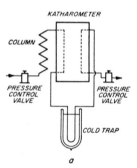

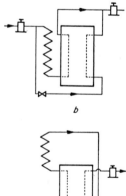

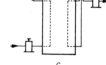

Figure 3.25. Flow systems in katharometers.

and first channel and (2) a controllable restriction, duplicating the column, and the second channel.

(c) This arrangement has series flow through (1) the first channel, (2) the column, and (3) the second channel.

If, in arrangement (a), the cold trap has no appreciable resistance, the gas rates and pressures in the two channels will be virtually equal. All that is required is a control of the gas rate for avoiding possible asymmetry, as described above. With this provision, system (a) can be expected to give a good base-line stability. It requires, however, an effective removal of sample components by chilling, a provision which may not be possible or convenient in every case. For routine analyses this requirement makes the arrangement less suitable.

With arrangement (b) it can be shown experimentally that if the bridge is balanced with an equal flow of the same gas through the parallel channels, and the flow in one of the channels is then increased, an appreciable out-of-balance voltage results. Figure 3.26, *a* illustrates this effect for 3, 6 and 10 l/h of nitrogen in one channel. From the equal slopes of the three lines it appears that the out-of-balance voltage is mainly dependent on the difference between the rates in the two channels and not on the actual flow rate. It is due to the fact that the small amount of heat removed by convection is now unequal in the two channels, i.e., not to asymmetry of the instrument. The practical disadvantage of the method is that equality of flow in the two channels depends on the resistances of the column and of the regulating restriction; if either of these varies during operation a variation in the base line must occur. In practice the required constancy of the restriction is not easily realized.

The influence of flow effects in arrangement (c) is slightly more complicated. The two channels are separated by a restriction (the column), so that the pressure in the first channel is higher than in the second and the volumetric flow rate is correspondingly lower. Suppose that with a certain inlet pressure at the first channel and a constant (say atmospheric) outlet pressure at the second the bridge is brought in balance. Now let the inlet pressure be altered, whereby the gas rate through the whole also changes. Two separate effects may now be expected: (1) the different gas pressure in the first channel will alter the response; (2) the (approximately equivalent) change in the gas rates through both channels may produce a zero drift owing to asymmetry, as discussed on p. 94, (Figure 3.24, d). The latter change may, however, be either positive or negative, according to the idiosyncrasies of the instrument. In this case it is important which of the two openings of the katharometer is taken as the inlet and which as the outlet. In the one case, any change occurring owing to effect (2) will increase effect (1); on reversing inlet and outlet, effect (2) will reduce effect (1).

System (c) is the simplest and most generally applicable in practice

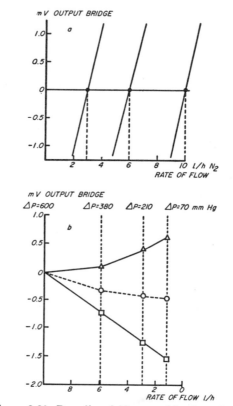

Figure 3.26. Base line drift caused by flow effects.
In *a*, arrangement *b* of Figure 3.25; in *b*, arrangement *c* of Figure 3.25.

and has been employed in the greater part of the writer's work. It is, however, very desirable to insure that the two flow effects discussed above shall tend to be subtractive and not additive. This may be carried out as follows. The two channels are connected in series, first without any intermediate restriction. The bridge is balanced at a certain gas rate, say 10 l/h, and the zero drift caused by a gradual reduction in gas rate is determined. The points are plotted, and some course as shown by the dotted line in Figure 3.26, b is obtained. The procedure is now repeated with a restriction (the column or an artificial gas resistance) between the two channels, the bridge being again balanced at, say, 10 l/h gas rate. The latter series is also repeated after reversing inlet and outlet. In this way the two solid lines in Figure 3.26, b might be found. The line having the least divergence from zero is the position to choose. (The dotted line should furnish a check by lying midway between the solid lines.) The entry and outlet of the cell should then be permanently marked as such.

Conclusions. After considering the various sources of error to which katharometers are subject, we can summarize the precautions that must be taken in designing and using them as follows.

(1) The two cells of the katharometer must have a high degree of geometric and physical symmetry. (This involves: identical wires at the same tension, identical channels, axial centering, etc.)*

(2) The katharometer must be maintained at a constant temperature. Regulation to within, say, $\pm0.05°C$ up to 100°C and $\pm0.1°C$ above 100°C will usually suffice.

(3) The heating current should be kept constant (say to within 0.1 per cent).

(4) By the use of sensitive pressure regulators, the gas rate should be controlled. As a rule it should not vary by more than 20 ml/h for packed columns.

(5) If the channels are connected in series, with the column in between, care should be taken that the errors due to variations in flow and pressure tend to compensate and not intensify one another.

Finally, it may be pointed out that the appearance of a component in the effluent gas causes a surge in the flow which also produces a signal. This surge effect (which, like the change in thermal conductivity, is proportional to concentration at the high dilutions occurring in practice) is, however, included in the calibration constant determined for the component. It need therefore not be taken into account, as long as calibration is carried out under the same conditions as are maintained in the actual analysis.

Differential Methods. *Hypersensitive Detectors*

In a chairman's address at the London Symposium on Gas Chromatography in 1956, A. T. James gave a critical comparison of the methods of detection used at that time, concluding with the words: "The field is open for the development of more sensitive and simpler detectors, and it is hoped that workers in this field will not rest content with the instruments at present available". In the intervening two years the speaker's hopes have been fulfilled, particularly as regards the evolution of more sensitive detectors. Among the principles which were suggested by James that based on ionization has proved to be the most fruitful.

The Low-Pressure Electric Discharge Detector. Harley and Pretorius[38] and Ryce and Bryce[39] have described electric discharge ionization detectors having sensitivities that are several orders of magnitude higher than the instruments previously used. Pitkethly[40] developed the low-pressure discharge detector into a practical form on the basis of Harley and Pretorius'

---

* The two other resistances in the Wheatstone bridge must have the same temperature. This is ensured by winding them on the same metal core.

design. The working of the instrument is founded on the sensitivity of low-pressure gas discharges to small changes in the composition of the gas. The apparatus incorporates two chromatographic columns, one of which is charged with a sample; the columns are connected to lengths of fine-bored capillary tubing (providing the required pressure drop), which are directly sealed to the discharge tubes, for which small commercial neon tubes (Philips type SBC) were employed. The two electrode gaps form arms of a bridge circuit supplied with about 400 volts stabilized D.C., the out-of-balance potential being amplified and recorded. Nitrogen was used as carrier gas and the optimum pressure in the discharge tubes was 3–5 mm. The ultimate sensitivity for C_3 and C_4 hydrocarbons was approximately 10^{-11} mole, the response being then of the same order as the base-line noise.

The Argon-β-Ray Detector. Earlier in this chapter a description was given of a detector depending for its action on the ionization of the effluent with β-rays and the determination of the current passing through the ionized gas between two electrodes under a constant D.C. potential. The carrier gas used in this method was hydrogen or nitrogen. Lovelock[41] has added to this detector a new element, that brings it into the same order of sensitivity as the discharge detector mentioned above.

Lovelock describes the principle of this instrument, and its difference with respect to the β-ray detector employing hydrogen or nitrogen, as follows:

"The absorption of ionizing radiation by gases produces ions and excited but unionized atoms and molecules. With most gases the lifetime of the metastable atoms is short, *ca* 10^{-9} secs., consequently under constant conditions of irradiation the ions, which have a comparatively long life-time, greatly outnumber the excited but nonionized atoms. The rare gases are unusual in their possession of long-lived metastable atoms, and in these gases the concentration of metastable atoms approaches that of ions during steady irradiation. In the pure gas the metastable atoms eventually decay to the normal state with the emission of radiation. In the presence of small traces of other gases the metastable rare atoms can, during their lifetime, transfer their energy of excitation by collision. If the ionization potential of the gas molecules is less than the excitation potential of the rare gas atoms the transfer of energy on collision leads to the ionization of the added gas. The molecules of most organic compounds have ionization potentials lower than the excitation potential of helium, neon and argon, and are ionized on collision with the metastable atoms of these noble gases".

The principal difference between the β-ray detector employing hydrogen or nitrogen and that making use of the rare gases is hence that in the latter the signal produced by the component is very much larger owing to the greater ionization induced by the excited atoms of carrier gas. The background is hence almost "silent" with respect to these signals.

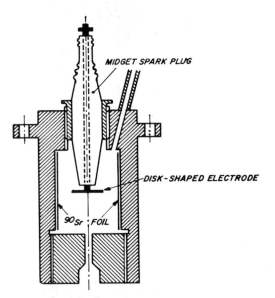

Figure 3.27. Argon β-ray detector (after Lovelock).

For practical purposes the use of helium and argon, which are both available in cylinders at reasonable prices, can be considered. The impurities in commercial argon are relatively harmless, whilst those in helium are not, so that Lovelock chose the former. (The use of pure helium, which, though expensive, is even more effective than argon might, however, be justified in modern columns with extremely low flow rates.)

The detector consists of an ionization chamber (see Fig. 3.27), having a central brass electrode which is insulated from the body by means of a Teflon washer. As in the β-ray method previously described, a ^{90}Sr source of ionizing radiation is employed, in the form of a leaf containing the isotope bonded between silver foil. The use of this dangerous isotope in the latter form involves no hazards if the usual precautions against direct radiation are taken. The ionization current is conveyed to a milliammeter or recorder by a D.C. amplifier.

The Lovelock detector is capable of responding to as little as 2.10^{-12} moles of most organic compounds, its response to different molecular species being closely similar and linear with concentration over a considerable range.

The Flame Ionization Detector. This detector has been developed by McWilliam and Dewar[42], and depends on changes in the electrical conductivity of a flame burning a mixture of hydrogen and nitrogen, on the introduction of a foreign compound.

The apparatus is similar to Scott's flame detector, but the thermocouple

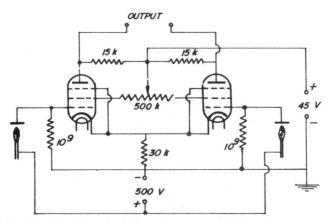

Figure 3.28. Dual-jet flame ionization detector with impedance conversion circuit (after McWilliam and Dewar). (Tubes: 4-V electrometer tubes ME 1400)

has been replaced by an electrode just over the flame, a D.C. potential of about 500 volts being applied between this electrode and the metal burner jet, which functions as second electrode. As a rule the best results were obtained by making the jet positive and the upper electrode negative. The air for combustion must be carefully filtered, as dust contributes greatly to the background "noise". In its most sensitive form, the detector has two flames, one burning the effluent, the other the pure carrier gas. McWilliam and Dewar, who employed a recorder of high imput impedance (100 kΩ), used a "long-tailed pair" circuit as shown in Fig. 3.28 for impedance conversion*). This dual jet detector has the same order of sensitivity as the argon β-ray detector. The base-line is remarkably insensitive to changes in nitrogen/hydrogen ratio, total flow rate, vibration, ambient temperature or minor variations in the supply of filtered air. The detector appears to be quite insensitive to carbon dioxide and inorganic vapours, e.g. water. The latter fact may be of importance in the analyses of water-containing samples, where a long "water tail" otherwise tends to mask the separation of superimposed components.

Ionization phenomena in a flame are as yet not fully understood. The ionization potential of most organic compounds lies between 9 and 12 eV. The actual degree of ionization occurring in a flame containing an organic material is much greater than would be expected from the normal I.P., the effective I.P. being rather of the magnitude of 5 eV. Stern[43] suggests an explanation by the formation of carbon aggregates and their subsequent ionization. (The I.P. of solid carbon is 4.6 eV.)

* A second impedance conversion stage would be required for a low-impedance recorder. Alternatively, the conversion may be performed directly with an instrument such as a vibrating reed electrometer, as used in the earlier β-ray method[45].

At present it seems that the Lovelock and the McWilliam detectors both offer great promise for the future. They are simple to construct, have little background and the response is linear to a considerable degree. The flame ionization detector has the advantage of being operable at elevated temperatures (300°C and higher), but the disadvantage that the sample is lost.

It should be noted that with all highly sensitive detectors, using very small samples, vapors of the stationary phase will tend to produce a noticeable signal unless its volatility is quite low. Another point of importance is that it is essential, if a rapid and sharp response is to be obtained from sensitive detectors, that the dead volume should be kept as low as possible. This applies particularly when they are used with certain highly efficient types of column recently developed (see Chapter 7), in which the gas rates and total volumes of carrier gas have been reduced to extremely small values.

Assemblies of Chromatographic Apparatus

Except perhaps for certain branches of laboratory research work and for incidental analyses, the various components constituting the apparatus for gas chromatography may with advantage be encased in suitable housing as a complete unit. This will have the recording equipment and the essential controls mounted on a panel; it must of course be so constructed that parts, such as the column, which may have to be interchanged or may need attention can be easily reached.

Since such unit assemblies can be built up in numerous ways and their form has no influence on the principles of gas chromatography, these aggregates will not be dealt with further in this book. Several complete sets of equipment are now available commercially.

REFERENCES

1. See, for instance, Ray, N. H., *Analyst*, **80**, 853 (1955).
2. James, A. T., and Martin, A. J. P., *Biochem. J. (London)*, **50**, 679 (1952).
3. James, D. H., and Phillips, C. S. G., *J. Sci. Instr.*, **29**, 362 (1952).
4. Ashbury, G. K., Davies, A. J., and Drinkwater, J. W., "A Versatile Gas-Liquid Partition Chromatography Apparatus Developed for Analytical Use," Dallas Symposium on Vapour Phase Chromatography, American Chemical Society, April 1956.
5. Porter, P. E., Deal, Jr., C. H., and Stross, F. H., *J. Am. Chem. Soc.*, **78**, 2999 (1956).
6. Deemter, J. J. van, Zuiderweg, F. J., and Klinkenberg, A., *Chem. Eng. Sci.*, **5**, 271 (1956)..
7. Craats, F. van de, private communication.
8. Craats, F. van de, *Anal. Chim. Acta*, **14**, 136 (1956).
9. Boer, H., "The Use of Ozonolysis in Oil Constitution Research," World Petroleum Congr., Proc. 4th Congr., Rome, 1955.
10. Demonstrated during Meeting on Gas Chromatography at Stevenston (Scotland), May 1955.
11. Janák, J., *Collection Czech Chem. Communs.*, **19**, 684, 917 (1954).

12. Ray, N. H., *J. Appl. Chem. (London)*, **4**, 82 (1954).
13. Griffiths, J., James, D., and Phillips, C., *Analyst*, **77**, 897 (1952).
14. Martin, A. E., and Smart, J., *Nature*, **175**, 422 (1955).
15. Martin, A. J. P., and James, A. T., *Biochem. J. (London)*, **63**, 138 (1956).
16. Dimbat, M., Porter, P. E., and Stross, F. H., *Anal. Chem.*, **28**, 290 (1956).
17. Otvos, J. W., and Stevenson, D. P., *J. Am. Chem. Soc.*, **78**, 546 (1956); Deal, C. H., Otvos, J. W., Smith, V. N., and Zucco, P. S., "A Radiological Detector for Gas-Liquid Partition Chromatography," Dallas Symposium on Vapour Phase Chromatography, American Chemical Society, April 1956.
18. Boer, H., Vapour Phase Chromatography, Desty, D. H. (ed.) London, 1957 (Proc. of London Symposium on V. Ph. Chr., May/June 1956), p. 169.
19. Shakespear, G. A., *Proc. Phys. Soc. London*, **33**, 163 (1921).
20. Daynes, H. A., Gas Analysis by Measurement of Thermal Conductivity, London, 1933.
21. Weaver, E. R., In: Berl, W. G. (ed), "Physical Methods in Chemical Analysis," Vol. II, pp. 387–437, New York, 1951.
22. Lindsay, A. L., and Bromley, L. A., *Ind. Eng. Chem.*, **42**, 1508 (1950).
23. Phillips, C. S. G., *Discussions Faraday Soc.*, No. 7, 241 (1949).
24. Davies, A. J., and Johnson, J. K., Vapour Phase Chromatography, Desty, D. H. (ed.), London, 1957 (Proc. of London Symposium on V. Ph. Chr., May/June 1956), p. 185.
25. Harrison, G. F., Knight, P., Kelley, R. P. and Heath, M. T., Gas Chromatography 1958, Desty, D. H. (ed.), London (Proc. of 2nd. Symposium on Gas Chr., Amsterdam, May 1958), p. 216.
26. Carle, D. W., *I.S.A. Proceedings*, 1957 International Gas Chromatography Symposium, Michigan, August 1957, p. 59.
27. Scott, R. P. W., Gas Chromatography 1958, Desty, D. H. (ed.), London (Proc. of 2nd. Symposium on Gas Chr., Amsterdam, May 1958), p. 189.
28. Zlatkis, A., and Ridgway, J. A., *Nature*, **182**, 130 (1958).
29. Munday, C. W., and Primavesi, G. R., Vapour Phase Chromatography, Desty, D. H. (ed.), London 1957 (Proc. of London Symposium on V. Ph. Chr., May/June 1956) p. 146.
30. Scott, R. P. W., *ibid.* p. 131.
31. Wirth, M. M., *ibid.* p. 154.
32. Henderson, J. I. and Knox, J. H., *J. Chem. Soc.* 2229 (1956).
33. Primavesi, G. R., Oldham, G. F. and Thompson, R. J., Gas Chromatography 1958, Desty, D. H. (ed.), London (Proc. of 2nd. Symposium on Gas Chr., Amsterdam, May 1958), p. 165.
34. Grant, D. W., *ibid.*, p. 153.
35. Taylor, B. W., *I.S.A Proceedings*, 1957 International Gas Chromatography Symposium, Michigan, August 1957, p. 133.
36. Felton, H. R., *ibid.* p. 113.
37. Stuve, W., Gas Chromatography 1958, Desty, D. H. (ed.), London (Proc. of 2nd. Symposium on Gas Chr., Amsterdam, May 1958), p. 178.
38. Harley, J. and Pretorius, V., *Nature* **178**, 1244 (1956).
39. Ryce, S. A. and Bryce, W. A., *ibid.* **179**, 54 (1957).
40. Pitkethly, R. C., Advances in Gas Chromatography (Proc. Symposium A.C.S., New York, September 1957) p. D-67.
41. Lovelock, J. E., *J. of Chromatography*, **1**, 35 (1958).
42. McWilliam, I. G. and Dewar, R. A., Gas Chromatography 1958, Desty, D. H.

(ed.), London (Proc. of 2nd. Symposium on Gas Chr., Amsterdam, May 1958), p. 142.

43. Stern, O., quoted by Lewis B. and Von Elbe, G. in: Combustion Flames and Explosions of Gases, p. 206, New York, 1951.

44. Brooks, J., Murray, W. and Williams, A. F., Vapour Phase Chromatography, Desty, D. H. (ed.), London, 1957 (Proc. of London Symposium on V. Ph. Chr., May/June 1956), p. 281.

45. Boer, H., private communication.

Chapter 4

GENERAL THEORY OF CHROMATOGRAPHIC
SEPARATIONS

Introduction

The important states and processes prevailing in a chromatographic column, such as adsorption or absorption equilibria, mass transfer between the two phases, diffusion and convection, may be expressed more or less accurately in mathematical terms. For this purpose the chromatographic column can be regarded as a macroscopically homogeneous medium, so that the main phenomenon—the transport of solute through the column—can be described by a one-dimensional differential equation. The microscopic phenomena are then considered as perturbations superimposed on the main phenomenon.

A general and exact treatment, however, leads to excessively complicated mathematics. By introducing simplifying assumptions various theories of limited validity are obtained, which nevertheless may yield the explanation of important chromatographic phenomena, such as the movement of bands or zones of solute through the column or the dispersion of these bands. The fact that in this way there now exist different chromatographic theories, according to the nature of the simplifications introduced, has led various critics to discredit these theories, but it will be shown that this attitude is unsound. The restricted theories, on the contrary, have proved to be valuable aids in the practical development of chromatography.

Before proceeding to deal with the theories and with simplifications to be adopted, it will be as well to introduce some conceptions that will be used in considering chromatographic processes.

The Distribution Isotherm

As we have seen in Chapter 1, a separation in chromatographic processes is founded on the distribution of the base material over two phases. The ratio of the concentrations of a substance distributed between two equilibrated phases under certain conditions (for instance, at a particular temperature) is termed the *distribution (partition) coefficient*. The numerical value of this quantity depends upon the units in which the concentrations are expressed, and also on which of these concentrations occurs in the numerator. In partition chromatography it has become common use to consider the distribution coefficient as a dimensionless quantity by expressing the concentrations in the moving and in the stationary phase per unit of volume. In adsorption chromatography the concentrations in the moving phase are usually expressed per unit of volume, those in the adsorbent, however, per unit of weight, because the adsorbent cannot be considered as homogeneous. Hence, in adsorption chromatography the distribution coefficient is not a dimensionless quantity.

In this book, which mainly deals with partition chromatography, we will define the partition coefficient k as,

$$k = \frac{\text{amount of solute per unit volume of stationary liquid phase}}{\text{amount of solute per unit volume of moving phase}}$$

The distribution coefficient may now be either (a) independent of the concentration of dissolved material or (b) variable with change in concentration.

In case (a) a plot of the concentration of material in the moving phase (horizontal axis) against concentration in the stationary phase at a given temperature gives a straight line through the origin (Figure 4.1a) and we

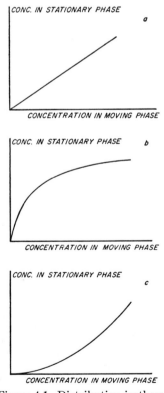

Figure 4.1. Distribution isotherms.

speak of a *"linear" isotherm*. The corresponding graphs (b) and (c) represent *non-linear isotherms*; these may be curved either toward or away from the horizontal axis.

In partition chromatography the conditions are often such that we can assume the isotherms to be linear. In adsorption chromatography, on the other hand, there is frequently no region of concentrations in which the isotherm is approximately straight and non-linear isotherms must be postulated.

The Plate Concept

A column may be considered as a device in which a number of elementary separation processes have been linked up.

A continuous countercurrent process, such as distillation and extraction, may (in theory and sometimes in practice) be carried out in a number of discrete stages, each constituting an elementary process in which perfect equilibrium is established between the opposed phases and in which the latter are then again separated. Such a stage is known as a "theoretical" stage or plate. In a packed column, however, the phases are continuously in motion and the establishment of complete equilibrium is impossible. In such cases it is usual to refer to a length of the column, over which the separation effected is equivalent to that of a theoretical plate, as the *"Height Equivalent to a Theoretical Plate"* or *"H.E.T.P."*

The plate concept has also proved fruitful in the theory of chromatography, where one phase is moving continuously and complete equilibrium can therefore also never be fully realized. Moreover, in certain chromatographic methods (L.L.C. and L.S.C.) the speed of flow is so small that no serious error is introduced by assuming the presence of equilibrium in describing certain phenomena, for instance the rate of transport of a band through a column. In gas chromatography, on the other hand, the speed of the moving phase is so large that such an assumption is in general not permissible, although the movement of the zone of maximum concentration of a band is still adequately described.

Classification of Chromatographic Theories

The simplified theories of chromatography may now be classified in the following manner according to the assumption that one or each of the two conditions mentioned below prevails (see, for instance, van Deemter, Zuiderweg, and Klinkenberg[1]).

(1) The distribution isotherm is either *linear* or *non-linear*.

(2) The prevailing conditions correspond to what is known either as *"ideal"* or *"non-ideal"* chromatography. In "ideal" chromatography the exchange process is thermodynamically reversible; the equilibrium between

particle and fluid is immediate (the mass transfer coefficient is infinitely high) and longitudinal diffusion and other processes having a similar effect can be ignored. In "non-ideal" chromatography these simplifying assumptions cannot be made.

One thus arrives at the following four possibilities:

	Ideal Chromatography	*Non-ideal Chromatography*
Linear isotherm	(I) Linear ideal chromatography	(III) Linear non-ideal chromatography
Non-linear isotherm	(II) Non-linear ideal chromatography	(IV) Non-linear non-ideal chromatography

These four cases will first be briefly reviewed before going into theoretical discussions.

Linear Ideal Chromatography. Case I is the simplest assumption involving the essential features of chromatography. The retardation of solute with regard to the moving solvent depends upon the product of the distribution (partition) coefficient between the two phases and the ratio of the amounts of these phases present in the column. The shape of a band, during its movement, thus remains unchanged. This is the case that was dealt with in the classical treatment of Wilson[2a]; it has been depicted schematically in Figure 4.2. An important feature is that different solutes, introduced as a mixture into a column, behave independently.

The requirements for the individual bands to be separated can be found by simple mathematics.

Non-Linear Ideal Chromatography. This case is of importance for the treatment of liquid-adsorption chromatography, where the effects of

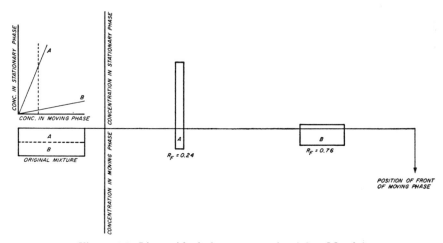

Figure 4.2. Linear ideal chromatography (after Martin).

non-linearity of the isotherm are usually appreciable. On the other hand, mass transfer is sufficiently fast and, in spite of the low linear velocity of the moving liquid, longitudinal diffusion still may be neglected. This case has been treated first by Wilson[2a], whereas a more correct treatment has been given by de Vault[2b] for a single solute; it has been depicted in Figure 4.3.

During their passage through the column the bands usually develop a sharp front and a long tail, a fact which renders the method less suitable for elution chromatography. A special complication is introduced by the fact that the solutes may affect each other, so that the case of two or more solutes cannot be derived by superposition of single-solute cases. Strictly speaking, it is not even accessible to rigorous treatment[3].

Linear Non-ideal Chromatography. In this case bands broaden during their passage through the column in an almost symmetrical manner; the elution bands approach the shape of a Gaussian curve (Figure 4.4). The case is of particular importance for the treatment of partition chromatography, either with a moving liquid or a moving gas, as the assumption of the linear isotherm is then usually a good approximation. The theory of this case can be dealt with in two ways.

In one form of treatment it has proved useful to regard the chromatographic column as a discontinuous medium analogous to a distillation or extraction column, built up of a large number of equivalent plates. The theory in question will be termed the *"plate" theory.*

A treatment which is at least as fruitful is that in which the column is visualized as a continuous medium in which mass transfer and diffusion phenomena are taken into account; this approach is referred to as the *"rate" theory.*

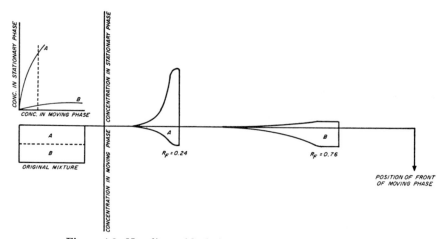

Figure 4.3. Non-linear ideal chromatography (after Martin).

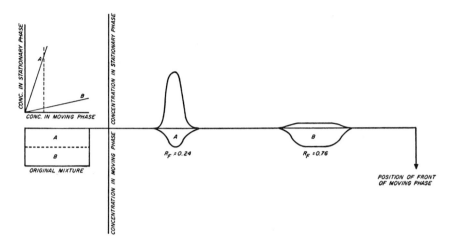

Figure 4.4. Linear non-ideal chromatography (after Martin).

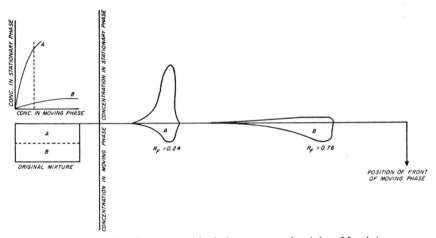

Figure 4.5. Non-linear non-ideal chromatography (after Martin).

The plate theory has been elaborated by Martin and Synge[5], Mayer and Tompkins[6] and Glueckauf[7]; the rate theory has been treated by Lapidus and Amundson[8], Glueckauf[9], Tunitskii[10], Giddings and Eyring[4] and by van Deemter, Zuiderweg and Klinkenberg[1].

The theories of Case III are the most important for the subject of this book and they will be dealt with fairly extensively later in this chapter.

Non-linear Non-ideal Chromatography. The elution bands are diffuse and distinctly asymmetric; neither front nor tail is sharp (Figure 4.5). Adsorption chromatography with a moving gas belongs to this type. Certain kinetic theories of Case IV are mentioned in the paper by Klinkenberg and Sjenitzer[11]. The mathematical treatment of these theories becomes very involved and will not be dealt with in this book.

A brief discussion of ideal chromatography (Cases I and II) will be given first. Case III will then be dealt with in more detail.

Theories of Chromatography

Theory of Ideal Chromatography

The theory will be given for the case of elution development. Frontal analysis can then also be understood, as it is a continuation of the phenomena occurring during the introduction of the sample in elution development. The theory of displacement development will be treated briefly in Chapter 8 on gas-solid chromatography.

Linear Isotherms. *Chromatography of a Single Solute.* Consider a column of some sorbent through which a gas or a solvent is percolating at a constant rate. Suppose now that this flow is replaced by that of a solution of some suitable substance. Owing to the sorption of the solute molecules the latter will be held back by the sorbent. There is an intimate contact between the solution and the sorbent, as a consequence of which the solute will distribute itself at equilibrium between the stationary and the moving phases, i.e., between the sorbent and the solution, respectively.

If in this dynamic sorption equilibrium a fraction $(1 - \varphi)$ of the total amount of solute is sorbed, the probabilities for any solute molecule to be in the sorbed or unsorbed state at any given moment are $(1 - \varphi)$ and φ, respectively. Consequently in a finite time interval any solute molecule will move along with the solvent only during a fraction φ of this time; during the remainder of the time it is sorbed and hence stationary. The average rate of movement of the solute molecules is therefore also a fraction φ of the rate of movement of the solvent.

The linearity of the distribution isotherm signifies that φ does not depend upon the concentration, so that the rate of movement of a band also does not vary with the concentration; bands of the same solute, having different concentrations, will all move at the same relative speed φ, hence a band of arbitrary shape during its progress through the column maintains its form.

Separation of Two Solutes. Consider now a column of an adsorbent (here supposed to have a linear isotherm) which, prior to the introduction of sample, has been wetted with a liquid E, the solvent or the eluent (see Figure 4.6). A small sample consisting of, say, equal amounts of components A and B (the latter being the more strongly adsorbed) is introduced into the top of the column, either as such or in eluent dilution. Just after the sample has entered the column a situation as pictured in Figure 4.6b prevails; both A and B are found in a small zone at the top. The amount of B on the adsorbent is larger than that of A $(1 - \varphi_B > 1 - \varphi_A)$ and hence the zone occupied by A is larger than that occupied by B. Thus

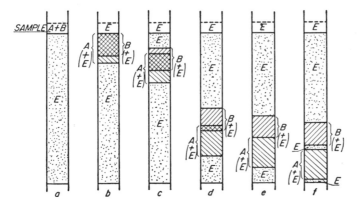

Figure 4.6. Elution development of two solutes A and B. B is more strongly adsorbed than A; E is the eluent.

at the leading edge of this band system a small zone of A has been formed. Continuation of sample introduction and the corresponding enlargement of that zone is equivalent to frontal analysis.

In elution development the introduction of the sample is followed by washing with the eluent; the various stages of the consequent development are pictured in Figures 4.6c to f. Since $\varphi_A > \varphi_B$, the band of A is moved down by the eluent faster than the band of the more strongly adsorbed component B. Consequently the zone of A at the front of the system becomes larger and larger, while at the trailing side of the system a zone of pure B is formed, which also increases in length during washing. In between the two zones of A and B a mixed band occurs, the height of which continuously decreases. Eventually this mixed band disappears, and a gap of pure eluent develops.

As a consequence of the infinite rate of mass transfer and absence of axial diffusion, the width of the two zones remains unchanged during their passage through the column. Separation is complete after the two bands have moved apart a distance equal to their mean width.

These conclusions may be expressed mathematically in a form in which the constants of the chromatographic column occur.

Let unit length of the column contain G_s grams of adsorbent and V_l ml of liquid, then the total solute content Q of a horizontal cross-section per unit length of column is given by

$$Q = V_l C_l + G_s C_s \qquad (1)$$

where C_s and C_l are the concentrations of the solute on the solid phase and in the liquid phase, respectively, expressed in suitable units*.

---

* In a more detailed consideration the accurate interpretation of C_s involves a complication that is not considered in this brief account of the theory.

The passage of a volume of eluent ΔV will produce a downward shift of the band equal to Δx. At the front of the solute zone a section of length Δx that was originally free of solute will now contain the amount $Q\Delta x$, supplied by the volume ΔV. This volume ΔV originally contained an amount $C_l\Delta V$ of the solute. The conservation of mass requires $Q\Delta x$ to be equal to $C_l\Delta V$ or

$$\frac{\Delta x}{\Delta V} = \frac{1}{Q/C_l} \tag{2}$$

Elimination of Q from (1) and (2) gives:

$$\frac{\Delta x}{\Delta V} = \frac{1}{V_l + G_s \cdot C_s/C_l} \tag{3}$$

Equation (3) shows that for large values of C_s/C_l (high adsorptivity) the transport velocity is low. Solutes with different values of C_s/C_l will travel at different rates. A simultaneous introduction of various bands, as is done on introducing a sample into the top of the column, will be followed by a development of the zones with different velocities and this again causes the components to be separated after the required volume of eluent has passed.

It is the ratio of the transport velocities (which will later be defined as the "separation factor") that determines whether components can be readily separated or not. It is convenient to take the transport velocity $(\Delta x/\Delta V)_{id.}$ of an idealized non-adsorbed component as a standard. The ratio

$$R_F = \frac{\Delta x}{\Delta V} \bigg/ \left(\frac{\Delta x}{\Delta V}\right)_{id.} \tag{4}$$

is frequently referred to in literature[12]. Since for the idealized component $C_s = 0$, $(\Delta x/\Delta V)_{id.} = 1/V_l$ and hence

$$R_F = \frac{1}{1 + \dfrac{G_s}{V_l} \cdot \dfrac{C_s}{C_l}} \tag{5}$$

The ratio of the transport velocities of two solutes equals the ratio of their R_F values (Equation 4).

Curved Isotherms. Suppose we introduce into the column successively, without a gap, three narrow bands of the same solute in different concentrations (see Figure 4.7). For the movement of these bands down the column two cases have to be considered as regards the relation between C_s and C_l, the isotherm $C_s = f(C_l)$ being linear if C_s/C_l is constant, and non-linear if C_s/C_l is not constant.

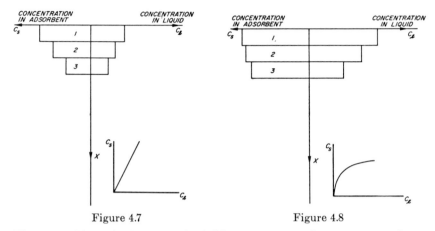

Figure 4.7   Figure 4.8

Figure 4.7. Linear isotherm: bands of different concentration move at equal rates.
Figure 4.8. Curved isotherm: bands of high concentration move faster than bands of low concentration.

Concentration on solid and in liquid have been plotted in opposite directions along horizontal axis. Bands have been introduced successively at the top and move in the direction of X.

If C_s/C_l is constant, as assumed hitherto, Equation (3) shows that the transport velocities of all zones in Figure 4.7 are equal; consequently the band system will be transported through the column unchanged. A band in which the concentration changes continuously can be considered as the limit of a large number of narrow bands each of constant concentration. Such a band preserves its shape; it does not broaden.

Now suppose that C_s/C_l is not constant, as is nearly always the case in adsorption chromatography.*

As C_s/C_l decreases with increasing C_l, it follows that zones of high concentration of solute, as represented by block 1 in Figure 4.8 will move faster (Equation 3) than zones of low concentration, such as block 3.

Furthermore, a band with continuously changing concentration will finally sharpen its front completely. With the tail of the zone the reverse is the case. A band of low concentration moves slowly and remains behind with respect to the bands of higher concentration. An originally sharp and symmetric band thus becomes an asymmetric one with a sharp front (see de Vault[2b]).

In this brief survey of the theories of ideal chromatography problems

* This fact can easily be explained as follows. For very low concentrations of the solute C_s/C_l will be nearly constant, but with increasing concentration the material to be adsorbed will find part of the adsorbent surface already occupied, so that the chance of becoming adsorbed is smaller for the additional molecules. C_s/C_l hence decreases with increasing C_l.

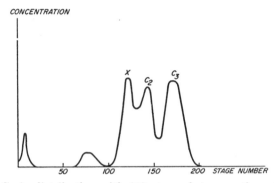

Figure 4.9. Craig distribution with 243 stages for separation of actinomycin C and actinomycin X. [After Brockmann (*Angew. Chem.*, **66**, 1) (1954)].

connected with mutual influence of various solutes on their adsorption have been ignored. In this respect the reader is referred to the original literature already mentioned.

Theory of Non-ideal (linear) Chromatography

"Plate" and "Rate" Theories. The elution diagrams shown in the examples of chapter 2, obtained with a differential technique of detection, consist of a number of bell-shaped curves, approaching fairly closely to symmetric Gaussian distribution curves, though some of them show definite signs of asymmetry. Usually the peaks are narrow near the injection point and broaden as they move further in the diagram, with a consequent reduction in peak height.

Distribution with Intermittent Flow—Craig Distribution (Binomial Type). Curves of this type are also encountered in other separation processes based on extraction. Such a procedure, to which reference has already been made in Chapter 1, is Craig's multiple extraction process[13]. In Figure 4.9 a 243-stage Craig extraction for the separation of Actinomycin C and Actinomycin X is illustrated. Although employing totally different equipment, this method, as already stated, shows very close analogies to chromatography.* In Craig's machine a large number of ideal extraction stages have been linked up; for the separation use is made of two immiscible phases between which the materials to be separated are distributed. One of these phases moves and the other is stationary.

The concept of the theoretical plate or stage can best be clarified by discussing the Craig extraction.

As was already pointed out, a stage is "ideal" if the phases are equilibrated in some way and thereafter completely separated. An ordinary

---

* See definition, Chapter 1.

laboratory separating funnel may act as an ideal stage and Craig's process may be conceived as a very large number of successive extraction funnels.

Let us consider a series of 11 separating funnels numbered from 0 to 10. We shall carry out a model extraction in which a system of two liquids—T (top liquid) and B (bottom liquid), which are assumed to be immiscible—is used. Initially all funnels contain an equal amount of B only, funnel zero in addition containing a certain amount of solute Y. We shall first deal with a solute Y having a distribution coefficient $k_Y = 1$. This means that after a volume of T equal to that of B has been introduced into funnel zero, and its contents have been shaken and allowed to settle, solute Y distributes itself equally between top and bottom layer.

The procedure is now as follows.

(1) T_0 (the subscript refers to the ordinal number of the funnel) is transferred to funnel 1; an equal amount of fresh T is introduced into funnel zero. Both funnels are equilibrated and allowed to settle. Funnels 0 and 1 now each contain $\frac{1}{2}Y$, which is equally distributed between T_0 and B_0, T_1 and B_1, respectively.

(2) T_1 is transferred to funnel 2 and T_0 to funnel 1; fresh T is introduced into funnel zero; the funnels are equilibrated and allowed to settle. Funnel 2 contains the amount $\frac{1}{4}Y$, transferred with T_1; this quantity is equally distributed between B_2 and T_2. Funnel 1, already containing $\frac{1}{4}Y$ in the bottom layer B_1, has received another $\frac{1}{4}Y$ by the transfer of T_0. Hence, this funnel contains $\frac{1}{2}Y$ equally distributed between T_1 and B_1. Funnel zero contains $\frac{1}{4}Y$.

(3) The procedure is repeated by taking into use a fourth and fifth funnel and so on, starting with the transference of top liquid from the last funnel to the one just included. With eleven funnels $(0 \cdots 10)$ the situations that are established successively are drawn up in Table 4.1. The fraction of Y present in each funnel can be found from the terms of the

TABLE 4.1

Funnel No.	0	1	2	3	4	5	6	7	8	9	10	
Amount of Y in the	1											$\times 2^0$
funnels	1	1										$\times 2^{-1}$
	1	2	1									$\times 2^{-2}$
	1	3	3	1								$\times 2^{-3}$
	1	4	6	4	1							$\times 2^{-4}$
	1	5	10	10	5	1						$\times 2^{-5}$
	1	6	15	20	15	6	1					$\times 2^{-6}$
	1	7	21	35	35	21	7	1				$\times 2^{-7}$
	1	8	28	56	70	56	28	8	1			$\times 2^{-8}$
	1	9	36	84	126	126	84	36	9	1		$\times 2^{-9}$
	1	10	45	120	210	252	210	120	45	10	1	$\times 2^{-10}$

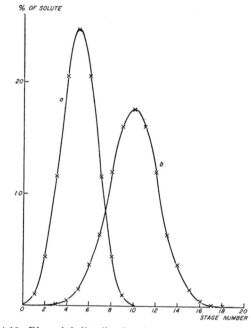

Figure 4.10. Binomial distribution for 11 stages (a); 21 stages (b).

binomial expansion $(a + b)^p$, where p is the ordinal number of the last funnel taken into use and a and b are each $\frac{1}{2}$. Figure 4.10a is the distribution curve corresponding to this case for 11 stages. Although the amounts of solute from funnel to funnel change stepwise, it is usual to connect the points by a smooth curve. The corresponding distribution curve for 21 funnels ($p = 20$) is shown in Figure 4.10b. A comparison of these figures shows the broadening of the curve and lowering of the peak.

For very large values of p (>100) the distribution closely approaches a Gaussian distribution.

In practice the distribution coefficient k will not be unity and the amounts of T and B may differ. It can easily be shown that for a system in which the volumes of T and B in each vessel are V_T and V_B and the distribution coefficient is k_Y, the distribution curve can be found by plotting the terms of the expansion of

$$\left(\frac{1}{E_Y + 1} + \frac{E_Y}{E_Y + 1} \right)^p \tag{6}$$

where

$$E_Y = k_Y \cdot \frac{V_T}{V_B}.$$

% OF SOLUTE

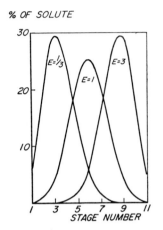

Figure 4.11. Distribution of a substance over 11 stages.

If two solutes Y and Z are introduced into funnel zero and $E_Y = 3$, $E_Z = \frac{1}{3}$, the first will be distributed according to the terms of $(\frac{1}{4} + \frac{3}{4})^p$ and the second according to $(\frac{3}{4} + \frac{1}{4})^p$. For 11 funnels $(p = 10)$ the distribution curves have been drawn in Figure 4.11.

A conclusion, the great importance of which is not always fully recognized, can be drawn from the latter figure. To effect an essentially complete separation between Y and Z one only has to increase the number of funnels to a suitable value. It is, however, not necessary to apply the procedure to all the funnels; after 11 funnels have been taken into use, the amounts of Y in the first and in the second funnel is already negligible (2^{-20} and 30.2^{-02} of the original amounts, respectively). Now this means that essentially the same separation can be attained by taking, for instance, only nine funnels and using the first as the tenth and the second as the eleventh funnel. Although the number of successive operations performed to effect a high degree of separation must increase, the number of equilibrations that have to be carried out in each of these successive steps may remain relatively small, because for the "front" funnels the equilibrations become useless. In terms of chromatography this fact signifies that in a column with a very large number of plates, only those plates where solute is present contribute to the separation. This is one of the reasons why the number of plates required to effect a chromatographic separation is considerably larger than the number of plates in countercurrent continuous distillation (see van Deemter et al.[1]).

Distribution with Continuous Flow (Poisson Type). An important difference between a Craig separation and a separation by chromatography is that the former operates with intermittent flow, whereas in the latter the

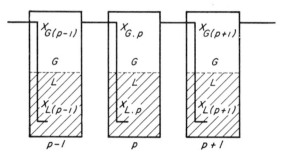

Figure 4.12. Three successive absorption vessels.

flow is uninterrupted. This aspect has been discussed by Glueckauf[7] and by Klinkenberg and Sjenitzer[11].

A procedure taking continuous flow into account and approaching gas-liquid chromatography very closely will now be described.

In Figure 4.12, three successive absorption vessels out of a series of $n + 1$, (ordinal numbers $0, 1 \cdots n$) have been drawn. The distribution procedure consists in introducing a volatile solute into vessel zero, where it dissolves in a nonvolatile liquid which is present there and exerts a vapor pressure above it. A constant flow of a gas, not soluble in the liquid, is passed through the vessels and carries the vapors above the liquid from one vessel to another.

In this procedure it is assumed that:

(1) The volume of the inert gas phase V_G and the volume of the non-volatile liquid V_L is the same in each vessel; further, that these volumes remain constant during the stripping process.

(2) Each vessel acts as an ideal plate, i.e., the two phases are in equilibrium at any moment.

(3) The equilibrium may be represented by

$$X_{L.p} = kX_{G.p} \qquad (7)$$

where $X_{L.p}$ is the concentration of the solute in the liquid phase of vessel p, and $X_{G.p}$ is the concentration of the solute in the (inert) gas phase of vessel p. The concentrations are expressed in units of volume of the phases. k is a constant, the equilibrium constant of the solute. (A constant k denotes that the distribution isotherm is linear.)

A volume dV of gas that is transferred from vessel p-1 into p carries with it the amount $X_{G.(p-1)}dV$ of the solute; an equal volume dV carries the amount $X_{G.p}dV$ of the solute from p into $p + 1$. As $X_{G.(p-1)} \neq X_{G.p}$ the solute content of p has altered; the concentration in the liquid phase has changed by $dX_{L.p}$, that in the gas phase by $dX_{G.p}$, hence the amount of solute in liquid and gas phase by $V_L.dX_{L.p}$ and $V_G.dX_{G.p}$, respectively.

The conservation of mass requires:

$$(X_{G.(p-1)} - X_{G.p})\, dV = V_G dX_{G.p} + V_L dX_{L.p} \tag{8}$$

Elimination of $X_{L.p}$ from (7) and (8) gives:

$$\frac{dX_{G.p}}{dV} = \frac{X_{G.(p-1)} - X_{G.p}}{V_G + kV_L} \tag{9}$$

If solute is initially present in the first vessel only, with a concentration $X_{G.o}$ in the gas phase (and consequently $X_{L.o}$ in the liquid phase) the solution of (9) reads

$$X_{G.p} = X_{G.o}\, \frac{e^{-v}.v^p}{p!} \tag{10}$$

with

$$v = \frac{V}{V_G + kV_L}$$

as may be verified by differentiation. The amount of solute introduced into the first vessel is equal to

$$V_G.X_{G.o} + V_L X_{L.o} = X_{G.o}(V_G + kV_L) \tag{11}$$

$V_G + kV_L$ is termed the "effective plate volume".

With the aid of Equation (10) the situation in each vessel can be calculated after an arbitrary "volume" v has passed through $[V = v(V_G + kV_L)]$.

In Figure 4.13 the quantity $x_p = X_{G.p}/X_{G.o}$ has been plotted against v for various relatively small values of p. (Observe that x_p and v are dimensionless parameters.) A family of curves is obtained which all have a maximum and two inflection points (except for $p = 0$). The *peak maximum* is situated at $v = p$, the *inflection points* at $v = p - \sqrt{p}$ and $v = p + \sqrt{p}$. The inflection tangents intersect the horizontal axis in two points $v = p + 1 \pm 2\sqrt{p}$. The *peak width* w will be defined as the distance between these two points; $w = 4\sqrt{p}$. The peak maximum,

$$x_p \text{ (max.)} = \frac{e^{-p}.p^p}{p!}.$$

Craig's distribution, as we have seen is of the *binomial type*, whereas the distribution obtained with continuous flow is of the *Poisson type*.

For sufficiently large values of p both distributions may be approximated by a Gaussian type distribution. Klinkenberg and Sjenitzer[11] (see also ref. 7) have shown that the variances* (and hence the peak widths) of the binomial and the Poisson distribution for an equal number of plates, with

* Variance is the square of the standard deviation σ.

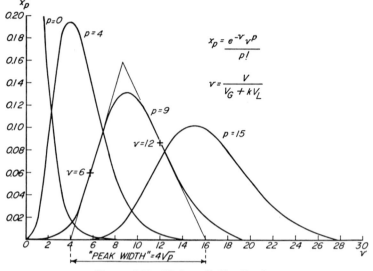

Figure 4.13. "Poisson" distributions.

the same amounts of the two phases in the plates and with the same throughput, differ. For the ratio of the variances they find

$$\frac{\sigma^2_{\text{binomial}}}{\sigma^2_{\text{Poisson}}} = 1 - \frac{V_G}{V_G + kV_L}$$

The formulas derived for the history of a solute, introduced into vessel zero, during its passage through a series of absorption vessels, immediately also apply without restriction to chromatographic columns, which are then conceived as built up of a large number of discrete plates, and where the amount of solute is so small that it can be introduced into the first plate.

If the total number of plates of such a column is $n + 1$, then

$$x_n = \frac{e^{-v}v^n}{n!} \qquad (10a)$$

represents the equation of the elution curve and

$$x_n = \frac{e^{-n}.n^n}{n!} \qquad (10b)$$

is the peak maximum which is reached at $v = n$. This signifies that the maximum of the elution curve breaks through after a volume of the mobile phase equal to n times the effective plate volume has passed through the column. This volume is called the retention volume v_R or V_R

$$v_R = n \qquad \text{or} \qquad V_R = n(V_G + kV_L) \qquad (12)$$

(see also Figure 1.4).

For large values of n, nV_G is the gas hold-up of the whole column, nV_L is the liquid hold-up of the column. The apparent retention volume defined in Chapter 1 is $V_R - nV_G = k.nV_L$. The initial and final retention volumes are found by adding or subtracting $2\sqrt{n}$ (half the peak width) from the retention volume (v_R) referred to the peak maximum.

Calculation of Number of Plates. With the aid of the formulas just derived the number of plates for a given column can be calculated from the elution diagram. This diagram is a plot of concentration against time. (The deflection of the recorder is assumed to be proportional to the concentration.) At a constant gas flow rate and constant speed of the recorder the distances along the base line on the chart, under constant conditions, are proportional to the volumes passed through. For many purposes, for instance for the determination of the number of plates, it is not necessary to convert the distances on the chart to time or to amounts of gas.

If we denote the distance between the injection point and the projection of the peak maximum on the base line (Figure 1.4) by d, the peak width by w (d and w expressed in the same units), $d = c.n$ and $w = c.4\sqrt{n}$, c being the proportionality factor. By eliminating c we find

$$\frac{d}{w} = \tfrac{1}{4}\sqrt{n}$$

or

$$n = \left(4\,\frac{d}{w}\right)^2 \tag{13}$$

Similar formulas may be derived for the initial and final retention volumes, respectively

$$n = \left(\frac{4d_I}{w} + 2\right)^2$$

and

$$n = \left(\frac{4d_F}{w} - 2\right)^2 \tag{13a}$$

Limitations of the Theory. In principle the formulas are suitable for calculating the number of plates and the overlap of the peaks to be separated with a given column, under certain conditions.

There is, however, a factor which may cause the state of affairs to be much more involved. In practice it will not be possible to introduce the total amount of sample into the first plate of the column, as has been assumed so far. Usually the amount of sample introduced will be many times the amount that can be contained in the first plate. This implies that a number of single plate chromatograms start simultaneously from a series of neighboring plates. The individual chromatograms overlap each other, so that the actual peak becomes broader; the single-plate formulas then do not apply strictly.

Another complication is the non-linearity of the distribution isotherm at higher concentrations, a fact which may cause the band to become asymmetric, the front usually being steeper than the rear. High concentrations occur particularly in the first part of the column when large samples are charged. It is clear that with asymmetric peaks, owing to the large amount of column charge, the peak maximum is no longer a true measure of the retention volume.

There is one quantity which is independent of the sample volume in cases where the distribution isotherm is linear or curves toward the horizontal axis; this is the final retention volume.* This fact is understandable, because the final retention volume refers to the amount of gas needed to wash the contents of the first plate out of the column. This volume is independent of whether solute has been present in the other plates or not.

In a few cases the initial retention volume, rather than the final retention volume or that referred to the peak maximum may be constant. If the isotherm curves away from the pressure axis and the sample is not introduced instantaneously as a plug, but is gradually evaporated into the column, the first amount of solute tends to behave independently of the remainder. Such a case has been observed by Dijkstra, Keppler and Schols[14].

The problem of large samples is very complicated; it has been tentatively treated by Glueckauf[7] and by van Deemter *et al.*[1]. In the treatment of the latter authors, the sample is taken to be charged at a constant concentration in the carrier gas during a certain period of time; they consider the charging period as the reverse of the washing period. The width of a peak is then to an appreciable extent determined by the length of the feed period. In the case of a large number of plates and small feed periods, these authors showed that the peak width is practically independent of the feed period. From their considerations it may be assumed that if the sample does not exceed $0.5 \sqrt{n}.(V_G + kV_L)$ it does not affect the peak width.

A practical manner employed by the present author for avoiding the complication of large samples is the method of extrapolation to "zero sample volume." By calculating the number of plates with the aid of Equation (13a) and dividing the length of the column by this number we obtain the "effective" H.E.T.P. In very many cases a plot of the effective H.E.T.P. against the sample size has proved to be a straight line from which [H.E.T.P.]$_0$ is found as the intercept of the axis in question. Phillips[15] has

* If not explicitly stated, the charge of sample is assumed to be instantaneous as a plug.

also studied the effect of sample size on the number of plates. A plot of his data for sample size against $1/n$ also yields a straight line.

Separation in Linear Non-ideal Chromatography. In G.L.C. volatile materials are separated by virtue of the differences of their volatilities or of their partition coefficients. If for two solutes A and B the partition coefficients are k_A and k_B ($k_A > k_B$), the ratio k_A/k_B is termed the "separation factor" or the "relative volatility"; it will be denoted by $\alpha_{A.B}$ or by α only if no confusion is possible.

Two substances are more readily separated the larger the value of α. In ideal linear chromatography the requirements for separation can easily be calculated. If a mixture of A and B is introduced into the top of the column, A will occupy a zone of width w_A and B a zone of width w_B (Figure 4.14). Separation is complete when the zones have moved apart a distance equal to $\frac{1}{2}(w_A + w_B)$. The length of column required for such a separation is

$$\tfrac{1}{2}(w_A + w_B)\cdot\frac{k_A}{k_A - k_B}$$

and depends upon the width of the bands introduced.

In linear non-ideal chromatography the state of affairs is more complicated because of the broadening of the bands. As this broadening is proportional to the square root of n and hence also roughly to the square root of the distance travelled through the column, whereas the distance over which the centers of the zones move apart is directly proportional to the column length, two substances having an α differing from unity can in principle always be separated. If α is close to unity the number of plates required to effect a desired degree of separation may become excessively large, in which case columns of unpractical lengths will be required.

Band broadening is also the reason for which two substances never can be completely separated; zero concentration of the solute is reached only at an infinite number of plates, i.e., in columns of infinite length. Complete separation, however, is not required in practice. Very high purities of separated bands can frequently be attained with a comparatively small number of plates.

The requirements for an "analytical separation" of an equimolecular

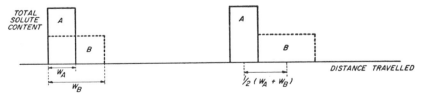

Figure 4.14. Separation of two solutes; ideal linear chromatography.

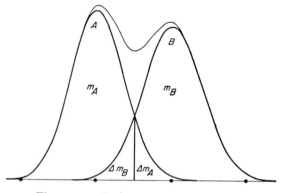

Figure 4.15. Definition of band impurity.

mixture of two substances have been dealt with in the paper by van Deemter *et al.*[1]. Glueckauf's treatment of this subject[7] is of a more general nature and will be followed here. Though the mathematics may be slightly involved, the results can be expressed in a very simple manner and they are of great importance for the calculation of columns in the case of difficult separations.

Figure 4.15 represents the elution curves of two substances A and B; the bands refer to amounts of m_A and m_B moles of A and B, respectively. The purity of each of the partially overlapping bands will depend upon the point where the cut is made. In the figure the minor cut-off Δm_B is the amount of substance B in substance A and Δm_A the amount of A in B.

A satisfactory way of making a cut is that in which the fractional impurities of both bands are equal, so that we have

$$\eta_A = \frac{\Delta m_B}{m_A - \Delta m_A} = \eta_B = \frac{\Delta m_A}{m_B - \Delta m_B} \tag{14}$$

where η_A and η_B are the respective fractional impurities. For a normal degree of separation $\Delta m_i \ll m_i$ and it follows that

$$\eta_A = \eta_B \approx \frac{\Delta m_B}{m_A} = \frac{\Delta m_A}{m_B} \tag{14a}$$

The amount of substance in any part of a band can be calculated from the equation of the elution curve. For the sake of convenience the equation

$$x_p = \frac{e^{-v} . v^p}{p!}$$

will be converted into an error function.

As x_p (max.) $= \dfrac{e^{-p} p^p}{p!} \approx \dfrac{1}{\sqrt{2\pi p}}$

we may write

$$x_p = \frac{e^{-p} \cdot p^p}{p!} \cdot e^{p-v} \left(\frac{v}{p}\right)^p \approx \frac{1}{\sqrt{2\pi p}} e^{p-v} \left(\frac{v}{p}\right)^p \tag{15}$$

For values of v differing appreciably from p, x_p becomes very small. (The whole elution curve is practically contained between $v = p - 2\sqrt{p}$ and $v = p + 2\sqrt{p}$). Hence $v - p$ is small compared with p. Substituting $v - p = \epsilon$ in (15) we obtain:

$$x_p \approx \frac{1}{\sqrt{2\pi p}} e^{-\epsilon} \left(1 + \frac{\epsilon}{p}\right)^p \tag{16}$$

For small values of ϵ/p, (16) may be further transformed. If

$$\psi = e^{-\epsilon} \left(1 + \frac{\epsilon}{p}\right)^p,$$

$$\log \psi = -\epsilon + p \log \left(1 + \frac{\epsilon}{p}\right) = -\epsilon + p \left(\frac{\epsilon}{p} - \frac{\epsilon^2}{2p^2} \cdots\right)$$

or, neglecting higher powers of ϵ/p.

$$\log \psi \approx -\frac{\epsilon^2}{2p}; \qquad \psi = e^{-\epsilon^2/2p},$$

hence

$$x_p \approx \frac{1}{\sqrt{2\pi p}} e^{-(v-p)^2/2p} \tag{17}$$

(Glueckauf's[7] formula 20 is equivalent to

$$x_p = \frac{1}{\sqrt{2\pi v}} e^{-(p-v)^2/2v} \tag{17a}$$

hence v and p have been interchanged, which is permissible for $v \approx p$). With Equation 17 (or 17a) the amount of solute contained in a section of the elution band and hence Δm_A or Δm_B can be calculated by integration. The result to which Glueckauf arrives is

$$\eta = \frac{2m_A m_B}{m_A^2 + m_B^2} \left(0.5 - \int_0^{f(n, \alpha)} e^{-\frac{1}{2}t^2} dt\right) \tag{18}$$

with

$$f(n, \alpha) = \sqrt{n}(\alpha^{\frac{1}{2}} - \alpha^{-\frac{1}{2}})$$

wherein

$$\sqrt{\frac{2}{\pi}} \int_0^{f(n, \alpha)} e^{-\frac{1}{2}t^2} dt = \text{erf } [f(n, \alpha)]$$

is the error function.

Equation (18) is the expression giving the relation between the impurity of a band η and the number of plates n, with the separation factor α as the parameter. The most practical way of employing this formula is to construct a graph. By using a log probability scale for the horizontal axis and a log scale for the vertical axis a family of parallel lines is obtained. Such a graph has been presented in Figure 4.16 for the case in which $m_A = m_B$,

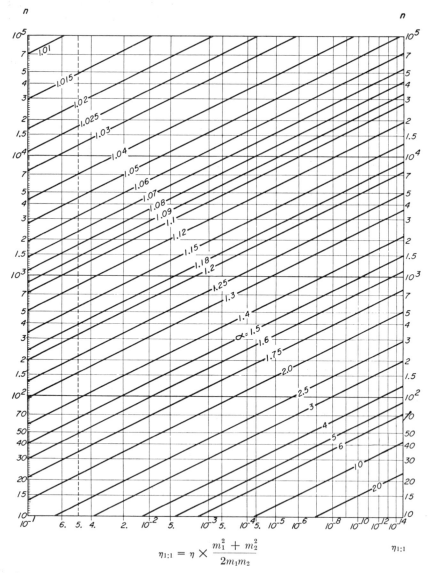

$$\eta_{1:1} = \eta \times \frac{m_1^2 + m_2^2}{2m_1 m_2}$$

Figure 4.16. Relation between number of plates (n), separation factor (α), and fractional band impurity (η). (After E. Glueckauf).

i.e., for the separation of equal amounts of two substances. The same graph, however, may be employed if unequal amounts have to be separated, as will be shown later by an example.

Equation 18 shows the unexpected feature that the impurity has a maximum at $m_A = m_B$.

The great practical importance of the graph and the way it is applied will now be demonstrated by means of an example. Suppose that two components A and B having a separation factor $\alpha = 1.3$ and present in the molar ratio 1:9 are to be separated. What is the number of plates required to effect a separation with 10^{-3} (0.1%) fractional impurity in each band? As $m_A = 0.1$ and $m_B = 0.9$; $(m_A^2 + m_B^2)/(2m_Am_B) = 4.55 \approx 5$. The number of plates required to effect the separation is now found by reading off the abscissa at the point 5×10^{-3}. On the line for $\alpha = 1.3$ we find a point corresponding to approximately 400 plates. If A and B had been present in equimolecular amounts, the reading would have been 10^{-3} and it is found that for a separation with the same band impurity the required number of plates is about 600.

The graph again shows that impossibly long columns are required for separating substances with a relative volatility close to unity. Substances with about the same volatility in the pure state may, however, show a considerable relative volatility when dissolved in a more suitable stationary liquid. It is therefore always advantageous to search for a stationary liquid giving a high value (preferably larger than 1.1) for the separation factor, although it may not always be possible to find one. Rules that may facilitate such a search will be given in Chapter 6.

We will now conclude this section with an instructive comparison of the minimum number of plates needed for chromatographic separations with that needed for a countercurrent process, for instance batch distillation (see Ref. 1). Figure 4.17 shows this comparison for the separation of equimolecular mixtures. In this figure the number of plates is plotted on a log scale against the separation factor. Particularly at low values of α the number of plates required for chromatographic separations is much higher than in distillation. The cause of this fact has been explained in discussing the Craig separation. The number of plates needed for chromatography is, however, much more easily realized than the lower number of plates required for distillation.

The "Rate" Theory. As we have seen, the plate concept is one way of explaining the phenomenon of band broadening that occurs when an initially narrow band of solute passes through a chromatographic column. It has been shown that the broadening of a band is proportional to the square root of the number of plates and that the width of a band can be used to calculate the effective number of plates which, together with the column length, gives the height equivalent to one plate.

The band broadening effect can also be approached from a kinetic angle. Such considerations may provide a relation between the practical measure, the H.E.T.P., and the factors operative in chromatography that determine the height of a plate.

We have seen that no broadening occurs in linear ideal chromatography. The conditions to be postulated for ideal chromatography will first be enumerated. It will then be demonstrated that these conditions involve assumptions that are quite unrealistic. A discussion of the effects of deviations from the postulated conditions will eventually lead to mathematical expressions for the broadening of a band.

In ideal chromatography the following conditions are assumed to prevail.

(1) The proportion of the two phases at all points of the column is constant.

(2) The flow of the mobile phase is uniform.

(3) Molecular diffusion of solute molecules (in longitudinal direction) does not occur in either of the two phases.

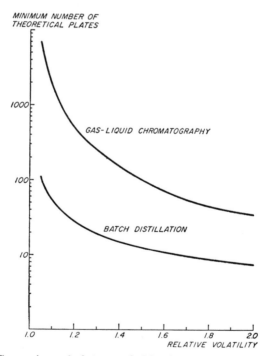

Figure 4.17. Comparison of plates needed in chromatography and batch distillation. Separation of equimolar mixtures into two fractions of 97.7% purity. (After v. Deemter *et al.*).

(4) Equilibrium between the two phases is instantaneous. Moreover, in linear chromatography the isotherm is linear.

If we consider the column in macroscopical respect conditions (1) and (2) are usually fulfilled. In microscopic respect, the condition of uniform flow does not prevail in a packed bed. Firstly, there is a pressure gradient along the length of the column, as a consequence of which the linear velocity of the carrier gas used in G.L.C. increases from the column inlet to the column outlet. This non-uniformity, however, affects all solute molecules to the same extent and will hence not cause band dispersion.

Secondly, as a result of the presence of the packing, gas molecules travel through the column along many different paths. These paths have somewhat different lengths; furthermore, the velocity is not axially directed and it also depends in magnitude on the width of the voids between the particles. These effects cause the residence time of gas molecules (and hence also of solute molecules constituting a band) in the column to spread; the result is a reduction of the peak height and widening of the band. This widening depends upon the size of the particles constituting the packing, their shape and the regularity with which they have been packed. This mechanism of band broadening is termed *"eddy diffusion"* on account of a certain analogy to eddy diffusion in turbulent flow.

Molecular diffusion of the solute molecules is superimposed on the forced flow of the carrier gas and solute molecules, and its axial component tends to enhance or counteract the transport of solute molecules. (The corresponding effect in the liquid phase is small as compared to that in the gas phase.) Molecular diffusion is a second mechanism of band broadening.

The fourth condition finally requires instantaneous equilibrium or an infinite rate of mass transfer between the two phases. This condition is not realized at the high rates of flow operative in G.L.C., although the distribution of the liquid phase as a very thin film is an effective means of enhancing the establishment of equilibrium. A consequence of the finite rate of mass transfer is that solute molecules either fail to go into solution, and then travel somewhat ahead of the band, or are slow in passing into the moving phase and then lag behind the band. The resistance to mass transfer* is the third important factor causing band broadening.

Longitudinal Diffusion as a Cause of Band Broadening. If there is no serious maldistribution of flow through the whole column, the effect of the residual irregularities may be taken into account by an "eddy diffusion coefficient" E. It should be emphasized that this procedure is only permissible if the irregularities have a statistical character. The eddy diffusivity describes the average effect over dimensions which are large as com-

---

* The effectiveness of mass transfer between the two phases is usually expressed in terms of the H.T.U.—height of a transfer unit.

pared to particle size and small as compared to column diameter. It has proved convenient to relate the eddy diffusivity E to the particle diameter d_p and the linear gas velocity u in the packed column by means of a dimensionless parameter λ

$$E = \lambda u d_p \qquad (19)$$

Under similar geometrical conditions and conditions of flow λ is independent of particle diameter and flow rate. λ may therefore be considered as a measure of packing irregularities; the higher λ, the more irregular the packing.

There are indications that regular packing is easier to realize with large than with small particles[11]. Values normally encountered are for instance $\lambda \approx 1$ for 20–40 mesh screen fractions (particle diameter 0.8–0.4 mm); $\lambda \approx 3$ for 50–100 mesh (0.3–0.15 mm); $\lambda \approx 8$ for 200–400 mesh (0.07–0.04 mm).

The effective longitudinal diffusivity $D_{\text{eff.}}$ is the sum of molecular and eddy diffusivity:

$$D_{\text{eff.}} = \gamma D_{\text{gas}} + E = \gamma D_{\text{gas}} + \lambda u d_p \,.$$

The factor γ is a correction for the tortuosity of the channels. With increasing particle size γ increases up to a limiting value of 1.

Finite Rate of Mass Transfer as a Cause of Band Broadening. The immobile liquid in G.L.C. is present in the pores of the supporting granules. It will, by capillary action, primarily accumulate in the smallest pores and holes (Figure 4.18). With increasing amounts of liquid larger pores also become filled. During mass transfer between the phases the molecules of the transported component have to travel by diffusion over a certain distance d_{gas} in the gas phase from the interstitial channels through the unfilled pores to the gas-liquid interface. The average distance d_{gas} is of the order of the particle diameter, or somewhat less. In the liquid phase the

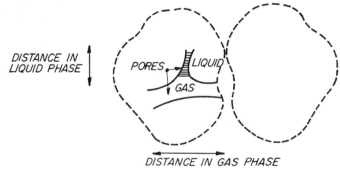

Figure 4.18. Distances travelled by diffusion.

distance d_{liq}. to be travelled by diffusion is equal to the average length over which the pores are filled with liquid. d_{liq}. of course varies from pore to pore; it has proved to be convenient to replace it by its statistical average d_f, which will be termed the effective film thickness. According to the Einstein diffusion equation the times required for traveling these distances in the gas and liquid phases, respectively, are

$$\frac{d_{\text{gas}}^2}{2D_{\text{gas}}} \quad \text{and} \quad \frac{d_f^{\,2}}{2D_{\text{liq}}}.$$

In order to decide in which phase the mass transfer resistance is mainly located, the ratio of these diffusion times

$$\left(\frac{d_{\text{gas}}}{d_f}\right)^2 \cdot \frac{D_{\text{liq}}}{D_{\text{gas}}}$$

must be considered. Since not much less than about half of the particle volume is usually filled with liquid, it is improbable that the average liquid-filled pore length d_f is much smaller than, say, one tenth of the particle radius, therefore $(d_{\text{gas}}/d_f)^2$ is of the order of 10^2, or perhaps 10^3. The ratio of diffusion coefficients $D_{\text{liq}}/D_{\text{gas}}$, on the other hand, is of the order of 10^{-4} to 10^{-5}. Consequently, the diffusion time in the gas phase is usually much smaller than the diffusion time in the liquid phase. Only in the case of very small amounts of liquids is it likely that the mass transfer in the gas phase becomes of importance.

The approach to equilibrium will now depend upon the diffusion time in the liquid, the gas velocity and the equilibrium distribution between the phases. The equilibrium is more closely approached if the gas velocity and the diffusion time in the liquid are small.

The above considerations can be given a more or less quantitative expression. The problems in question have been approached in two ways, both leading to the same results.

Klinkenberg and Sjenitzer[11] followed a statistical approach. These authors discuss the history of a peak load of a sample introduced into the column and the resulting distribution of the sample components in the effluent. They observe that this distribution often can be approximated by a Gaussian probability curve around a mean value and they analyze the various mechanisms that give rise to such Gaussian curves. As Klinkenberg and Sjenitzer point out, however, there are methods of deriving the Gaussian distributions directly, based on the general principle that the *mean* equals the sum of the individual means, and that the *variance* (square of standard deviation) equals the sum of the individual variances. The width of a curve is then expressed in a standard form as the ratio of the standard deviation to the mean (σ/μ).

It is also possible that various mechanisms operate independently at the same time. In that case, the squares of σ/μ due to the individual mechanisms must be added.

According to the results of Klinkenberg and Sjenitzer, it now becomes possible to express the height of a theoretical plate as the sum of a number of contributing terms, one of which is proportional to D/u and accounts for molecular diffusion, the second being proportional to u and accounting for finite rate of mass transfer, while the third, accounting for eddy diffusion, is independent of u. The derivation of the expression involves a fair amount of statistical mathematics and will not be gone into here.

The Van Deemter Equation for the H.E.T.P. The second method of approach was followed by van Deemter, Zuiderweg and Klinkenberg.[1] Their theory is a valuable extension of that developed by Glueckauf[9] and other investigators. They demonstrate that the diffusional effects may be described by two differential equations for the material balance in each of the phases. The derivation of these equations and the meaning of the terms occurring in them may be understood by referring to Figure 4.19, in which the transport phenomena occurring in a small section of the column are represented schematically.

If gas passes through a section of height Δx, it takes with it the solute in a concentration C_{gas} by convection. The amount transported by diffusion in the gas phase (in longitudinal direction) is proportional to the concentration gradient $\partial C_{gas}/\partial x$. Through the top layer of the section, similar transports take place, but with a different value of the concentration (viz. $C_{gas} + \Delta C_{gas}$) and a different concentration gradient.

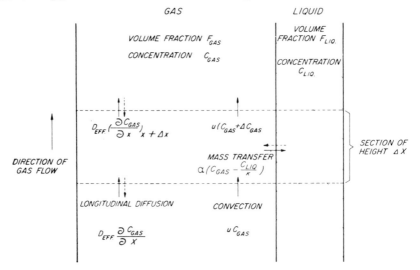

Figure 4.19. Schematic representation of the transport phenomena in a section Δx of a G.L.C. column.

The amount of solute transported by mass transfer to or from the liquid is proportional to the difference $(C_{liq.}/k - C_{gas})$ as a driving force (k is the distribution coefficient). As the result of transport by convection, diffusion and mass transfer, the concentration and amount of solute in the section has changed. For the gas phase the material balance requires:

$$F_{gas}\frac{\partial C_{gas}}{\partial t} = D_{eff}.F_{gas}\frac{\partial^2 C_{gas}}{\partial x^2} - uF_{gas}\frac{\partial C_{gas}}{\partial x} + \alpha(C_{liq.}/k - C_{gas}) \quad (20)$$

| Change in the amount of the component in the section Δx. | Amount of component transported by longitudinal diffusion. | Amount of component transported by convection | Amount of component transported by mass transfer to or from the liquid. |

For the corresponding phenomena in the liquid phase the equation reads:

$$F_{liq.}\frac{\partial C_{liq.}}{\partial t} = \alpha(C_{gas} - C_{liq.}/k) \quad (21)$$

mass transfer

In these equations the concentrations C_{gas} and $C_{liq.}$ are expressed in suitable units per unit of volume (mol/cm^3 for instance), so that the diffusion can be described as simply as possible. The distribution coefficient k refers to the same units. $F_{liq.}$ and F_{gas} are the volume fractions of liquid and gas in the column. α is the mass transfer coefficient; according to van Deemter *et al.* the latter is given by

$$\alpha = \frac{\pi^2}{4}\cdot\frac{F_{liq}.F_{gas}}{d_f^2},$$

which is the inverse of the diffusion time in the liquid layer d_f .

It can be shown that the solution for a single peak may be approximated by a Gaussian curve of the same type as results from the plate theory. The use of the latter theory is now in fact justified, since both theories lead to essentially the same mathematical expression. Furthermore, a comparison of the two expressions yields the relation between the H.E.T.P. and the diffusional effects. This expression, which forms the basis of our further considerations, reads:

$$H = 2\lambda d_p + 2\frac{\gamma D_{gas}}{u} + \frac{8}{\pi^2}\frac{k'}{(1 + k')^2}\cdot\frac{d_f^2}{D_{liq.}}u \quad (22)$$

| H.E.T.P. | longitudinal diffusion (eddy) (molecular) | non-equilibrium effect |

This result is the same as that arrived at in the statistical treatment of Klinkenberg and Sjenitzer. As already stated, the H.E.T.P. is composed of three terms, the first and the second constituting the contributions of axial (eddy and molecular) diffusion, the third term representing the contribution due to the resistance to mass transfer. For small values of the gas flow rate u the H.E.T.P. is mainly determined by the second term; in the case of very low gas velocities the H.E.T.P. may, in other words, become very large (and the number of plates for a given column length correspondingly low) owing to the molecular longitudinal diffusion. This influence becomes negligible for large values of u, in which case the H.E.T.P. may become large as a consequence of the resistance to mass transfer. Somewhere in between the H.E.T.P. has a minimum; the molecular diffusion term and the mass transfer term have equal values at this minimum. Particularly in the vicinity of the minimum the term $2\lambda d_p$ may play an important role. This term, the contribution by eddy diffusion, is a characteristic of the column packing, particle diameter and packing irregularities.

In the mass transfer term

$$\frac{8}{\pi^2} \frac{k'}{(1 + k')^2} \cdot \frac{d_f^2}{D_{\text{liq.}}} u,$$

the factor k' is given by $k(F_{\text{liq.}}/F_{\text{gas}})$. Hence, this term depends upon the distribution coefficient k, which is a function not only of the stationary liquid, but also of the components to be separated and the temperature at which the column is operated. It follows that the number of plates is not a characteristic of the column packing only. It depends also on the operating conditions and on the solutes; under the same set of conditions different numbers of plates are found for different solutes.

A plot of H against u and a similar plot of H versus $1/u$ for arbitrary values of the parameters (Figures 4.20 and 4.21) show two curves with a minimum and (for high values of u and $1/u$, respectively) an approximately straight part. In both cases the intercept of the "straight" part on the H axis is equal to $2\lambda d_p$, so that, if d_p is known, λ can be calculated and a measure of the packing regularity is obtained. From the slope of the straight part of the H-u curve the film thickness d_f can be estimated if $D_{\text{liq.}}$ and k' are known.

Like most theories involving limitations and assumptions, those dealt with above have met with some criticism. Van Deemter himself, in a chairman's lecture given at the Second Gas Chromatography Symposium in Amsterdam (1958), pointed out that there were several points in his theory which still needed confirmation. There is no doubt, however, that the theories in question have had an important influence on the development of gas chromatography by providing a clearer insight into the influence of operational parameters, and by indicating the way in which these parameters must be adjusted and combined if optimum separating efficiencies are desired. In Chapter 7 two highly efficient columns, chiefly based on such considerations, will be described. In connection with one of these the following is worth noting. Van Deemter's theory of a packed column is founded on a model in which the column is visualized as a bundle of capillaries. The

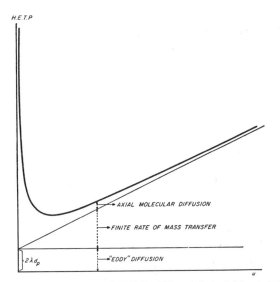

Figure 4.20. Analysis of H.E.T.P. ($H = 0.1 + 0.1/u + 0.05u$).

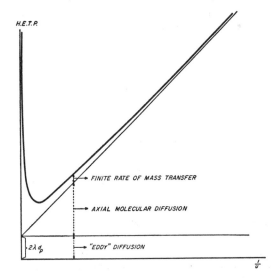

Figure 4.21. Analysis of H.E.T.P. ($H = 0.1 + 0.1/u + 0.05u$).

column independently developed by Golay actually takes the physical form of a single long capillary.

Before going into the design of high-efficiency columns (a subject that will be treated in Chapter 7), it will, however, be necessary to discuss in some detail the roles played by the mobile phase (carrier gas) and the stationary phase (the support and solvent). These subjects will be dealt with in Chapters 5 and 6.

List of Important Formulas for Linear Non-ideal Chromatography
(see list of symbols on page ix.)

Elution curve:

$$x_p = \frac{e^{-v}v^p}{p!} \tag{10}$$

Peak maximum:

$$x_p \text{ (max.)} = \frac{e^{-p}p^p}{p!} \tag{11}$$

Peak width at base: $w = 4\sqrt{p}$
Inflection points: at $v = p \pm \sqrt{p}$
Base line intercepts of inflection tangents: $v = p + 1 \pm 2\sqrt{p}$
The above formulas apply to any value of p ($o \cdots n$). For $p = n$ the formulas refer to the elution curve.
Retention volumes: $v_R = n$ $V_R = n(V_G + kV_L)$
Apparent retention volume: $V'_R = nkV_L$
Initial and final retention volume: $V_{R_{I,F}} = n(V_G + kV_L)(1 \mp 2\sqrt{n})$
Gas hold-up (V_{gas}) and liquid hold-up ($V_{liq.}$) of column: nV_G and nV_L
Number of plates:

$$n = \left(4\frac{d}{w}\right)^2,$$

alternatively:

$$n = \left(4\frac{d_I}{w} + 2\right)^2$$

$$n = \left(4\frac{d_F}{w} - 2\right)^2$$

H.E.T.P. $= L/n$
Definition of small sample*: $<0.5\sqrt{n}\,(V_G + kV_L)$

* The factor 0.5 refers to a particular manner of introducing the sample. In G.L.C. with instantaneous injection of the sample as a plug the factor is much smaller (see page 194).

For large values of p:

$$\frac{e^{-v}v^p}{p!} \approx \frac{1}{\sqrt{2\pi p}} \, e^{-(v-p)^2/2p} \tag{17}$$

van Deemter equation:

$$H = 2\lambda d_p + 2\frac{\gamma D_{\text{gas}}}{u} + \frac{8}{\pi^2} \cdot \frac{k'}{(1+k')^2} \cdot \frac{d_f^2}{D_{\text{liq}}} \, u. \tag{22}$$

REFERENCES

1. Deemter, J. J. van, Zuiderweg, F. J., and Klinkenberg, A., *Chem. Eng. Sci.*, **5,** 271 (1956).
2a. Wilson, J. N., *J. Am. Chem. Soc.*, **62,** 1583 (1940).
2b. De Vault, D., *J. Am. Chem. Soc.*, **65,** 532 (1943).
3. Baylé, G. G., and Klinkenberg, A., *Rec. trav. chim.*, **73,** 1037 (1954).
4. Giddings, J. C., and Eyring, H., *J. Phys. Chem.*, **59,** 416 (1955).
5. Martin, A. J. P., and Synge, R. L. M., *Biochem. J. (London)*, **35,** 1358 (1941).
6. Mayer, S. W., and Tompkins, E. R., *J. Am. Chem. Soc.*, **69,** 2866 (1947).
7. Glueckauf, E., *Trans. Faraday Soc.*, **51,** 34 (1955).
8. Lapidus, L., and Amundson, N. R., *J. Phys. Chem.*, **56,** 984 (1952).
9. Glueckauf, E., "Principles of Operation of Ion Exchange Column," paper read at the Conference on Ion Exchange, London, 5th-7th April 1954.
10. Tunitskii, N. N., *Doklady Akad. Nauk S.S.S.R. (Compt. rend. acad. sci. U.R.S.S.),* **99,** 577 (1954).
11. Klinkenberg, A., and Sjenitzer, F., *Chem. Eng. Sci.*, **5,** 258 (1956).
12. Consden, R., Gordon, A. H., and Martin, A. J. P., *Biochem. J. (London)*, **38,** 224 (1944).
13. Craig, L. C., *J. Biol. Chem.*, **155,** 519 (1944).
    Craig, L. C., and Craig, D., Chapt. IV of Vol. III of "Technique of Organic Chemistry," New York, Interscience, 1950.
14. Dijkstra, G., Keppler, J. G., and Schols, J. A., *Rec. trav. chim.*, **74,** 805 (1955).
15. Littlewood, A. B., Phillips, C. S. G., and Price, D. T., *J. Chem. Soc.*, **1955,** 1480.

Chapter 5

THE MOBILE PHASE IN GAS-LIQUID CHROMATOGRAPHY

INTRODUCTION

In the previous chapter, while discussing the theories on the separation effected by a G.L.C. column, we have seen that phenomena caused by (or occurring in) the moving gaseous eluent play an all-important part. The phenomena in question have, however, so far only been dealt with very generally. Several points arising in this connection must now be discussed in greater detail. These points are mainly contained in the following questions that might arise:

(1) Is it immaterial what kind of carrier gas is used?

(2) The velocity of the carrier gas has proved to have an important influence on the efficiency of the column. What are the results of the fact that this velocity varies along the length of the column, owing to the resistance of the packing and the compressibility of the gas?

(3) Is the pressure level at which a certain (average) gas velocity is established of importance?

In partition chromatography with elution development the ideal state of affairs is for the eluent to be a good solvent for the components, but it should be insoluble in the stationary phase. The latter condition (which is usually far from being satisfied in L.L.C.) has been assumed to be fulfilled in G.L.C. Fortunately this assumption is very close to the truth: the carrier gases mostly used in G.L.C.—nitrogen, carbon dioxide, hydrogen and helium—are almost completely insoluble in the normal types of stationary liquids.

In their primary function—the transport of a band through the column—the four gases mentioned above are therefore entirely equivalent. The conclusion should not, however, be drawn that it is indifferent which gas is used. Secondary physical effects must be considered: the gases have different viscosities and thus give rise to different pressure gradients in the column; diffusion effects also vary from gas to gas. These factors will be dealt with later in this chapter.

Another difference of practical importance, which has already been discussed in Chapter 3, lies in the fact that the response of the detector employed and the interpretation of this response may be dependent on the

140

carrier gas chosen. This point has already been dealt with in Chapter 3 and will not be further considered here.

Effects of the Compressibility of the Carrier Gas

In any form of chromatography a pressure gradient is required to move the mobile phase through the column. In gas chromatography (as opposed to L.L.C and L.S.C.) the mobile phase is readily compressible. Consequently the linear velocity of the carrier gas increases along the column from the high-pressure end to the low-pressure end. The same applies to the rate of transport of a volatile component, which is proportional to the rate of the carrier gas. A single figure for the gas velocity (as usually reported in chromatography) therefore provides an inadequate description of the prevailing conditions.

In order to describe the actual distribution of gas velocities in the column we must consider the flow of a gas through a packed bed. Though the theory of this mechanism is complicated in a general sense, a chromatographic column represents a simple case—as was pointed out by James and Martin[1] —since the macroscopic flow may be regarded as unidirected and laminar.

The pressure gradient in the column results from two factors: the dynamic viscosity (η) of the gas and the resistance to flow afforded by the packing. Instead of the "resistance," it is preferable to introduce the concept of "permeability"*(K).

Let us consider a packed column, as depicted in Figure 5.1, of length L, through which gas is passing in unidirectional laminar flow. At any point (x) the linear gas velocity (u) in the cross-sectional area (a) occupied by the gas phase is inversely proportional to the dynamic viscosity η (which is nearly independent of pressure) and directly proportional to the pressure gradient dp/dx, the proportionality factor being the permeability.

$$u = -\frac{K}{\eta}\frac{dp}{dx} \qquad (1)$$

(The negative sign is due to the fact that the direction of u is opposed to that of increasing pressure p.)

By a development of this equation we can calculate, for any point in the column, the pressure and rate of flow, expressed in the quantities that are observed in practice: the pressures p_i and p_o at the inlet and outlet, respectively, and the volume V_t of gas (converted if necessary to the temperature prevailing in the column) emerging from the outlet in unit time.

---

* "Permeability" should be distinguished from "porosity." Although porosity and permeability are both related to particle size and shape, the porosity is associated with the ratio of the spaces occupied by gas and solid, whilst the permeability is a measure of the ease with which the gas flows through the erratically distributed voids between the particles.

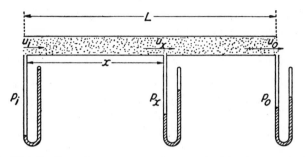

Figure 5.1. Distribution of pressures and gas velocities in a packed column.

If η is known the equation further allows us to calculate K, a quantity that can be used for characterizing the column packing.

In the case of isothermal flow (a condition which can be assumed to prevail in gas chromatography) of an ideal gas the volumetric throughput $a.u$ is inversely proportional to the pressure:

$$a.u.p = a.u_o.p_o$$

which is more conveniently written as:

$$a.u = \frac{V_t.p_o}{p} \tag{2}$$

From Eqs. (1) and (2) it follows that

$$V_t p_o.dx = -a \frac{K}{\eta} p.dp \tag{3}$$

By integration, and by putting $p = p_i$ when $x = 0$, this becomes:

$$V_t p_o x = \frac{a}{2} \frac{K}{\eta} (p_i^2 - p^2) \tag{4}$$

When $x = L$, $p = p_o$ and we obtain

$$V_t p_o L = \tfrac{1}{2} a \frac{K}{\eta} \cdot (p_i^2 - p_o^2) \tag{5}$$

Elimination of K/η from Eqs. (4) and (5) gives

$$\frac{x}{L} = \frac{p_i^2 - p^2}{p_i^2 - p_o^2} = \frac{(p_i/p_o)^2 - (p/p_o)^2}{(p_i/p_o)^2 - 1} \tag{6}$$

This equation enables us to calculate p at any place in the column for any values of p_i and p_o. It is instructive to draw a graph, based on Equation (6), in which the pressure ratio p/p_o is plotted against the relative distance x/L from the inlet. This has been done in Figure 5.2, with various values of

p_i/p_o as parameter. Since $u_o/u = p/p_o$ expression (6) can also be used to construct similar curves for u/u_o against x/L with p_i/p_o as parameter, as given in Figure 5.3.

It will be seen from these graphs that the pressure falls off slowly and almost proportionally in the first part of the column, but more rapidly toward the outlet. The increase in gas velocity shows a corresponding trend. The bend in the latter curves becomes very abrupt for high ratios of the inlet and outlet pressures. As has been shown in Chapter 4, the efficiency of a column has an optimum corresponding to a certain gas velocity, so that in the case of high pressure ratios a part of the column may operate very inefficiently. It should, however, be observed that with a proper choice of gas velocity the inefficient part constitutes only 10 to 20 per cent of the whole column length. Hence it follows that the consequences of using, for instance, low outlet pressures and correspondingly high p_i/p_o ratios need not necessarily affect the column efficiency seriously. Great care must nevertheless be taken, as will be shown further, to insure that the velocity

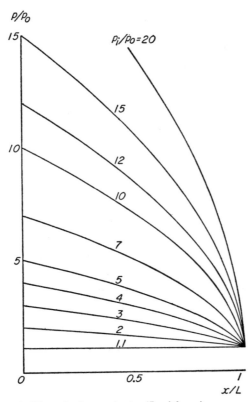

Figure 5.2. Plot of p/p_o against x/L with p_i/p_o as parameter.

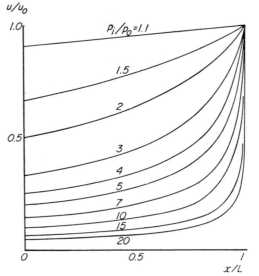

Figure 5.3. Plot of u/u_o against x/L with p_i/p_o as parameter.

of the gas at the exit is such that the main part of the column is actually operating in the region of efficient gas rates.

For values of p_i/p_o close to 1, say less than 1.5, the pressure gradient may be considered as constant without introducing a serious error.

The compressibility of the moving phase naturally also affects the retention volumes in gas chromatography. Fortunately, the conversion of the measured retention volumes to standard conditions presents no difficulties. A derivation of the required formula has been given by James and Martin[1]. The derivation that will be given here requires the introduction of a few simple concepts.

The Average Pressure in the Column

As the pressure is not a linear function of x, the average column pressure differs from the arithmetic mean of inlet and outlet pressures; for high values of p_i/p_o it may be considerably higher.

The average column pressure $\bar{p}$ is defined as

$$\bar{p} = \frac{\int p.dx}{\int dx} \tag{7}$$

by substituting

$$dx = -\frac{a}{V_i p_o} \cdot \frac{K}{\eta} . p.dp$$

from Eq. (3) and carrying out the integration between the limits of $p = p_i$ and $p = p_o$ we find:

$$\bar{p} = \tfrac{2}{3}p_o \, \frac{(p_i/p_o)^3 - 1}{(p_i/p_o)^2 - 1} \tag{8}$$

(It can easily be shown that it is only permissible to replace $\bar{p}$ by $\tfrac{1}{2}(p_i + p_o)$ for low p_i/p_o ratios, say less than 1.5; at this value of p_i/p_o the error becomes less than $1\tfrac{1}{2}$ per cent of p_o.)

Residence Time of the Carrier Gas

If V_{gas} ($=aL$) is the volume occupied in the column by the gas phase and V_t, as before, is the volume of gas emerging from the column in unit time, then, for a noncompressible moving phase, the average residence time of a molecule of the carrier gas in the column would be $t_g = V_{gas}/V_t$. If further the pressure p prevailing inside the column is different from the pressure p_o at the outlet (where V_t is measured) the average residence time is

$$t_g = \frac{V_{gas}}{V_t} \cdot \frac{p}{p_o} \tag{9}$$

Because of the compressibility of the gas, p changes continuously, but it can be shown that it may be replaced by $\bar{p}$, since

$$t_g = \int \frac{dx}{u} = \frac{1}{u_o p_o} \int p dx = \frac{\bar{p}L}{u_o p_o} = \frac{\bar{p}aL}{p_o a u_o} = \frac{\bar{p}V_{gas}}{p_o V_t}$$

From Eqs. (8) and (9) it follows that

$$t_g = \tfrac{2}{3} \frac{V_{gas}}{V_t} \cdot \frac{(p_i/p_o)^3 - 1}{(p_i/p_o)^2 - 1} \tag{10}$$

Retention Volume

In G.L.C. a constant proportion has been assumed between the rate of movement of a volatile solute and the rate of movement of the carrier gas. Consden, Gordon and Martin[2] have introduced the retardation factor, R_F, to denote this transport ratio under the prevailing circumstances:

$$R_F = \frac{\text{rate of movement of the solute}}{\text{rate of movement of the fluid}}$$

The slower rate of movement of the solute relative to that of the carrier gas causes the average residence time of a solute molecule to be $1/R_F$ times the average residence time of a carrier gas molecule. The average volume V_R of carrier gas required to transport a solute molecule through the column (corresponding to the volume required to transport the centre of a solute band), hence will be:

$$V_R = V_t t_g / R_F \qquad (11)$$

Substituting t_g from Eq. (10) we obtain:

$$V_R = \tfrac{2}{3} \cdot \frac{V_{gas}}{R_F} \cdot \frac{(p_i/p_o)^3 - 1}{(p_i/p_o)^2 - 1} \qquad (12)$$

The limit to which V_R approaches when p_i approaches p_o (i.e., when the pressure differential tends to zero) may be termed the "limiting retention volume" $V_R{}^o$.

In that case the quotient

$$\frac{(p_i/p_o)^3 - 1}{(p_i/p_o)^2 - 1} \text{ becomes } \frac{3}{2},$$

so that

$$V_R{}^o = \frac{V_{gas}}{R_F} \qquad (13)$$

and we may write

$$\frac{V_R}{V_R{}^o} = \tfrac{2}{3} \cdot \frac{(p_i/p_o)^3 - 1}{(p_i/p_o)^2 - 1} = \frac{\bar{p}}{p_o} \qquad (14)$$

In this manner James and Martin (*loc. cit.*) expressed the actual retention volume for an outlet pressure p_o in terms of the limiting retention volume at the average column pressure.

For large pressure differentials (p_i/p_o say >5) Eq. (14) gives

$$V_R/V_R{}^o \approx \tfrac{2}{3} \frac{p_i}{p_o},$$

while for small pressure differentials (p_i/p_o say <1.5),

$$V_R/V_R{}^o \approx \frac{p_i + p_o}{2p_o}.$$

THE PERMEABILITY OF THE COLUMN

The pressure differential to be applied across the column in order to produce the desired carrier gas velocity depends, as we have seen, on the viscosity of the gas, the length of the column and its permeability. It is obvious that the permeability of a column will increase as the diameter of the particles constituting the packing increases. For the present purpose it will not be necessary to discuss this relation in detail. From chemical engineering studies on fluid flow in a packed bed (Kozeny, Carman, Ergun, Rose[3]) it is found that K can be expressed by a relation which we will write in the following form:

TABLE 5.1. VALUES OF K FOUND FOR VARIOUS PARTICLE DIAMETERS

Sterchamol Screen Fraction	Average Particle Diameter (mm)	$K \times 10^7$ (cm²)
20/30	0.715	48.4
30/50	0.444	16.6
50/80	0.237	4.6
80/100	0.163	2.7

$$K = \frac{1}{C} \cdot f(\epsilon) \cdot d_p^2 \tag{15}$$

in which:

d_p is a measure of the "diameter"* of the particles;

C is a factor depending on the shape of the particles, but varying only between narrow limits;

ϵ is the fractional void volume of the packing (porosity).

It follows that if, for fractions of progressive particle size of a particular type of packing, we assume that C and ϵ are constants, K must be proportional to the square of the particle diameter.

A test of this relation has been carried out by the writer on a number of screen fractions of Sterchamol support, impregnated in each case with 30 parts (wt) of a stationary liquid to 100 parts (wt) of support. Nitrogen was used as carrier gas. In each experiment the observations comprised measuring the inlet and outlet pressures p_i and p_o and the volume V_t of gas (at p_o) in unit time, corrected for the vapor pressure of water (from the wet gasmeter) and converted to column temperature. By employing Equation (5), K/η could then be calculated after inserting the proper value of L and a. The latter figure was computed from the volume and diameter of the column, the volume occupied by the support and the volume occupied by the stationary liquid. The values found checked very well with the value for a obtained from the "retention" volume of a non-absorbed gas (see Figure 1.4). After multiplication by η (the known viscosity of nitrogen at the column temperature), K is found (c.g.s. units were used, K/η then has the dimensions cm³.g⁻¹. sec. and K the dimensions cm²). In Table 5.1 the values of K so obtained are listed against the screen fraction in question and the average particle diameter.

Figure 5.4 shows a plot of K against the square of the average particle diameter. It will be seen that the linearity of the relationship is satisfactory.

The measurements were carried out for each column at various values of p_i and p_o and at a number of column temperatures. It was found that the val-

---

* As the particles may have any shape, we must define what is understood by its diameter. It may, for instance, be expressed as the volume of the particle divided by the part of the surface area contributing to the frictional resistance.

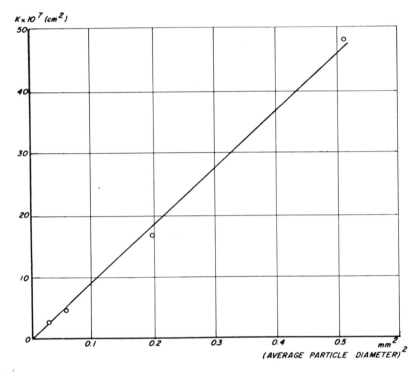

Figure 5.4. Plot of permeability, K, against the square of particle diameter for various Sterchamol screen fractions.

ues of K agreed within the limits of experimental error. These results also serve to show that the simplified theory of flow assumed in the derivation of the formulas is sufficiently valid.

Velocity Gradient and Column Efficiency

Application of the Van Deemter Equation

We can now consider the second question raised in the introduction to this chapter, namely, in how far the gradient in gas velocity along the length of the column affects its efficiency. This subject can best be approached by considering the equation (22) due to Van Deemter, given in the later part of Chapter 4. This equation for the H.E.T.P. as a function of u, the linear gas velocity, can be written in a simplified form with three coefficients:

$$H = A + B/u + Cu \tag{16}$$

The equation is that of a hyperbola (see Figures 4.20 and 4.21) having a minimum at $u = \sqrt{B/C}$ and $H = A + 2\sqrt{BC}$. Consequently there is only one value of the linear gas velocity, corresponding to this minimum, at which a particular column is operating at its maximum efficiency.

Since a certain velocity gradient in a packed bed is inevitable, it will be clear that a G.L.C. column can, strictly speaking, never function at optimum efficiency along its whole length. Depending on the distribution of velocities, the over-all efficiency may, however, be more or less satisfactory.

It will be obvious that the closest approach to optimum efficiency will be realized if the range of gas velocities is small (a condition implying a low pressure differential, namely, a low column resistance) and if these velocities lie around the optimum. Since the left-hand branch of the hyperbola is usually steep it is also evident that very low gas velocities may transplant the operation into the very inefficient region where molecular diffusion becomes serious. (This point will be gone into later.) On the other hand, it will be less disadvantageous if the average velocity is somewhat higher than the optimum because the right-hand branch of the curve is usually not so steep. The use of higher velocities also possesses the practical advantage of giving a proportional shortening of the time required for the analysis.

As a rule the position of the minimum will, of course, be unknown. It varies from case to case, and is dependent not only on the length of the column, the particle size of the support, etc., but also on the nature of the stationary liquid, carrier gas and solute, the temperature and other operational parameters. Some experimental determinations of H-u curves (which incidentally agreed well in shape with that predicted by theory), carried out by the writer and co-workers[4] on columns with various types of support, various amounts of stationary liquid and several kinds of carrier gas, confirmed that the minima lie at different linear gas rates. These data, however, also showed that the volumetric gas rate of 100 ml/min, quoted in Chapter 2 as a good average for columns of 6 mm I.D., is a reasonable figure for practical use; the equivalent linear gas rate (about 10–15 cm/sec at the outlet) may lie somewhat to the right of the average optimum found, but not sufficiently to affect the efficiency seriously.

In the case of critical separations it may, however, be necessary for the experimenter to adopt an empirical procedure and to vary the gas velocity so as to observe whether the efficiency of separation undergoes noticeable changes.

In the following paragraph we shall mainly take the practical criterium— the shortening of residence times and duration of the analysis—for judging the effects resulting from alterations in the gas velocity by changing the inlet and outlet pressures.

Influence of Varying Inlet and Outlet Pressure

If an analysis is carried out at certain values of the inlet and outlet pressures, p_i and p_o, and it is desired to increase the gas velocity so as to shorten the time of analysis, this result may be obtained by changing either p_o or p_i, or both. It will be shown by a few examples that it is not immaterial which of the pressures is altered. We will consider a column that is operated at inlet and outlet pressures p_i and p_o, after which these pressures will be changed to p_i' and p_o'. If originally the volumetric gas rate (measured at the outlet) and the residence time of the carrier gas were V_t and t_g, respectively, these quantities become V_t' and t_g'. The ratio of the gas rates V_t/V_t' follows from Eq. (5):

$$\frac{V_t}{V_t'} = \frac{p_o'}{p_o} \cdot \frac{p_i^2 - p_o^2}{(p_i')^2 - (p_o')^2} \tag{17}$$

and that of the residence times t_g/t_g' from Eq. (10):

$$\frac{t_g}{t_g'} = \frac{V_t'}{V_t} \cdot \frac{(p_i/p_o)^3 - 1}{(p_i/p_o)^2 - 1} \cdot \frac{(p_i'/p_o')^2 - 1}{(p_i'/p_o')^3 - 1} \tag{18}$$

so that the ratio of gas rates and residence times can be calculated.

We will now consider three experiments.

Let the first be carried out at atmospheric inlet pressure, outlet pressure 0.25 atm. In a second run the inlet pressure is kept constant at 1 atm. and the outlet pressure is reduced to 0.1 atm., in a third case the outlet pressure is maintained at 0.25 atm. and the inlet pressure is increased to 1.15 atm. The calculated values of the volumetric gas rate at the outlet, the relative residence times and the ratio of linear outlet to inlet gas speeds, u_o/u_i, are then found to be as in Table 5.2.

A comparison of these figures is very instructive. In the second run a reduction in outlet pressure by a factor of $2\frac{1}{2}$ has produced a shortening of residence time by but 9 per cent. At the same time the spread of the velocity gradient has become $2\frac{1}{2}$ times larger, so that the chance is now considerably greater that a part of the column is operating at a low stage efficiency. In the third experiment the increase in inlet pressure has resulted in a 15 per cent reduction in residence time, whilst the non-uniformity in the gas rate has increased only slightly. For shortening residence times an increase

TABLE 5.2. PARAMETERS FOR VARIOUS COLUMN PRESSURES

	I	II	III
Inlet pressure (atm.)	1	1	1.15
Outlet pressure (atm.)	0.25	0.1	0.25
Volumetric gas rate (outlet)	V_t	$2.64\ V_t$	$1.34\ V_t$
Residence time	t_g	$0.91\ t_g$	$0.847\ t_g$
Ratio u_o/u_i	4	10	4.6

in inlet pressure is therefore a far better measure than a reduction in outlet pressure.

Low column pressures have frequently been employed in G.L.C. (even
in published experiments) under the assumption that there exists an
analogy with vacuum distillation, in other words that the rate of transport
of a component of low volatility will thereby be increased. *This assumption
is, however, erroneous.* The transport velocity of a solute in G.L.C., at a
certain gas rate, is dependent on its partition coefficient with respect to
the column liquid and is independent of the absolute gas pressure. Though
the use of a low column pressure need not necessarily result in a low efficiency if the resistance of the packing is not excessive, particular care
should be taken that the velocity at the inlet is sufficient to insure its
operation outside of the "bad" portion of the H-u curve. An example of
the unsatisfactory results that might be obtained by carrying out G.L.C.
"in vacuum" is illustrated in Figure 5.5. In this figure u_i and u_o represent
the speeds at the inlet and outlet of the column that might prevail in run I
of Table 5.2 ($u_o = 4u_i$). The circle on the curve shows the estimated
"average" H.E.T.P. at which the column is operating, the distribution of
velocities (Figure 5.3) being taken into account. It has been assumed that
this value of the H.E.T.P. lies close to the optimum. If now the column were
operated at $p_i = 0.1$ atm. and $p_o = 0.01$ atm., the calculated limiting gas
velocities become u_i (vac.) and u_o (vac.). The column thus functions largely
in the unfavorable part of the H-u curve, the estimated average H.E.T.P.
being as shown by the second circle: the average column efficiency is reduced to less than half on account of this fact alone.

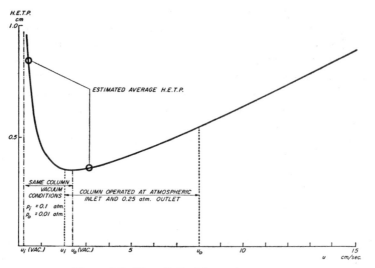

Figure 5.5. The effect of low column pressures.

In operating columns of high resistance it will be preferable to work at somewhat elevated pressures, so as to establish a u_o/u_i ratio as close to unity as possible.

Although, as we have shown, the use of low column pressures should be discouraged from the point of view of separation efficiency, it should be observed that reduction of column pressure is a good means of increasing the concentration of the solutes in the effluent, and hence of increasing the signal from the detector.

THE EFFECT OF GAS DIFFUSION

The Coefficient B in the simplified Van Deemter Equation (16) is equal to $2\gamma D_{gas}$ (Eq. 22, p. 125), in which D_{gas} is the gas diffusivity and γ is a factor for the tortuosity of the gas channels. An increase in D_{gas} lowers the maximum efficiency by increasing $H_{min.} = A + 2\sqrt{BC}$ and alters the value of $u = \sqrt{B/C}$ at which this value of $H_{min.}$ is established. From a standpoint of column efficiency, therefore, carrier gases of low diffusivity (nitrogen and carbon dioxide) are preferable to those of high diffusivity (hydrogen and helium).

In the Van Deemter equation the factor γ is assumed to lie between 0.5 and 1, dependent on the packing. In order to verify this point, values for D_{gas} must be known. Gas diffusion coefficients can be calculated from a relation given by Gilliland[5]. The values so obtained for the systems propane and butane in nitrogen and hydrogen are as follows:

$$\left. \begin{array}{l} D(C_3H_8 \text{ in } N_2) = 0.0765 \text{ cm}^2/\text{sec} \\ D(C_3H_8 \text{ in } H_2) = 0.283 \text{ cm}^2/\text{sec} \\ D(C_4H_{10} \text{ in } N_2) = 0.0663 \text{ cm}^2/\text{sec} \\ D(C_4H_{10} \text{ in } H_2) = 0.252 \text{ cm}^2/\text{sec} \end{array} \right\} \quad 20°C, 1 \text{ atm.}$$

By systematic chromatographic measurements it is possible to determine points on the H-u curve experimentally and from this curve to calculate values of the three coefficients A, B and C. This was done for the four above-mentioned systems.* From B and D_{gas} a figure for γ could then be obtained. The values so found lay between 0.55 and 0.77, and therefore were of the right order of magnitude. For a first approximation γ may, in fact, be regarded as constant.

We are now also in a position to estimate more quantitatively the effect of the nature and the pressure of the carrier gas. The coefficient D_{gas} for hydrogen is about four times that for nitrogen. In Figure 5.6 curves have been plotted, corresponding to the equations:

$$H = 0.1 + 0.07/u + 0.05\ u \quad \text{(nitrogen)}†$$
$$H = 0.1 + 0.28/u + 0.05\ u \quad \text{(hydrogen)}$$

From these curves it may be seen that a carrier gas of low diffusivity

---

* Work, partly unpublished, carried out in the author's laboratory; see also Ref. 4.
† See Ref. (4) and chapter 7 for the values of A and C.

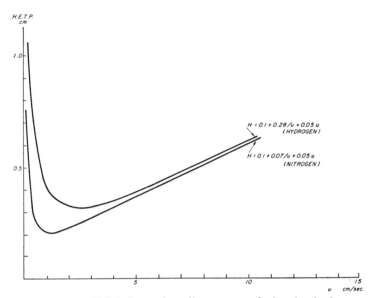

Figure 5.6. Plot of H.E.T.P. against linear gas velocity for hydrogen and nitrogen.

(such as nitrogen or CO_2) gives rise to higher column efficiencies than a gas of high diffusivity (hydrogen or helium). The difference is particularly striking at low gas velocities; at high gas rates it becomes small.

It should be noted that the diffusivity is inversely proportional to the gas pressure. This fact provides another argument against the use of low column pressures.

In the above discussion of the diffusion effect it has been assumed that the resistance of the column is small, so that inlet and outlet velocities do not differ appreciably. Hydrogen is less viscous than the other gases and this fact gives a good motive for using it in densely packed columns. As pointed out previously, the use of this gas also gives a high sensitivity in a katharometer.

REFERENCES

1. James, A. T., and Martin, A. J. P., *Biochem. J. (London)*, **50**, 679 (1952).
2. Consden, R., Gordon, A. H., and Martin, A. J. P., *Biochem. J. (London)*, **38**, 224 (1944).
3. Kozeny, J., *Sitzber. Akad. Wiss. Wien, Math. naturw. Kl. Abt.* IIa **136**, 271 (1927). Carman, P. C., *Discussions Faraday Soc.*, No. 3, 72 (1948). Ergun, S., *Chem. Eng. Progr.*, **48**, 89 (1952). Rose, H. E., *Inst. Mech. Engrs. London, Proc.*, **153**, 141 (1945).
4. Keulemans, A. I. M. and Kwantes, A., Vapour Phase Chromatography, Desty, D. H. (ed.), London, 1957 (Proc. of London Symposium on V. Ph. Chr., May/June 1956), p. 15.
5. Gilliland, E. R., *Ind. Eng. Chem.*, **26**, 681 (1934).

Chapter 6

THE SOLID SUPPORT AND THE STATIONARY LIQUID

The Solid Support

The Function of the Support

In gas-liquid chromatography the column packing* consists of an inert solid material supporting a nonvolatile liquid. As was stated in Chapter 2, the amount of the latter varies in practice from 15 to 50 parts per 100 parts (wt/wt) of the support. This relatively large amount of liquid must be present as a coating that is as thin and uniform as possible. Two conditions are thereby insured. In the first place, the liquid will actually be stationary, viz., it will not move by gravity or be transported by the carrier gas. Secondly, a rapid establishment of the gas-liquid equilibrium will result, since the solute molecules need not travel far in the liquid phase, where the speed of diffusion is small.

The support must therefore have a large specific area and should hence consist either of small particles or of particles with a high accessible porosity.

In the case of massive, uniform spherical particles the specific area is inversely proportional to the diameter of the particles. If the particles are porous this proportionality does not hold, since the contribution to the area due to the pores (which is frequently a large proportion of the total) does not increase with diminution in size. Furthermore, the packing density scarcely increases when the particles become smaller. The specific area of a highly porous material is consequently very little dependent on particle size.

Nonporous solids are usually of little practical interest as supports for G.L.C. Even if the particles are extremely fine the surface is not sufficiently large to prevent filling of the voids and transport of the liquid. Neither is every porous substance suitable. In materials such as silica gel the large surface area is for the greater part due to the presence of extremely fine pores. The latter fill up with solvent, exposing but a small surface for exchange. Since the length of the pores is relatively great, a considerable time

---

* In the present chapter, only the conventional packed column is considered. The recently developed coated capillary column is referred to in Chapter 7.

TABLE 6.1. PERCENTAGE PARTICLE SIZE DISTRIBUTION OF "CELITES"

Range of Particle Size	Celite 535	Celite 545
$>40 \mu$	17.5%	24%
40–20 μ	32%	52%
20–10 μ	32%	18.5%
10–6 μ	16%	4.5%
$<6 \mu$	2.5%	1%

is required for diffusion; the elution peaks consequently broaden, as explained in Chapter 4. Furthermore, such substances usually retain a certain adsorptive capacity after impregnation and then give rise to "tailing" of the peaks.* Many surface-active substances, including active charcoal, cracking catalysts, etc., belong to the latter class.

Two kinds of material that have been widely used as support are diatomaceous earth and ground fire-brick. "Celite," a brand of the former material, was utilized by the inventors of G.L.C., James and Martin[1], and has subsequently been employed by many investigators. Two types of "Celite" that have proved suitable are "Celite" 535 and 545, which differ in grading (among other properties), as appears from Table 6.1.

These grades of "Celite" are frequently submitted to elutriation for removal of the fines and are sometimes also given an after-treatment.†

Ground fire-brick was first proposed by the author and A. Kwantes[3] and has since then been advocated by several workers in the field[4, 5, 6, 7]. Not all kinds of fire-brick are satisfactory. The writer employed a German make, Sterchamol No. 22. It has been shown by Dimbat, Porter and Stross[5] that an American fire-brick—Johns-Manville C 22 grade—is an equivalent material, having a somewhat greater strength.

For most purposes the fire-brick can be impregnated directly after

* Surface-active solids of this type are employed in gas-adsorption chromatography. It has recently been proposed to use for this purpose adsorbing agents that have been impregnated with small amounts of liquid, the latter then acting as a "tailing reducer." This development will be described in Chapter 8.

† James and Martin size-graded Celite by repeated suspension in water in a beaker 18 cm high; all fine material not settling in 3 minutes was rejected. About 50 per cent of the material was so removed[2]. (The particles must consequently have been larger than 20 μ.)

The graded Celite was heated in a muffle furnace for 3 hours at 300°C, washed with dilute hydrochloric acid for the removal of iron and basic compounds, subsequently with water, and was dried at 145°C. This treatment effectively eliminated the adsorptive capacity observed in the separation of fatty acids. For the separation of amines, however, the treatment with HCl had to be followed by one with 5 per cent methanolic NaOH. The support then still had slight adsorptive properties, but not enough to interfere with its use in most applications.

grinding, screening and the removal of dust with a suitable liquid (see Chapter 3).

Dimbat and co-workers* investigated the effects of some characteristics of various solid supports, including "Celite", Sterchamol and Johns-Manville C 22 fire-brick, on the resolution of solute mixtures in G.L.C. The surface area, pore volume and bulk density were measured. Of these properties the latter was the only one showing a correlation with resolution. The bulk densities of the materials investigated ranged from 0.31 to 1.4. Good resolution was exclusively observed with supports having a bulk density below 0.45; above a value of 0.65 results were definitely unsatisfactory.

Quantitative Aspects of Particle Diameter and Liquid Film Thickness

A more quantitative treatment of the influence of the support and the film of stationary liquid can be undertaken with the aid of the equation derived for the H.E.T.P. by Van Deemter (Equation 22, p. 135). It was shown in Chapter 5 that the term $2\gamma D_{gas}/u$ allows the effects due to the nature of the carrier gas to be estimated. A consideration of the two other terms will be found to provide information on several factors of importance for constructing and operating columns intended for separations at high efficiencies.

Particle Diameter of the Support. The term $2\lambda d_p$ in Equation 22, p. 135 is characteristic of the column packing and is independent of the solute, the solvent and operating conditions.

The most obvious way to reduce this term (and so increase column efficiency) would be to diminish d_p, the particle diameter. However, the value of λ—a factor dependent on the manner in which the particles are packed—proves to be adversely affected (increased) by small values of d_p. This fact shows that regular packing is easier to realize with large than with small particles; a fine support is more liable to cause channeling than a coarse one. Values quoted by Van Deemter et al.[8] for λ are: ca. 8 for a 200–400 mesh screen fraction (diameter 74–37 μ), ca. 3 for 50–100 mesh (297–149 μ), less than 1 for 20–40 mesh (840–240 μ).

The same authors compared columns packed with "Celite" (300–400 mesh or $d_p \approx 40\ \mu$) to columns packed with a 50–80 mesh fraction of ground fire-brick (average particle diameter ca. 250 μ). The values of $2\lambda d_p$ for these two columns were obtained from the intercepts of the asymptotes to the H-u curve on the H axis (see Figures 4.20 and 4.21) and proved to be about equal, or even slightly higher for the "Celite" column. It hence follows that the advantage of a six times smaller particle diameter in the case of "Celite" is nullified by a value of λ that is at least six times as large.

* Private communication.

Since the coarser material has a far higher permeability than "Celite" (with the important resulting advantages discussed in Chapter 5), the writer considers a 30–50 or 50–80 screen fraction of a suitable fire-brick to be a better support for most types of work*.

The Amount of Stationary Liquid. The effect of the quantity of stationary liquid on the support shows up in the term

$$\frac{8}{\pi^2} \cdot \frac{k'}{(1 + k')^2} \cdot \frac{d_f^2}{D_{\text{liq.}}} \cdot u$$

of Equation 22 (p. 135), in which the thickness d_f of the liquid film enters in the second power. If d_f is small in comparison to the particle diameter, as is usually the case, the total volume of stationary liquid is about equal to the product of surface area of the support and effective film thickness. We have seen that the surface area only varies appreciably with particle size in the case of smooth particles; in the case of the porous materials normally used the specific surface area scarcely increases with a reduction in particle size. Hence d_f will vary little with particle diameter, and for a certain type of support will always be roughly proportional to the ratio of stationary liquid to solid.

The coefficient of the mass transfer term does not, however, increase directly in proportion to the square of the film thickness d_f , since the quantity $k' = k \dfrac{F_{\text{liq.}}}{F_{\text{gas}}}$ is also affected. For a given column packing $F_{\text{liq.}} + F_{\text{gas}}$ is constant, so that an increase in $F_{\text{liq.}}$ will reduce F_{gas} and cause an increase in $F_{\text{liq.}}/F_{\text{gas}}$. With the double purpose of checking the validity of the mass transfer term in the Van Deemter equation and of obtaining practical information on the influence of variations in the amount of stationary liquid, Keulemans and Kwantes[9] determined a number of H-u curves on columns containing different ratios of solvent to support. The columns employed were packed with 30–50 mesh ground fire-brick, coated with 5, 15, 30 and 45 parts per 100 of n-hexadecane; propane and n-butane were chosen as solutes. The results are shown in Figure 6.1. The most important data from these experiments are listed in Table 6.2.

* Recent results have shown, however, that fractions of firebrick, if impregnated with a stationary liquid of low polarity, will retain a certain adsorptivity for solute components of higher polarity, so that some tailing will then result. If such polar compounds are present in the mixture to be analyzed, the alternatives are hence: (a) to use a stationary liquid having approximately the same polarity as the compound in question, or, if a stationary phase of low polarity is essential, (b) to employ Celite, which produces the effect described to a lower, though not entirely negligible degree. An alternative method of diminishing residual adsorption, communicated by Scott[21], consists in "silver plating" the supporting solid by treating it with silver nitrate solution and a reducing agent.

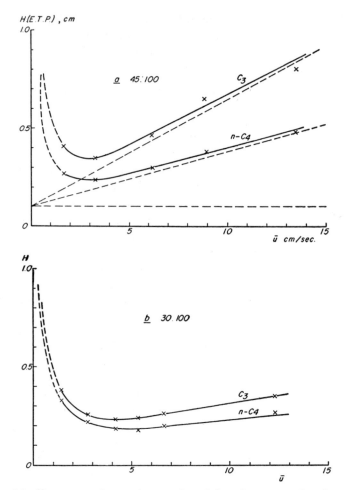

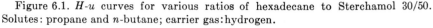

Figure 6.1. *H-u* curves for various ratios of hexadecane to Sterchamol 30/50. Solutes: propane and *n*-butane; carrier gas:hydrogen.

(a) 45:100   (b) 30:100

Of the figures in Table 6.2 those for $F_{\text{liq.}}$ and F_{gas} could be determined directly from measured column data. The values for k' and $k'/(1 + k')^2$ could be calculated from known partition coefficients k (see Chapter 7), which at the temperature of the experiments (30°C) were 11.4 ± 0.3 for propane and 38.0 ± 0.3 for *n*-butane with respect to *n*-hexadecane. The true effective value of d_f is not easy to estimate, and a relative procedure was therefore adopted. If a thickness of unity is assigned to the film in the 5 per cent column, the thicknesses in the 15, 30 and 45 per cent columns will not have been more than 3, 6 and 9, respectively and the proportion-

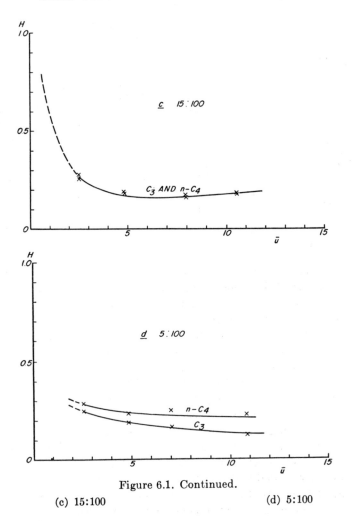

Figure 6.1. Continued.

(c) 15:100   (d) 5:100

ality of d_f^2 will not have exceeded $1:9:36:81$; the latter values were taken for computing $d_f^2 k'/(1 + k')^2$.

A satisfactory check of the theory might have been obtained by measuring the slopes of the asymptotes in one experiment, calculating those in the others and comparing them with observed values. Unfortunately, the slopes of the 5, 15 and 30 per cent asymptotes were too small to be measured with sufficient accuracy. The values calculated from the 45 per cent curves, however, agree with observations in two respects:

(a) the slopes are equal for the 15 per cent column, and

(b) the order of slopes is reversed in the 5 per cent column.

TABLE 6.2. COMPARISON OF DATA FOR COLUMNS WITH VARIOUS AMOUNTS
OF STATIONARY LIQUID

Hexadecane in Per cent (wt/wt)	5	15	30	45
$F_{liq.}$	0.0067	0.0233	0.0426	0.0629
F_{gas}	0.213	0.215	0.191	0.165
$k' - C_3$	0.36	1.24	2.54	4.34
$k' - nC_4$	1.2	4.1	8.5	14.5
$k'/(1 + k')^2 - C_3$	0.149	0.247	0.203	0.152
$k'/(1 + k')^2 - nC_4$	0.248	0.158	0.094	0.060
$k'd_f^2/(1 + k')^2 - C_3$	0.15	1.86	7.31	12.30
$k'd_f^2/(1 + k')^2 - nC_4$	0.25	1.42	3.38	4.86
Slope of curve as calculated from 45% column C_3	0.0006	0.008	0.033	0.055*
C_4	0.0015	0.008	0.019	0.028*

* Experimental values.

The experiments therefore give a qualitative confirmation of the Van
Deemter term, which is probably all that can be expected in view of the
assumptions made in the derivation of the equation and the relatively
small contribution of the mass transfer term.

In spite of its inherent uncertainties this term can provide us with
valuable indications in several respects. Firstly, we can look into the influence of temperature on column efficiency. The factor $k'/(1 + k')^2$ has a
maximum of 0.25 at $k' = 1$. Normally k' will be appreciably larger than 1
and will decrease with increasing temperature, so that $k'/(1 + k')^2$ then
becomes larger and tends to reduce the column efficiency. On the other
hand, an increase in temperature increases the diffusion coefficient $D_{liq.}$,
partly owing to a reduction in viscosity of the liquid. The two effects tend
to compensate each other, and the over-all influence on the column efficiency is not easily predictable. The fact that an increase in temperature
has sometimes been found to have a favorable, and sometimes an unfavorable effect on column efficiency thus becomes explicable.

The mass transfer term of the Van Deemter equation also furnishes the
possibility of measuring $D_{liq.}$. Admittedly, this procedure has the disadvantage of requiring a value to be assigned to d_f if $D_{liq.}$ is to be determined
absolutely. By using one and the same column it is, however, possible to
obtain relative values for $D_{liq.}$ (since d_f^2 cancels out) and so gather valuable information on the diffusion coefficients for various solutes, their de-
pendency on temperature, etc. It should be noted that the diffusivity (which
is small in magnitude, but is a determining parameter in G.L.C.) is not
readily accessible to accurate measurement by other methods.

The Use of Solid Detergents as Stationary Phase

It has been demonstrated by Gohlke and McLafferty[22] that it is possible to use household solid detergents in G.L.C. as a substitute for the usual support coated with a non-volatile liquid. Desty and Harbourn[23] have further investigated this suggestion and have found that various spray-dried commercial detergents of the alkylaryl sulphonate class, after being graded if necessary, form an excellent general-purpose packing, for instance for the analysis of hydrocarbon mixtures. Advantages are: low cost, convenience, suitability up to relatively high temperatures, e.g. 250°C; disadvantages are: lack of uniformity in quality (samples vary appreciably) and hygroscopic properties.

THE STATIONARY LIQUID

Liquid Solutions

The practical rules and suggestions that are given in Chapter 2 and Appendix I for choosing the stationary liquid will probably be sufficient for the majority of separations to be carried out by G.L.C.

In attempting to consider the most important role played by the stationary liquid in greater detail, one is confronted by the difficulty that a theory of the liquid state, sufficiently valid for a rigid treatment, is still lacking. The various theories that have been developed are at present able to describe the observed phenomena only in a qualitative or semi-quantitative sense. Nevertheless, they can frequently provide guidance of value.

Among these theories, those developed by Hildebrand[10] and co-workers have had a great influence and should first be mentioned. Hildebrand introduced, for instance, the concept of the "solubility parameter," a quantity that is characteristic of a liquid substance. In the case of liquid binary mixtures, their behavior as regards demixing in a certain range or the partial vapor pressure of the components can be predicted from the solubility parameters of each of the components. Hildebrand himself stresses, however, that the assumptions in the theory are approximations only, and that the consequent uncertainty, together with that in the available data, renders it impossible to predict solubilities exactly.

Solubility parameters are useful for selecting solvents for a particular solute in G.L.C. However, in selecting a solvent that will effect the separation of two similar solutes, one has to depend on small differences in relative volatility and for this purpose an accuracy higher than that attainable by Hildebrand's theory is essential. It is doubtful, in fact, whether the required accuracy can be obtained by considering a single parameter for each of the two components of the binary mixture, particularly since in G.L.C. the solute and the solvent usually differ widely in nature.

In the following we shall first consider the theory of solution behavior from a rather qualitative point of view and then proceed to a more quantitative treatment.

In a separation by G.L.C. the volatile solute molecules are for the greater part of the time dissolved in the stationary liquid and are, during that time, not transported. During a small part of their total residence time in the column the solute molecules are in the gas phase, where they are transported by the moving carrier gas. The separation of two solutes is based on the difference in their rate of transport and hence on the difference in the fraction of these solutes in the gas phase. We therefore have to deal with the theory of vapor-liquid equilibria in mixtures of two components; only one of these components, however, exerts a measurable vapor pressure.

Our considerations will be founded on two fundamental laws of solution, both referring to the partial vapor pressure of solutes above their liquid solutions. The first law refers to *ideal liquid solutions*.

Raoult's Law. According to *Raoult's law*, the partial vapor pressure, p, of a constituent of an (ideal) liquid solution is equal to the product of its mole fraction, x, in the liquid and its vapor pressure in the pure state, p^0; hence

$$p = xp^0 \tag{1}$$

For a binary ideal liquid solution the vapor pressures of the constituents are given by

$$p_1 = (1 - x_2)p_1^0 \quad \text{and} \quad p_2 = x_2p_2$$

where x_2 is the mole fraction of the second component.

According to these equations the plot of the partial vapor pressure of each constituent against its mole fraction in the liquid will be a straight line, as shown in Figure 6.2. The total vapor pressure P is the sum of the two partial pressures;

$$P = p_1 + p_2 = (1 - x_2)p_1^0 + x_2p_2 = p_1^0 - x_2(p_1^0 - p_2^0);$$

hence, the total vapor pressure P also varies in a linear manner with the mole fraction of either component in the liquid phase.

Ideal liquid solutions are exceptional, although systems are known which approximate to ideality very closely (for instance pentane-hexane, methanol-ethanol, n-chlorobutane-n-bromobutane). A binary liquid mixture will form an ideal solution only if the solute molecules interact in the same way with the surrounding solvent molecules as they do with neighboring molecules in the pure state.

In G.L.C. there is always a large difference in volatility between solute and solvent, arising either from a large difference in the dimensions of their molecules (as in the case of butane-hexadecane), from a large difference in polarity (butane-dimethylformamide) or from both factors (benzene-polyethyleneglycol). These differences are sufficient to upset

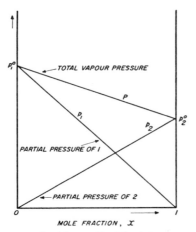

Figure 6.2. Vapor pressures of a binary liquid mixture according to Raoult's law.

ideality completely, so that ideal liquid solutions need scarcely be considered in G.L.C.

The deviations from ideality may be positive or negative, depending on whether the actual partial vapor pressure of a constituent is greater or smaller than it should be if Raoult's law were obeyed. Instances of these two cases have been depicted in Figure 6.3.

While on the one hand non-ideality leads to a complication in the treatment of solution behavior, the fact that the solute molecules predominantly occur in very low concentrations introduces a simplification. In G.L.C. solute molecules are seldom close enough together to exert a mutual influence; the direct environment of a solute molecule can hence often be considered as a medium consisting of solvent molecules only. Instead of referring to "ideal" liquid solutions we may then speak of "ideally dilute" solutions or "infinitely dilute" solutions. In such solutions the volatility of the solute molecules (or their escaping tendency) is mainly determined by the intermolecular forces between solute and solvent molecules, and scarcely at all by the intermolecular forces between solute molecules, as in the case of the pure solute in the liquid state.

Henry's Law. It is to this type of non-ideal liquid solutions that the second fundamental law, Henry's law, applies. According to this law the partial vapor pressure of a solute in dilute solution is proportional to its mole fraction. In Figure 6.4, there are shown vapor pressure lines for, I, an ideal solution agreeing with Raoult's law, II, a solution with a positive deviation, III, a solution with a negative deviation. It may be seen that a part of the two curves near the origin almost coincides with the tangents in the origin. The almost straight part of the curves near the origin may some-

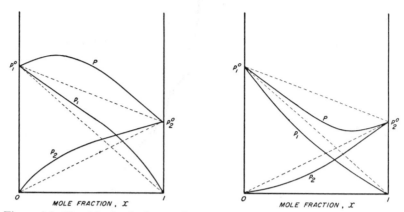

Figure 6.3. Non-ideal solutions. (Left) Positive deviation from Raoult's law. (Right) Negative deviation from Raoult's law.

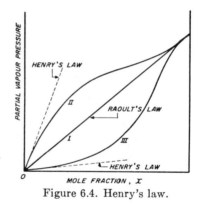

Figure 6.4. Henry's law.

times be very small. This will be the case, for instance, for associated solute molecules, which frequently dissociate in an appropriate solvent, the degree of dissociation depending upon the dilution, even at very small concentrations. If Henry's law applies in practice for the whole region of solute concentration encountered in G.L.C., it follows that the assumption of a linear distribution isotherm is fulfilled and, as has been shown in Chapter 4, the elution curves will be symmetric. On the other hand, distinctly asymmetric elution curves may be caused by curved distribution isotherms, which means that there is a departure from Henry's law. (Sometimes the asymmetry may be caused by adsorption on the support.)

Qualitative Observations on the Stationary Liquid

The Cohesive Energy. In qualitative considerations valuable practical guidance may be obtained from simple models. Let us illustrate such a case by a discussion of the phenomenon of vaporization.

Molecules, either in a pure state or in solution, are kept in the liquid state by *cohesive forces* and tend to escape from the liquid by *thermal agitation*. As soon as a particular molecule has acquired sufficient kinetic energy to overcome the forces of attraction exerted by the surrounding molecules in the liquid state, it may escape into the vapor.

The forces of cohesion may be of various types. In the case of a solute that is kept in a liquid solution they are:

(a) forces between permanent dipoles of solute and solvent;

(b) forces between a permanent dipole, either of solute or solvent, and the induced dipole of the other;

(c) non-polar forces between solute and solvent molecules.

(In the case of association the forces of attraction between a pair of solute molecules have also to be considered.)

In the same order the above forces have been termed (see[10])

(a) orientation forces (Keesom)

(b) induction forces (Debye)

(c) dispersion forces (London).*

A particular type of orientation forces, the so-called "hydrogen bonding" deserves special mention. These forces are much larger than the normal cohesive forces, although they are smaller than the forces of the chemical bond. It should, moreover, be noted that cases also occur in G.L.C. in which use is made of the chemical bond, viz., the formation of loose chemical adducts between certain solutes and stationary liquids.

Each of the three types of forces mentioned contributes to the total cohesive energy, although the relative magnitudes of the contributions may differ considerably. If, besides London forces, strong orientation forces are also present (as in the case of water, fatty acids, alcohols), the volatility is much reduced in comparison with that of non-polar molecules of the same size.

The contribution of the induction forces is always relatively small. Table 6.3, which has been taken from Ketelaar[11], may serve to give some impression of the relative magnitudes of the energies constituting the cohesive energy for a number of pure compounds.

Mathematical expressions have been derived for each of these three energies (see Hildebrand[10]) which allow some conclusions to be drawn:

(1) The energy of attraction between two molecules increases with the inverse 6th power of their distance. Solvents with large dipoles concentrated in small molecules—as in dimethylsulfolane or dimethylformamide, for instance—must therefore be capable of producing very selective separations.

---

* The term van der Waals forces is sometimes used to denote the dispersion forces; it would be slightly more correct to denote the combined forces by this name. In order to avoid confusion the term van der Waals forces will not be used in this book.

TABLE 6.3. COHESIVE ENERGIES IN KG CAL/MOLE

(a = orientation energy; b = induction energy; c = dispersion energy), dipole moments (μ) in Debye units (10^{-18} e.s. units of charge $\times$ cm) and polarizabilities (α) in cm³ of various compounds.

Compound	a	b	c	$a + b + c$	μ	α in 10^{-24} cm³
A	0.000	0.000	2.03	2.03	0	1.63
CO	0.0001	0.002	2.09	2.09	0.12	1.99
HI	0.006	0.027	6.18	6.21	0.38	5.40
HBr	0.164	0.120	5.24	5.52	0.78	3.58
HCl	0.79	0.24	4.02	5.05	1.03	2.63
NH₃	3.18	0.37	3.52	7.07	1.50	2.21
H₂O	8.69	0.46	2.15	11.30	1.84	1.48

(2) The capability of a stationary liquid for effecting selective separations decreases with increasing temperature.

The effect of decreased selectivity at higher temperatures is particularly large for the orientation energy because the latter is, even at constant volume, inversely proportional to the absolute temperature.

Examples. As has been mentioned, the induction energy is always small in comparison with the other energies of attraction. Its effect on the separation of volatile compounds may nevertheless be appreciable, as will be demonstrated in the following examples.

(1) Benzene and cyclohexane, with boiling points of 80.10 and 80.81°C, respectively, have no permanent dipoles; benzene, however, is more polarizable per unit of volume than cyclohexane. If a moderately polar substance, such as dinonyl phthalate, is used as the solvent, a certain dipole will be induced by the electric field of the molecules of this stationary liquid; this dipole is larger in the case of the benzene molecules than in that of the cyclohexane molecules. The cohesive forces of induction will be increased selectively for benzene and consequently this solute will become less volatile than cyclohexane. With a non-polar solvent, such as a paraffin, on the other hand, benzene will become the more volatile. This fact may, at least partly, be explained as follows. From the lower molecular weight of benzene with respect to cyclohexane the first might be expected to have a boiling point a few degrees below that of cyclohexane. The "induction forces" in pure benzene, however, cause these molecules to have an additional cohesive energy (which for instance finds its expression in its smaller molecular volume). If we now bring the benzene molecule into a paraffin medium this additional energy is lost and, in accordance with its lower molecular weight, benzene will become more volatile than cyclohexane.

(2) Butene-1 and isobutene have boiling points of −6.3 and −6.9°C, respectively. The first has a small permanent dipole (0.3 D), while isobutene has no dipole. The polarizability of isobutene is much greater than that of

butene-1. If a strongly polar liquid is used, such as dimethylformamide, it is possible to separate one olefin from the other and the order of elution is the reverse of what would be expected from the volatility of the pure substances.

(3) A third example may be taken from the work of Bradford, Harvey and Chalkley[12], who investigated the separation of a mixture of hydrocarbon gases by G.L.C. with the aid of three stationary liquids:

(a) Triisobutylene (a polymer of isobutene boiling between 190 and 200°C);

(b) Acetonyl acetone;

(c) A saturated solution of silver nitrate in glycol.

The observed retention volumes, relative to that of ethene, are shown in Table 6.4.

Triisobutylene, a non-polar liquid, does not give rise to induced dipoles and therefore, as might be expected, causes a separation according to boiling point, acetylene forming the only marked exception.

Acetonyl acetone is moderately polar. It induces dipoles in the polarizable unsaturated hydrocarbons and consequently retains them selectively. *Trans*- and *cis*-butene-2 are also readily separated on account of their difference in polarizability.

In the case of stationary phase (c) there exist forces of attraction between the silver ions and the unsaturated hydrocarbons[13], and the stationary liquid forms loose chemical adducts with specific olefins. The chemical bond is stronger in the case of butene-1 than in that of isobutene, and

TABLE 6.4. RELATIVE RETENTION VOLUMES (ETHENE = 1) FOR COMPONENTS OF A HYDROCARBON MIXTURE WITH

(a) triisobutylene, (b) acetonyl acetone and (c) AgNO₃/glycol as stationary liquids

Hydrocarbon	Boiling Point (°C)	Relative Retention Volumes		
		(a)	(b)	(c)
Methane	−161.5	0.8	0.7	0.75
Acetylene	−84.0	0.95	3.8	—
Ethene	−103.7	1.0	1.0	1.0
Ethane	−88.6	1.2	1.0	0.75
Propene	−47.7	2.4	2.2	1.0
Propane	−42.1	2.7	1.5	0.75
Methylacetylene	−23.2	2.85	11.5	—
Isobutane	−11.7	5.6	2.2	0.75
Isobutene	−6.9	6.7	4.75	3.25
Butene-1	−6.3	6.7	4.75	6.25
Butadiene	−4.4	6.7	10.0	10.0
n-Butane	−0.5	7.5	3.0	0.75
Trans-Butene-2	+0.88	8.0	5.85	1.75
Cis-Butene-2	+3.72	8.9	6.8	5.5

these two olefins (which have equal retention volumes with stationary phases a and b) are now completely separated. The paraffins from methane to butane overlap with this stationary liquid, and the same applies to ethene and propene.

As will be apparent from the foregoing, the separation of two substances under a given set of conditions depends both upon their differences in boiling point and upon the differences in ideality of their solutions in the stationary liquid. With a stationary liquid not giving rise to induction forces compounds are separated primarily on the basis of their boiling points; with a liquid causing polarization, both boiling point and type play a role. Materials closely alike both in boiling point and type can be separated only with difficulty. Substances with different boiling points and of different type can be separated unless the two effects just compensate each other.

The examples show that, in spite of the smallness of the induction energy, all three types of cohesive force have to be taken into account, since it is not the volatility of a substance that must be considered in the first place, but the relative volatility (ratio of volatilities) of two substances when dissolved in the stationary liquid.

As compared with the energies playing a role in the formation of stable chemical compounds the cohesive energy is small. There are, however, dipoles in which hydrogen is linked to N, O or F, that exert effects upon each other far greater than those to be expected from normal dipoles. The reason for this phenomenon is that the bare proton of compounds with strongly negative atoms, being so small, can come very close to a second negative atom, so that a " hydrogen bond" is formed. Its exceptional nature is due to the closeness of approach of the two dipoles that is possible owing to the small size of the proton. The influence of this fact upon the total cohesive energy is considerable, as the energy is proportional to the inverse sixth power of the distance. The strength of the bond falls off approximately in the order F-H, O-H, N-H. Phenomena such as association and solvation are the result of hydrogen bonding. Its energy lies somewhere between that of the chemical bond and the normal cohesive energy.

Classification of Solvents. As has already been said, current theories of solutions do not allow the separation effected by a solvent to be accurately predicted from the properties of this solvent and from those of the components to be separated. The considerations given in the previous pages can, however, prove of some assistance in selecting a suitable solvent for a particular purpose. Admittedly, the indications so obtained are as yet far from precise. Nevertheless it is possible to draw up a very rough qualitative scheme for dealing with a specific problem, by defining five classes of substances into which the volatile materials and stationary liquids fall. These classes are arranged in the order of decreasing cohesive energy (see, for instance, Hecker[14]).

(I) The molecules form a three-dimensional network of hydrogen bonds. Examples are: water, polyalcohols, aminoalcohols, oxy-acids, polyphenols, di- and tricarboxylic acids.

(II) The molecules possess active hydrogen atoms as well as electronegative atoms with free pairs of electrons (O, N, F). Examples: alcohols, fatty acids, phenols, primary and secondary amines, oximes, nitro compounds and nitriles with α-H atoms.

(III) The molecules possess electronegative atoms, but no active hydrogen. Examples: ethers, ketones, aldehydes, esters, tertiary amines, nitro compounds and nitriles without α-H atoms.

(IV) The molecules possess active hydrogen atoms and negligible dipoles only ($CHCl_3$, CH_2Cl_2, CH_3CHCl_2, CH_2Cl—CH_2Cl, CH_2Cl—CH_2—$CHCl_2$ etc., aromatic and olefinic hydrocarbons).

(V) Molecules without functional groupings, such as saturated hydrocarbons, carbon disulfide, tetrachloromethane, etc.

This classification (which amounts to a more detailed form of the "rule of similarity" given in Chapter 2) does not explicitly take into account the effects of mutual polarizability. Furthermore, it does not allow for the fact that forces similar to those of the chemical bond may produce extremely selective retentions (by the formation of loose adducts) for particular solutes with specific stationary liquids. Apart from these effects, a certain solute will be retained more powerfully by a stationary liquid as the classes to which they belong are closer together.

The use that can be made of this rough classification can be illustrated by an example.

Take the case of a mixture of two components having nearly the same boiling points, but belonging to different classes: ethanol (b.p. 78°C, Class II) and 2,2-dimethylpentane (b.p. 79°C, Class V). For a good separation we could now choose either a stationary liquid falling in Class II (or in the adjacent Classes I or III), say a poly-alcohol such as glycerol, or else one at the other end of the scale, for instance "liquid paraffin" (Class V). With the former the alcohol will be selectively retained and the paraffinic solute will emerge first. With "liquid paraffin" as stationary phase the order will be reversed. In the latter case the volatility of the alcohol will be promoted by the dissociation of its associated molecules in the paraffinic solvent. If only these two substances had to be separated, it would be immaterial in practice which stationary liquid were selected.

If, however, a third substance—benzene, b.p. 80°C, Class IV—were present, the use of a polar solvent from the head of the scale would be preferable. The latter will induce a small dipole in the slightly polarizable benzene molecule and thus retain it somewhat more powerfully than the aliphatic hydrocarbon, the order of emergence then being 2,2-dimethylpentane, benzene, ethanol.

Quantitative Observations on the Stationary Liquid

The Activity Coefficient. It is recalled that in Chapter 4 the partition coefficient k of a solute was defined as the ratio of the amount of solute per unit volume of the liquid phase to the amount of solute per unit volume of the gas phase.

For ideal solutions k is independent of concentration. In practice k is sometimes nearly a constant at very low concentrations (infinitely dilute solutions); this fact is equivalent to the existence of an almost linear portion of the partition isotherm.

For an ideal solution of a volatile solute in a (nonvolatile) solvent Raoult's law requires that

$$p = xp^0 \tag{1}$$

where p^0 is the vapor pressure of the pure solute, x, the molecular fraction of the solute in solution and p the partial vapor pressure of the solute above the solution.

As two liquids seldom form ideal solutions relation (1) generally does not hold. We can, however, introduce a factor $\gamma(x)$ having such a value that the relationship

$$p = \gamma(x).x.p^0 \tag{2}$$

is satisfied, irrespective of whether the solution is ideal or not. (For ideal solutions $\gamma(x) = 1$ and Raoult's law applies, for dilute non-ideal solutions $\gamma(x)$ is sometimes a constant, and Henry's law is fulfilled). The correction factor $\gamma(x)$, which has been termed the *activity coefficient*, depends upon the nature of the volatile component itself, and upon the environment in which this component exists. It therefore follows that the quantity p/x and hence the rate at which a solute travels through a G.L.C. column, depends on the vapor pressure p^0 of the pure compound and on its activity coefficient γ in the particular solvent. The reason for relating p in this way to the vapor pressure of the pure solute will later become clear.

The partial pressure, p, may also be expressed in terms of the total pressure P above the solution and the mole fraction y of the component in the gas phase, $p = yP$, hence

$$yP = x.\gamma.p^0 \tag{3}$$

For dilute solutions the ratio of the mole fractions x/y is related to the partition coefficient, k, by:

$$k = \frac{x}{y} \cdot \frac{N_{\text{liq.}}}{N_{\text{gas}}} \tag{4}$$

in which $N_{\text{liq.}}$ and N_{gas} are the moles of stationary liquid and gas, respectively, per unit volume.

From Eqs. (3) and (4) it follows that

$$k = \frac{P}{\gamma p^0} \cdot \frac{N_{\text{liq.}}}{N_{\text{gas}}} \tag{5}$$

Assuming that Boyle's law applies* to the gas phase we may put RT for P/N_{gas}, and we get:

$$k = \frac{N_{\text{liq.}} RT}{\gamma p^0} \tag{6}$$

In the above manner k has been formulated as an expression containing a solvent-dependent factor, $N_{\text{liq.}}$ (moles of stationary liquid per unit volume), a solute-dependent factor p^0 (vapor pressure of pure solvent at the temperature of operation) and a factor $\gamma(x)$ which is dependent on both the solute and the solvent. Porter, Deal and Stross[15], and Pierotti, Deal, Derr and Porter[16], among others, have shown that such a formulation permits of a convenient treatment of solvent effects and partition coefficients in G.L.C.

The expression for k will now be related to the retention volume by means of Eq. (12), page 112,

$$V_R = nV_G + knV_L = V_{\text{gas}} + kV_{\text{liq.}}$$

which in view of Eq. (6) becomes

$$V_R = V_{\text{gas}} + \frac{N_{\text{liq.}} RT}{\gamma p^0} \cdot V_{\text{liq.}} \tag{7}$$

The assumption of a constant k implies a constant $\gamma(x)$ and hence either a constant concentration or a very low concentration. Neither of these conditions is always entirely fulfilled in G.L.C., but the solute concentrations are usually so low that, under certain conditions they can be considered to approach infinite dilution. In this case we speak of γ^0, the activity coefficient at "zero" concentration, which is a constant. It should, however, be realized that in a band of solute in the chromatographic column all concentrations between zero and the maximum concentration occur and that, particularly near the column inlet, the assumption of constant γ or k is frequently quite unrealistic.

It has been experimentally established (see Chapter 7) that the retention volume of a solute for a particular column and a particular solvent is indeed determined by γ^0 and p^0. This fact means that the solid carrier in G.L.C. does not affect retention volumes. Values of k derived from G.L.C. experiments are true k values, they do not depend upon the solid support,

* It would be more correct to replace p^0 by the fugacity f^0 (see also Chapter 7).

on the column dimensions or on column efficiency (see also Littlewood Phillips and Price[17]).

Relative Volatility of Two Solutes. Let us look further into the question how the solvent affects the retention volume by changing the partition coefficient k. The quantity $N_{liq.}$ is the number of moles of solvent per unit volume, or the reciprocal of the molal volume, and is thus purely a solvent property. A change from one solvent to another involves a change in $N_{liq.}$ and thus affects the absolute magnitude of k and hence the retention volume.

For two solutes with partition coefficients k_1 and k_2 we have

$$\alpha_{1,2} = \frac{k_2}{k_1} = \frac{\gamma_1^0 p_1^0}{\gamma_2^0 p_2^0} \tag{8}$$

We see that, although $N_{liq.}$ affects k, it does not affect the relative volatility α of two solutes.

The factors p^0, the vapor pressures of the pure solutes, depend only on the solute in question and on the temperature. For a given set of components the values of p^0, and hence their effects are fixed. Although the absolute magnitudes of p^0 change rapidly with temperature, the relative values for several components do not change greatly as long as their heats of vaporization are similar. It is only when large temperature changes are involved (see Chapter 2) that the relative values alter appreciably.

We are here again touching on the problem—already considered from one aspect in the first part of this chapter—how an increase in temperature affects a separation by G.L.C. The foregoing considerations on the stationary liquid and the volatility of the solution show that this influence cannot be very pronounced. It is true that at higher temperatures p^0 will be higher, k correspondingly lower and that the plate capacity $V_{eff.}$ (which is proportional to $V_G + kV_L$) will also fall. However, we have seen in Chapter 4 that a column operates at its maximum efficiency as long as the size of the sample is smaller than $\frac{1}{2}V_{eff.}\sqrt{n}$.*

The above, in conjunction with the conclusions reached in the early part of the chapter, denotes that a column will not decrease in efficiency with increasing temperature if care is taken that the sample is always "small," viz., less than $\frac{1}{2}V_{eff.}\sqrt{n}$.

The factor γ, finally, is the only quantity which depends on the chemical structure of both the solvent and the solute. It is thus the only factor which can greatly affect the relative magnitude of k or the relative volatilities of the various components. Hence the separability of components can be changed only through changes in γ, brought about by changes in solvent type. Like $N_{liq.}$ and p^0, γ also affects the absolute values of k and hence the absolute retention volumes.

---

* See Chapter 4, page 124 and Chapter 7, page 194.

A solvent for G.L.C. must possess certain properties of stability, volatility and viscosity, factors which principålly affect the mechanical aspects of operation. However, the choice of a satisfactory solvent is primarily a matter of choosing a material which provides suitable values of γ such that a maximum ratio of k values, the relative volatility, results and thus ultimately a maximum ratio of retention volumes.

Before proceeding with the treatment of the relation between γ values and structure it may be as well to summarize a few points.

In the separation by G.L.C. it is primarily the *relative volatility* α of two compounds that must be considered. We have seen that this value cannot be affected by changes in the molecular volume of the solvent and that it will normally not be greatly affected by changes in temperature.

The absolute magnitude of the k values is also of importance since it affects the plate capacity, and hence the separation obtainable with a sample of given size. Solvents of low molecular weight and low temperatures increase the absolute values of k. Even though the relative volatility of two components may in a certain case be satisfactory, the separation can be vitiated by the column inefficiency due to a small absolute value of the partition coefficient. This influence can, however, frequently be offset to a large degree by a reduction in the temperature of operation and a decrease in sample size. Briefly, therefore, the proper procedure is to choose a solvent giving a satisfactory relative volatility and then to reduce the temperature to a level at which the value of k is high enough.

We have shown that three somewhat analogous quantities may be used for characterizing solute-solvent systems:

(1) Retention volumes. These quantities depend on the operational variables. (Retention volumes relative to that of a standard substance are, however, free of most of these variables. Retention volumes may also be corrected for operational variables in the manner described by Littlewood, Phillips and Price[17] and are then approximately equivalent to k values.)

(2) Partition coefficients (k). For a given solute-solvent system values of k are dependent on temperature. ($\log k$ is roughly a linear function of $1/T$.)

(3) Activity coefficients (preferably at infinite dilution, γ^0). These values are much less dependent on temperature.

As γ^0 can be calculated from k^0 and p^0 and vice versa*, it is not important in the practice of separation whether k or γ is used. For discussing solvent effects, γ^0 is, however, the more suitable parameter.

The treatment of non-ideal solutions on the basis of molecular interactions has only in a few cases led to a quantitative estimation of k and γ, though it has qualitatively sometimes been useful. In the special case of "regular solutions"[10], the Scatchard-Hildebrand relation permits of a fairly good estimate of γ from the energies of vaporization and molecular volumes.

---

* k^0 is the value of k at infinite dilution.

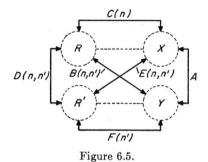

Figure 6.5.

This relation, however, is not applicable to solutions of which one or both components are polar, a type of primary importance in G.L.C.

The need for a more quantitative approach has led Pierotti and a number of co-workers[15, 16] to develop a more empirical method of correlating γ with structure. These investigators have determined activity coefficients prevailing in a large variety of binary mixtures, so chosen that variations within homologous series of solutes and solvents could be systematically studied. Although much of this work has involved solvents of volatilities too high to be of direct interest for G.L.C., certain regularities in behavior are more broadly applicable and are worthy of note. In a book of this scope it is not possible to enter into details of Pierotti's method; the interested reader is referred to the publications quoted. The present account must therefore be confined to a brief description of the principles of the method, which constitutes a development and extension of procedures suggested previously[18, 19, 20].

Pierotti's "Building Block" Method. Pierotti *et al.* drew up a semi-empirical model in which the quantity $RT \log \gamma^0$, the so-called "partial molal excess-free energy"* of a solute at infinite dilution is considered as the sum of several terms, each of which is associated with a pair of characteristic groups of the solute and the solvent molecules.

Consider a solute molecule RX at infinite dilution in a solvent $R'Y$, R and R' being homologous alkyl groups, X and Y functional groups. The interactions (the sum of which constitutes $\log \gamma^0$) between these "building blocks" are shown in Figure 6.5.

The interaction between the functional groups X and Y will be a more or less constant term, A, to some extent influenced by the number of carbon atoms n and n' in R and R'. The interaction between R and R' will be a function of n and n' and likewise the interactions R-Y and R'-X.

By means of experimental data obtained from phase equilibrium meas-

---

* Note that at $\gamma = 1$, $RT \log \gamma = 0$, hence the term excess free energy for non-ideal solutions.

urements (vapor-liquid, liquid-liquid, and liquid-solid) the type of function was in each case established by first taking simple pairs such as two paraffinic hydrocarbons, where only the interaction $R\text{-}R' = f(n, n')$ is involved, since no functional groups are present. After the $R\text{-}R'$ term had been established for numerous hydrocarbon pairs, the values obtained were then used for handling the next more complicated case of a hydrocarbon RH in a solvent $R'Y$. Proceeding in this way Pierotti *et al.* described the various functions constituting $\log \gamma^0$ for the solute RX in the solvent $R'Y$ by

$$\log \gamma^0 = A + \frac{Bn}{n'} + \frac{C}{n + C'} + D(n - n')^2 + \frac{F}{n' + F'} \qquad (9)$$

n representing the number of CH_2 or CH_3 groups in the solute, n' the number of such groups in the solvent, and A, B, C, D and F being coefficients. D is a constant, expressing the interaction between methyl or methylene groups in the two types of molecules, and it is independent of the nature of both the solute and the solvent functional groups. C and C' are constants characteristic of the solute functional group X and apply to an entire homologous series of solutes. F, F' and B are characteristic of a solvent functional group and apply to an entire homologous series of solvents. A is characteristic of both the solute and the solvent functional groups. (The coefficient E, characteristic of the $R'\text{-}X$ interaction, is usually found to be negligible and is here included in the A term.) The application of this complex equation to a few special cases will now be discussed.

Homologous series of solutes in a particular solvent.

In this case n' is constant, as is also the F term. The B term is a function of n only. For a series of paraffins, for instance, we have no X functional group, and thus the A and C terms drop out. The equation now simplifies to

$$\log \gamma^0 = K'_{\text{par.}} + B_{\text{par.}} n + D(n - n')^2 \qquad (10)$$

For the homologous series of n-alkanes up to C_{30} the experimentally determined values of $\log \gamma^0$ have been plotted in Figure 6.6A against the number of C atoms, for the (volatile) solvents n-heptane, methyl ethyl ketone, phenol, triethylene glycol and water, respectively. For any given solvent, n' is constant and all constant terms have been grouped in $K'_{\text{par.}}$.

We now may write

$$\log \gamma^0 = K_{\text{par.}} + B_{\text{par.}} n \qquad (11)$$

the contribution of the term $D(n - n')^2$ being so small that $\log \gamma^0$ may be represented for most purposes by a straight line of slope $B_{\text{par.}}$, the latter being characteristic for the solvent. For n-heptane as the solvent, B equals zero and a nearly constant value of γ^0 (approx. 1) results.

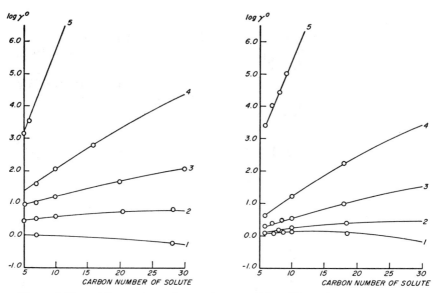

Figure 6.6A. *n*-Alkanes in various solvents. (After Pierotti *et al.*). Figure 6B Alkylbenzenes in various solvents. (After Pierotti *et al.*).

1 *n*-Heptane at 90°C
2 Methyl ethyl ketone at 90°C
3 Phenol at 90°C
4 Triethylene glycol at 90°C
5 Water at 25°C

For the alkylbenzenes the relation is slightly more complex. As these have a functional group (the phenyl group), a C term is involved, which, however, is only significant for small values of n, and so gives a slight curvature for the lower aromatics. The curves are thus again essentially straight lines with a slope determined by the same $B_{par.}$ values found for the paraffins (see Figure 6.6B).

It is of interest to note that chain branching has been found to have only second-order effects upon γ so that the curves also represent branched-chain hydrocarbons. Table 6.5 shows the various coefficients for paraffins and alkylbenzenes in the solvents employed.

Homologous series of solutes in homologous series of solvents.

Eq. 9 is rearranged to

$$\log \gamma^0 = \left[A + \frac{F}{n' + F'}\right] + \frac{Bn}{n'} + \frac{C}{n + C'} + D(n - n')^2 \quad (12)$$

If we study the change of the B term for a homologous series of solvents, it is found that this term varies linearly with the reciprocal of the carbon num-

TABLE 6.5. CONSTANTS FOR ACTIVITY COEFFICIENT CORRELATIONS AT 90°C
Solutes: Paraffins and alkylbenzenes (Pierotti *et al.*)

Solvent:	Heptane	Methyl Ethyl Ketone	Phenol	Triethylene Glycol	Water (25°C)
$K_{par.}$	0	0.330	0.620	0.680	0.69
K_B	0.202	0.239	0.420	0.730	3.55
$B_{par.}$	0	1.019	0.058	0.134	0.63
C	−0.350	−0.350	−0.350	−0.350	(0.466)
C'	−4	−4	−4	−4	−4
D	−0.0006	−0.0006	−0.0006	−0.0006	—

ber. For large carbon numbers the term approaches zero, which actually is the value for heptane. This term thus depends upon the concentration of functional group in the solvent molecule and is independent of the solute.

Likewise the term

$$\left[A + \frac{F}{n' + F'} \right]$$

is experimentally found to depend on $1/n'$ or the concentration of the functional group. Thus when one takes any solute and varies the solvent structure by increasing the carbon number, the terms characteristic of the solvent groups change in this regular manner.

A hypothetical example:

In order to illustrate how solvent effects can be utilized in G.L.C. separations, the partition coefficients for a homologous series of paraffins and alkylbenzenes have been estimated for three type cases:

(1) a hypothetical solvent, forming ideal solutions with all components,

(2) a non-polar solvent (a C_{30} paraffin), which gives negative deviations from ideal behavior,

(3) a polar solvent, triethylene glycol, giving large positive deviations.

The log k versus n plot at 90°C for these three cases is given in Figure 6.7.

In the case of the ideal solvent, differences in k arise solely from differences in vapor pressures of the solutes and separations with such a solvent are thus based on solute boiling points. The relative volatility of two successive paraffins or aromatics is about 2.25, that of a paraffin relative to the aromatic of the same carbon number about 1.25. We also can say that paraffins have the same volatility as aromatics which are only 0.3 lower in carbon number. In the case of the C_{30} paraffin as solvent the separation of successive paraffins or successive aromatics is again controlled by p^0 effects and is thus according to boiling points. Values of partition coefficients are slightly lower than in the ideal case, primarily because $N_{liq.}$ for this high molecular-weight solvent is lower than that assumed in the ideal case.

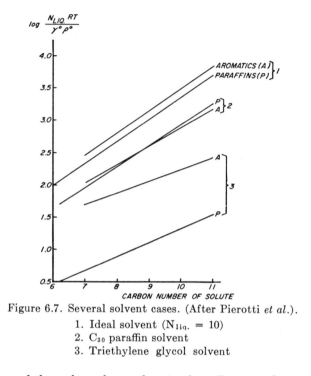

Figure 6.7. Several solvent cases. (After Pierotti *et al.*).

1. Ideal solvent ($N_{liq.}$ = 10)
2. C_{30} paraffin solvent
3. Triethylene glycol solvent

In the case of the polar solvent the γ^0 value effects predominate and result in a considerable change in the possible separations. Relative volatilities of successive paraffins or aromatics are still high, but only 1.7 as compared to 2.25 in the ideal case. However, the separation of types having equal carbon numbers is now very easy, the relative volatility being 9. As a result of the spreading of the curves together with the decrease in slope, the carbon number spread for equal volatility has now become 5 as compared to 0.3 only in the ideal case. Values of k are markedly lower than in the ideal case, a result primarily of the γ^0 effect.

The high γ^0 values for polar solvents lead to low absolute partition coefficients or to low emergence volumes. Thus polar solvents may make it necessary to lower the temperature and work with extremely small samples.

A much wider choice of effective solvents is involved in the separation of moderately polar compounds such as alcohols, ketones, esters, etc. We will discuss as an example the separation of a mixture of acetone, diisopropyl ether, methyl ethyl ketone, isopropyl alcohol and secondary butyl alcohol, which would emerge in the same order (that of their boiling points) from an ideal solvent. Such a solvent, of course, does not exist, because the compounds themselves cover a wider range of polarity.

From a paraffinic oil, in which the relatively polar compound isopropyl alcohol has a high γ^0 value, it emerges soon after acetone, which boils 25°C lower. The ether, having a small dipole only, is retarded and emerges closely adjacent to secondary butyl alcohol. Only methyl ethyl ketone comes out well-separated from the other components.

In a moderately polar solvent, dinonyl phthalate, the ether has a higher γ^0 value than before and moves up near isopropyl alcohol, which now is separated from acetone.

Finally with a highly polar solvent, diglycerol, the ether emerges first, isopropyl alcohol is retarded, but the ketones come out relatively close together.

The choice of the best solvent thus depends upon what objectives are in view. There may be no single solvent which will achieve a complete separation of all components, but consideration of the γ^0 and p^0 factors will greatly aid in a more quantitative orientation.

Identification Plots. Let us consider the activity coefficients of a homologous series of solutes in two different solvents A and B. In the equation for log γ, C is dependent on the functional group of the solute and is thus here a constant; the F term is a constant for each solvent case, the D term is small. Grouping the constant terms into one constant we find:

$$\log \gamma_A{}^0 = K_A{}' + \left(\frac{B_A}{n_A{}'}\right) n \quad \text{and} \quad \log \gamma_B{}^0 = K_B{}' + \left(\frac{B_B}{n_B{}'}\right) n \quad (13)$$

Since

$$k = \frac{N_{\text{liq}}.RT}{\gamma^0 p^0}, \quad (6)$$

$$\log k_A = -\log p^0 + \log RTN_A - K_A{}' - \left(\frac{B_A}{n_A{}'}\right) n \quad (14)$$

and

$$\log k_B = -\log p^0 + \log RTN_B - K_B{}' - \left(\frac{B_B}{n_B{}'}\right) n \quad (15)$$

which leads to

$$\log k_B = K'' + \left(\frac{B_B n_A{}'}{B_A n_B{}'}\right) \log k_A \quad (16)$$

A plot of log k_A (i.e., the k value in solvent A) against log K_B for the members of a homologous series is linear and the slopes are the same for all homologous series, since the factors in $B_B n_A{}'/B_A n_B{}'$ are characteristic only of the two solvents (see Fig. 2.6, p. 31). Such a figure provides a clear description of the differences in separation obtainable by the two solvents. For instance, any horizontal line in Fig. 2.6 (p. 31) shows those compounds which are inseparable by diisodecyl phthalate, while a vertical line shows the same for triol.

Before concluding this chapter we must point out that the above discussions apply to solutions which do not form co-ordination or other loose complexes with the components to be separated. This very important field of complexes is one which has hardly been explored; furthermore, it is one that is not susceptible to a general treatment. However, when a difficult separation is encountered one should always be alert to the possibilities of the reversible formation of a molecular complex or loose adduct between solute and solvent, as in the case of picric acid-fluorene and silver nitrate solutions discussed in Chapter 2.

REFERENCES

1. James, A. T., and Martin, A. J. P., *Biochem. J. (London)*, 50, 679 (1952).
2. Martin, A. J. P., private communication.
3. Keulemans, A. I. M., and Kwantes, A., "Analysis of Volatile Organic Compounds by Means of Vapour-phase Chromatography," World Petroleum Congr., Proc. 4th Congr., Rome, 1955.
4. Whitham, B. T., Vapour Phase Chromatography, Desty, D. H., (ed.), London, 1957 (Proc. of London Symposium on V. Ph. Chr., May/June 1956), p. 194.
5. Dimbat, M., Porter, P. E., and Stross, F. H., *Anal. Chem.*, 28, 290 (1956).
6. Craats, F. van de, *Anal. Chim. Acta*, 14, 136 (1956).
7. Adlard, E. R., Vapour Phase Chromatography, Desty, D. H., (ed.), London, 1957 (Proc. of London Symposium on V. Ph. Chr., May/June 1956), p. 98.
8. Deemter, J. J. van, Zuiderweg, F. J., and Klinkenberg, A., *Chem. Eng. Sci.*, 5, 271 (1956).
9. Keulemans, A. I. M., and Kwantes, A., Vapour Phase Chromatography, Desty, D. H., (ed.), London, 1957 (Proc. of London Symposium on V. Ph. Chr., May/June 1956), p. 15.
10. Hildebrand, J. H., and Scott, R. L., "The Solubility of Non-Electrolytes," 3rd ed., New York, Reinhold Publishing Corporation, 1950.
11. Ketelaar, J. A. A., "Chemical Constitution," p. 330, Amsterdam, New York, Elsevier Publishing Co., 1953.
12. Bradford, B. W., Harvey, D., and Chalkley, D. E., *J. Inst. Petroleum*, 41, 80 (1955).
13. Irving, H. M. N. H., and Williams, R. J. P., *Science Progr.*, 41, 418 (1953).
14. Hecker, E., "Verteilungsverfahren im Laboratorium," Weinheim, Verlag Chemie G.m.b.H., 1955.
15. Porter, P. E., Deal, C. H., Jr., and Stross, F. H., *J. Am. Chem. Soc.*, 78, 2999 (1956).
16. Pierotti, G. J., Deal, C. H., Jr., Derr, E. L., and Porter, P. E., *J. Am. Chem. Soc.*, 78, 2989 (1956).
17. Littlewood, A. B., Phillips, C. S. G., and Price, D. T., *J. Chem. Soc.*, 1955, 1480.
18. Martin, A. J. P., Biochem. Soc. Symposia (Cambridge, Engl.) Nos. 1–5, 4 (1948–50).
19. Cohn, E. J., and Edsall, J. T., "Proteins, Amino-acids and Peptides as Ions and Dipolar Ions," New York, Reinhold Publishing Corp., 1943.
20. Alders, L., *Appl. Sci. Research*, A4, 171 (1954).

21. Scott, R. P. W., Gas Chromatography 1958, Desty, D. H. (ed.), London (Proc. of 2nd Symposium on Gas Chr., Amsterdam, May 1958), p. 197.
22. Gohlke, R. S., and McLafferty, F. W., presented at 29th A.C.S. Meeting, Dallas, April 1956.
23. Desty, D. H., and Harbourn, C. L. A., "Advances in Gas Chromatography" (A.C.S. Symposium, New York, September 1957), p. D-157.

Chapter 7

MORE ADVANCED APPLICATIONS OF G.L.C.

This chapter will be devoted to some applications of the theories of G.L.C. developed in the previous chapters.

Firstly, the determination of certain parameters entering into the theory of solutions will be dealt with; this treatment more or less forms a continuation of that developed in Chapter 6. Secondly, the evaluation of chromatographic columns will be considered; this is a subject of importance for constructing equipment capable of performing difficult separations.

THE DETERMINATION OF SOLUTION PARAMETERS

The fact that G.L.C. is more than a powerful analytical tool was fully recognized by its inventors. In concluding a review of the work he had carried out with James, Martin[1] wrote the following words:

"The method provides perhaps the easiest of all means of studying the thermodynamics of the interaction of a volatile solute with a non-volatile solvent, and its potential value for providing this type of data should be very great."

A number of more recent publications[2, 3, 4, 5, 6] shows that the interest in this non-analytical application is rapidly growing.

As we have seen, a satisfactory method of describing the behavior of solutions is to start from the simple theory of ideal solutions and to consider the deviations from ideality. In the case of systems involving volatile components an obvious line of attack, which has already been discussed, is to measure the effective vapor pressure in its relation to the concentration of the components in the liquid mixture, and to derive the activity coefficients γ. Measurements of this kind, if carried out by the "classical" methods, require a high degree of experimental precision and are very laborious; consequently but few reliable figures have been determined by such means. (See, however [7, 8, 9].)

Vapor pressure measurements on solutions of a volatile solute at very low concentrations in a virtually non-volatile solvent appear to be especially difficult to carry out. It is precisely these figures, however, that are of the greatest value, not only from a theoretical aspect, but also on account of their obvious bearing on practical separations by gas chromatography. It has now been found[2, 5, 6], as predicted by Martin, that G.L.C. provides a rapid means of obtaining such data with much less trouble than required in the older methods.

In discussing the practical procedures of determining figures for effective vapor pressures or Henry coefficients from chromatographic diagrams, we shall first confine the treatment to systems departing from ideality which can be treated as "infinitely dilute" solutions. For these systems the region of low concentrations of the partition isotherms can be approximated by the tangent to the isotherm in the origin, so that a constant value of γ may be assumed to exist; the elution curves are then highly symmetric, at all events for small concentrations of the solute. Subsequently a procedure will be suggested for systems that do not have these properties and consequently produce noticeably asymmetric elution curves.

Calculation of γ^0 from Symmetric Elution Curves

The following quantities are determined:

(a) The volumetric gas and liquid hold-up of the chromatographic column, V_{gas} and $V_{liq.}$, respectively, at the temperature prevailing in the column. These quantities can be found directly from the volume of the empty column, the skeleton density of the support, the weight of the support and that of the stationary liquid, and the density of the latter (see p. 192). (The quantity V_{gas} can, however, also conveniently be measured from the distance IO in Figure 1.4 (p. 16), correcting for the dead space from column to detector and converting to average column pressure.)

(b) The retention volume $V_R{}^0$ of the solute. This quantity is obtained by converting the distance IG (Figure 1.4) to the volume of (dry) gas at column temperature and average column pressure (see Chapter 5 for the conversion).

From these values we then calculate

(c) the partition coefficient k, by means of formula (12), page 122

$$V_R{}^0 = V_{gas} + kV_{liq}.$$

and finally we obtain:

(d) γ^0 either in the form of $\gamma_p{}^0$ or $\gamma_f{}^0$ from formula (6), page 171

$$k = \frac{N_{liq}.RT}{\gamma_p{}^0 \cdot p^0} \quad \text{or} \quad k = \frac{N_{liq}.RT}{\gamma_f{}^0 \cdot f^0}$$

where f^0 is the fugacity of the solute at temperature T.

Generally speaking, values of $\gamma_p{}^0$ are more readily accessible than those of $\gamma_f{}^0$, since accurate vapor pressure data are available for many volatile solutes (see for instance API project No. 44[10]), while fugacity data are scarce, though they are known for most volatile hydrocarbons. It should, however, be observed that the quantity $\gamma_p{}^0$ is not a true measure of the imperfection in solution only, but rather a measure of the combined imperfections in gas and solution. Experimentally it has been found that in many cases the quantity $\gamma_p{}^0$ is more sensitive to changes in temperature than $\gamma_f{}^0$.

Values of $\gamma_f{}^0$, derived from normal G.L.C. analyses[21] with very small samples, have been listed in Table 7.1. The values of p^0 were calculated from the Antoine equations (API Project No. 44)[10] and converted into fugacities f^0 by means of the fugacity coefficients. The latter were obtained from Maxwell's[11] data book on hydrocarbons, and the critical data necessary for their calculation from API Project 44.

The question whether values of γ^0 obtained from G.L.C. measurements are sound and do not depend upon such operational factors as the nature of the support, the rate of gas flow, the amount of stationary liquid, etc., has already been answered by Porter et al.[5] and Pierotti et al.[6] in the positive sense. There are no data available, for comparison with Table 7.1, on activity coefficients determined from direct vapor pressure measurements at exactly the same temperatures. However, if the figures in this table are compared with the values calculated by the relation of Brønsted and Koefoed[7] for 20°C and with those found by van der Waals[8] at 72°C (as has been done in Table 7.2 for n-heptane in four normal paraffins), it will be found that a satisfactory agreement exists.

Table 7.2 gives rise to the following comments.

(a) Though $\gamma_f{}^0$ must vary with temperature, this variation is apparently very slight; the figures are not sufficiently accurate to show this effect.

Bosanquet and Morgan[12] have calculated the heat of solution of propane and of propene in triisobutene from G.L.C. measurements and have observed that this quantity is virtually equal to the heat of vaporization of the solutes. This fact supports the smallness of the effect of temperature on γ^0. Deviations from ideality in systems of aliphatic hydrocarbons seem to be caused mainly by the entropy of mixing as a consequence of the difference in size of the molecules of solute and solvent. (It should be observed that values of $\gamma_p{}^0$ are more temperature-sensitive because of imperfection of the vapors.)

(b) As regards the values of γ^0 calculated by means of the Brønsted relation, it should be noted that this formula is only intended for hydrocarbons up to C_{16}. This fact was expressly pointed out in the author's paper:

"Although this formula, as we are now justified in assuming, holds very closely for systems of n-paraffins from $n = 6$ to $n = 16$, it is obvious that it cannot hold for an unlimited increase in the chain length. Further measurements are therefore required to test the formula outside these limits."

TABLE 7.1. VALUES OF γ_f^0 FROM G.L.C. DATA FOR A NUMBER OF VOLATILE HYDROCARBONS IN VARIOUS NONVOLATILE HYDROCARBON SOLVENTS

	Solvent: n-Hexadecane		Solvent: n-Tetracosane		
	30°C	60°C	60°C	80°C	105°C
n-Pentane	0.88	0.87	0.71	0.74	0.74
n-Hexane	0.89	0.88	0.72	0.73	0.73
n-Heptane	—	0.89	0.73	0.73	0.73
n-Octane	—	—	0.74	0.74	0.73
Isopentane	0.92	0.90	0.73	0.73	0.73
2,2-Dimethylbutane	0.93	0.91	0.75	0.76	0.77
Cyclopentane	0.74	0.72	0.56	0.58	0.57
Methylcyclopentane	0.78	0.77	0.61	0.61	0.62
Cyclohexane	0.77	0.75	0.58	0.58	0.57
Methylcyclohexane	—	0.77	0.60	0.60	0.58
Benzene	—	0.90	0.64	0.63	0.60
Toluene	—	0.89	0.64	0.64	0.62
Ethylbenzene	—	—	—	0.69	0.66
Paraxylene	—	—	—	0.64	0.63

	Solvent: Pentatriacontane		Solvent: Squalane (C_{30})		Solvent: Squalane + 10% Fluoranthene	
	80°C	105°C	80°C	105°C	80°C	105°C
n-Pentane	0.62	0.62	0.67	0.66	0.76	0.75
n-Hexane	0.61	0.62	0.66	0.65	0.74	0.75
n-Heptane	0.63	0.63	0.68	0.66	0.75	0.74
n-Octane	0.65	0.64	0.70	0.68	0.77	0.76
Isopentane	0.62	0.62	0.66	0.67	0.76	0.73
2,2-Dimethylbutane	0.64	0.64	0.68	0.70	0.79	0.79
Cyclopentane	0.48	0.46	0.52	0.49	0.58	0.57
Methylcyclopentane	0.50	0.50	0.55	0.54	0.61	0.61
Cyclohexane	0.48	0.46	0.52	0.50	0.58	0.57
Methylcyclohexane	0.50	0.49	0.54	0.53	0.60	0.60
Benzene	0.51	0.49	0.59	0.56	0.65	0.61
Toluene	0.52	0.50	0.61	0.58	0.66	0.63
Ethylbenzene	0.56	0.55	0.65	0.62	0.71	0.67
Paraxylene	0.52	0.52	0.62	0.60	0.67	0.64

Experimental conditions: Columns: 1800 mm or 3600 mm x 6 mm coiled copper.
Support: 30/50 Sterchamol fire-brick.
Carrier gas: nitrogen or hydrogen.
Weight ratio: liquid/support 20/100 and 30/100.
Gas rate: 60 ml/min.
Samples appr. 3 mg.

TABLE 7.2. ACTIVITY COEFFICIENTS (γ_f^0) OF n-HEPTANE IN n-PARAFFINS

Source	a	b	c			
Temperature, °C	20°	72°	30°	60°	80°	105°
Solvent:						
n-Hexadecane (C_{16})	0.91		0.91			
n-Tetracosane (C_{24})	(0.73)			0.73	0.73	0.73
n-Dotriacontane (C_{32})	(0.50)	0.67		(0.67)*		
n-Pentatriacontane (C_{35})	(0.42)				0.63	0.63

* By interpolation.
  (a) Calculated from the Brønsted-Koefoed relation for 20°C, log $\gamma^0 = -0.00048 \times (n - n')^2$, n and n' being, as in Eq. (9) (p. 175), the number of CH_2 or CH_3 groups in the solute and solvent molecules, respectively.
  (b) Measured by van der Waals.
  (c) Calculated from G.L.C. data (Table 7.1).

The data in the table indicate that the values calculated by Brønsted's formula for n-heptane in dotriacontane and solvents of higher molecular weight are too low.

The general impression gained from the table is that the values obtained by G.L.C. are reliable. The figures quoted cannot, however, pretend to be highly accurate, since they were derived from incidental analyses carried out for other purposes. There is no reason why a greater accuracy should not be obtainable by means of special experiments in which particular care is taken in the control of the essential operational parameters.

The data of Table 7.1 show that within the system of aliphatic hydrocarbons, which frequently have been regarded to form almost ideal solutions, appreciable deviations from ideality occur and that they do not even constitute "regular" solutions according to Hildebrand. It is further interesting to note that the addition of 10 per cent of an aromatic to a C_{30} paraffin affects the magnitude of the activity coefficients considerably. This fact suggests the use of G.L.C. for characterizing a nonvolatile solvent of great complexity (as for instance a mineral oil fraction) by the activity coefficients of a number of suitably chosen volatile solutes.

Calculation of γ^0 from Asymmetric Elution Curves

In the above-mentioned cases the determination of activity coefficients is simplified by the fact that the systems in question can be considered as infinitely dilute solutions and that in practice linear partition isotherms may be postulated. If, however, solute and solvent differ largely in polarity, the assumption of a linear part of the partition isotherm is not permissible, even not for the low concentrations encountered in gas chromatography; hence the retention volumes, partition coefficients and activity coefficients depend on the solute concentration, which decreases continuously from column inlet to column outlet. Values of γ^0 for a number of systems depart-

TABLE 7.3. VALUES OF γ_p^0 CALCULATED FROM PARTITION COEFFICIENTS MEASURED BY PORTER, DEAL AND STROSS FOR VARIOUS SOLUTES IN DIISODECYLPHTHALATE

	75°C	95°C	105°C	115°C	135°C
n-Hexane	—	0.92	0.94	—	—
n-Heptane	1.01	0.97	0.96	0.98	0.90
n-Octane	1.07	0.99	1.00	0.99	0.94
n-Nonane	—	1.10	1.09	1.07	—
Methylcyclopentane	0.74	0.75	0.72	0.70	0.65
Cyclohexane	—	0.66	0.65	0.69	—
Methylcyclohexane	0.75	0.72	0.71	0.71	0.67
Toluene	—	0.49	0.53	0.48	—
Methanol	—	1.37	1.24	—	—
Ethanol	—	1.34	1.16	—	—
Propanol-1	1.42	1.22	1.05	(1.05)	0.87
Butanol-1	1.43	1.08	0.96	0.86	0.78
Propanol-2	—	1.16	1.04	—	—
2-Methyl 2-butanol	0.97	0.83	0.79	0.75	0.66
3-Methyl 2-butanol	0.98	0.86	0.78	0.76	0.71

ing slightly more from ideality than those of Table 7.1 have been calculated by the writer according to the normal procedure from partition coefficient measurements published by various investigators[5, 13]. These data (Tables 7.3 and 7.4) are chiefly included for purposes of comparison. On account of the departures from ideality and the consequent asymmetry of the elution curves they do not represent the highest attainable accuracy.

The writer has evolved a procedure for calculating values of γ^0 in the case of very imperfect systems. Though this procedure has not yet been extensively verified, it appears to yield figures but slightly less accurate than those obtained for ideally dilute solutions. The suggested method relies mainly upon experimental observations and may be described as follows.

It has been found that in asymmetric elution curves the location of the peak maximum is a function of the sample size of the solute (see for instance Littlewood, Phillips and Price[2]). In many cases of asymmetry either the "initial" or "final" retention volume (distances OA or OB in Figure 1.4, p. 16) appear to be independent of the charge. (See also Pollard and Hardy[14].) This behavior is not unexpected, since the initial or final retention volume in question refers to the rate of motion of a zone of very low concentration and such a zone is always present in a solute band with diffuse edges. A zone of low concentration will move at constant speed. In systems involving γ values lower than unity this zone will be found at the rear of a band and hence the final retention volume is almost constant; in systems

TABLE 7.4. VALUES OF $\gamma_p{}^0$ CALCULATED FROM PARTITION COEFFICIENTS MEASURED
BY ADLARD AT 100°C FOR VARIOUS SOLUTES IN POLYETHYLENE GLYCOL 400
(P.E.G. 400), METHOXY-P.E.G. 350 AND POLYPROPYLENE GLYCOL 425

Solute	P.E.G. 400	Solvent Methoxy P.E.G. 350	P.P.G. 425
n-Pentane	4.661	2.853	1.307
n-Hexane	6.207	3.667	1.474
n-Heptane	7.790	4.605	1.674
n-Octane	10.138	5.582	1.921
n-Decane	17.225	8.318	—
Benzene	0.868	0.671	0.501
Toluene	1.226	0.900	0.613
m-Xylene	1.710	1.181	0.744
o-Xylene	1.550	1.096	0.714
Mesitylene	2.352	1.553	0.902
Methanol	0.423	0.454	0.412
Ethanol	0.553	0.564	0.494
n-Propanol	0.640	0.593	0.496
n-Butanol	0.753	0.666	0.518
n-Pentanol	0.852	0.708	0.520
Acetone	1.159	0.629	0.569
Methyl ethyl ketone	1.214	0.765	0.626
Methyl isopropyl ketone	1.489	0.935	0.679
Diethyl ketone	1.380	0.905	0.665
Methyl isobutyl ketone	1.727	1.114	0.767
Ethyl acetate	1.031	0.839	0.603
n-Propyl acetate	1.325	1.012	0.671
n-Butyl acetate	1.752	1.234	0.776

with a γ greater than 1 the initial retention volume is nearly constant. (It is assumed that samples are charged as a small plug.)

The calculation of γ^0 from asymmetric curves will become possible if the peak maximum of the hypothetical zone of low concentration can be determined. The peak width of such a zone can be found by the following procedure of extrapolation.

Elution curves are determined for at least three small samples of different size. (At the same time it is verified that the retention volume OA or OB is actually constant.) From each of these curves the "effective" number of plates is then calculated by means of formula (13a) (p. 123). (The number of plates decreases with increasing sample size.) In each case the [H.E.T.P.]$_{eff.}$ is next computed and plotted against sample size. Experimentally it has been found that an almost straight line is obtained, which can be extrapolated to sample size zero. The number of plates at sample size zero is then calculated and from the number of plates the peak width, with the aid of formula (13a) (p. 123). The location of the peak maximum is found by adding or subtracting half the hypothetical peak width either to the initial or from the final retention volume.

This section will now be concluded with a brief discussion of the effect of non-linearity on the transport of solutes through the chromatographic column. Two cases will be distinguished[5].

(a) If the components of the solution are very similar in polarity, but have a large difference in molecular magnitude (or if the components tend to form transient adducts) a "negative" deviation from Raoult's law (log $\gamma < 0$) usually results. The partition coefficient, and hence the retardation of the solute, is smaller for a more concentrated zone of the band than for a more dilute portion. The effect shows up as a sharpening of the band's leading edge and in a dispersion of its tail as it proceeds through the column. At the same time the concomitant depletion of the zone of maximum concentration causes the net motion of the band to become relatively slower, until it obtains the limiting rate of motion corresponding to "zero" concen-

TABLE 7.5. APPARENT HEATS OF SOLUTION FROM G.L.C. MEASUREMENTS
(Porter, Deal and Stross[5])

Solute	Solvent	a	b	c
n-Pentane	squalane	5.22	5.25	−0.72
n-Hexane	"	6.21	6.36	−0.60
n-Heptane	"	7.37	7.58	−0.54
Cyclohexane	"	6.60	6.77	−0.58
Methylcyclohexane	"	7.28	7.53	−0.50
n-Hexane	diisodecylphthalate	6.54	6.36	−0.93
n-Heptane	"	7.00	7.58	−0.17
n-Octane	"	8.00	8.64	−0.11
n-Nonane	"	9.14	9.77	−0.12
Methylcyclopentane	"	5.95	6.45	−0.25
Cyclohexane	"	(7.35)	6.77	(−1.33)
Methylcyclohexane	"	6.90	7.53	−0.12
Ethylcyclohexane	"	8.46	8.63	−0.58
Toluene	"	7.78	8.13	−0.40
Methanol	"	4.91	8.15	+3.24
Ethanol	"	(5.00)	9.61	(+4.61)
Propanol-1	"	7.35	9.94	+1.41
Butanol-1	"	7.45	10.00	+1.80
2-Methyl 2-butanol	"	8.08	9.28	+0.45

a = Apparent heat of solution; $\dfrac{\partial \ln k}{\partial (1/T)} = \dfrac{\Delta H_v - RT - \overline{\Delta H_s}^{\mathrm{E}}}{R}$.

b = ΔH_v = heat of vaporization of the solute.

c = $\overline{\Delta H_s}^{\mathrm{E}}$ = excess partial heat of solution of the solute in the solvent.

TABLE 7.6. HEATS OF SOLUTION FROM G.L.C. MEASUREMENTS
(Littlewood, Phillips and Price[2])

Solute	Heats of Solution in		ΔH_v
	Tritolyl Phosphate	Silicone 702	
Ethanol	8.1	5.9	9.6
Propanol-1	9.4	7.0	9.9
Methyl acetate	7.7	7.1	7.3
Ethyl acetate	8.3	7.8	7.8
Propyl acetate	9.0	8.4	8.1
Benzene	9.2	7.4	7.4
Toluene	9.0	7.9	8.1

tration. The result is that the retention volume referred to the maximum of the curve (IG) is less than it would be in the hypothetical case of zero concentration throughout the column.

(b) If there is a great difference in the polarity of solute components, the partition coefficient is greater in the more concentrated portions of a band than in dilute portions. The elution curve will have a sharpened trailing edge and a more diffuse front. In this case the decreasing concentration at the band's maximum causes the band to move relatively faster, and hence the measured retention volume will be greater than in the limiting case of zero concentration ($\log \gamma > 0$, positive deviation from Raoult's law).

These effects are appreciable in the very first part of the column only; they become smaller as longer columns are used. For the measurement of accurate values of γ^0 columns of considerable length (3–6 meters) must hence be recommended.

Heats of Solution

G.L.C. has been used for calculating the heat of solution from the change of partition coefficients with temperature. Free energies of solution can be calculated from the partition coefficient at one temperature and hence entropies of solution may also be computed. Data on heats of solution taken from literature are presented in Tables 7.5 and 7.6.

THE DESIGN OF COLUMNS FOR DIFFICULT SEPARATIONS

In Chapter 2 it was stated that for most analytical purposes the design of an appropriate column and the assessment of the operating variables do not present great difficulties. This is mainly due to the circumstances that the separation factors usually involved differ sufficiently from unity and that separation can be obtained with columns having between 1000 and 2000 plate equivalents. For critical separations, however, the number of plate equivalents required may be considerably higher; the design of the column and the manner of operation should then be given due attention.

TABLE 7.7. BOILING POINTS AND VAPOR PRESSURES[10] AT 30°C OF HYDROCARBONS
PRESENT IN A TECHNICAL "HEXANE" FRACTION

Component	B.p. (°C)	Vapor Pressure (mm Hg/30°C)	Vapor Pressure Ratio
n-Pentane	36.0	615	
			1.60
Cyclopentane	49.2	385	
			1.00
2,2-Dimethylbutane	49.7	385	
			1.35
2,3-Dimethylbutane	58.0	286	
			1.10
2-Methylpentane	60.3	259	
			1.11
3-Methylpentane	63.2	233	
			1.25
n-Hexane	68.8	187	

As an example, the analysis of a technical distillate fraction of "hexanes," containing the isomeric hydrocarbons listed in Table 7.7, will be discussed. In this table the boiling points, vapor pressures at 30°C and the relative volatilities of the successive hydrocarbons have been stated. By normal distillation the separation of cyclopentane from 2,2-dimethylbutane is almost impossible.

In gas-liquid chromatography the relative volatility of the volatile hydrocarbons is affected by the column liquid. The effect will be fairly small for the isomeric paraffins, but may be appreciable for cyclopentane, as will be seen from Table 7.8, which gives partition coefficients at 30°C in two liquids differing largely in polarity, viz., dimethyl sulfolane (D.M.S.) and n-hexadecane (n-C$_{16}$). In both cases the emergence of cyclopentane proves to be selectively retarded; with D.M.S., cyclopentane is even less volatile than n-hexane.

With both solvents the separation between 2,3-dimethylbutane and 2-methylpentane appears to be the most critical. In the case of n-C$_{16}$ the relative volatility is 1.07; from Glueckauf's graph (Figure 4.16) it may be seen that for a 98 per cent separation of small and equal quantities of these hydrocarbons, columns with at least 4000 plate equivalents are required.

TABLE 7.8. PARTITION COEFFICIENTS OF HYDROCARBONS PRESENT
IN "HEXANE" FRACTION
(dimethyl sulfolane and n-hexadecane at 30°C)

Solvent: Dimethyl Sulfolane			Solvent: n-Hexadecane		
Component	Part. Coeff.	Ratio	Component	Part. Coeff.	Ratio
n-Pentane	19		n-pentane	122	
		1.37			1.50
2,2-Dimethylbutane	26		2,2-dimethylbutane	182	
		~1.4			1.25
2,3-Dimethylbutane	~36		cyclopentane	227	
		~1.0			1.13
2-Methylpentane	37		2,3-dimethylbutane	257	
		1.19			1.07
3-Methylpentane	44		2-methylpentane	276	
		1.16			1.15
n-Hexane	51		3-methylpentane	317	
		1.10			1.23
Cyclopentane	56		n-hexane	389	

In the following we will discuss a tentative evaluation for this purpose of two columns of equal length, but provided with different stationary liquids and operated with different carrier gases. The main purpose of this evaluation is to demonstrate how use can be made of the theoretical principles developed in the previous chapters. First it will be shown what column data are required for an evaluation, then an estimate will be made of the coefficients in the Van Deemter equation. It will be found that the estimation of these coefficients involves a number of uncertainties, but that the latter partly cancel out in comparing the two columns.

With the Van Deemter equation the H.E.T.P. under optimum conditions can be calculated and also the linear gas velocity at which the H.E.T.P. is a minimum. From the gas velocity determined in this manner the theory of Chapter 5 permits of calculating column pressures and elution times. Finally, the maximum permissible sample size can be roughly computed.

Two fictitious columns will be compared; they are 720 cm in length and 6 mm in internal diameter. The support is ground fire-brick (30/50 mesh), the column temperature 30°C. The calculations refer to 2-methylpentane.

Column data

Volume empty column ($V_{col.}$)................................. 205.6 cm³
Weight of support employed.............................. 81.51 grams
True density of support................................... 2.17
True volume of support ($V_{sup.}$)......................... 37.56 cm³

	Column I Solvent: Dimethyl sulfolane	Column II Solvent: *n*-Hexadecane
Weight of solvent	32.604 grams	16.302 grams
Wt ratio solvent/support	40/100	20/100
Density of solvent at 30°C	1.128	0.765
Volume of solvent ($V_{liq.}$)	28.90 cm³	21.31 cm³
$V_{gas} = V_{col.} - V_{liq.} - V_{sup.}$	139.14 cm³	146.73 cm³
Liquid cross section ($F_{liq.}$)	0.040 cm²	0.030 cm²
Gas cross section ($a \sim F_{gas}$)	0.193 cm²	0.204 cm²
Gas cross section dry column (F)	0.233 cm²	0.233 cm²

For the computation of the coefficients A, B and C in equation (16, p. 148) several assumptions have to be made, particularly as regards the quantities d_f and $D_{liq.}$ occurring in coefficient C.

For the 20/100 *n*-C_{16} column d_f was estimated by various means to be about 5 μ. Correspondingly the value of d_f for column I was taken to be

$$\frac{V_{liq.}(\text{D.M.S.})}{V_{liq.}(n\text{-}C_{16})} \times 5 = 6.8 \ \mu.$$

The liquid diffusivity was assumed at 0.4×10^{-6} cm²/sec for both liquids.

The A term $(2\lambda d_p)$ was evaluated at 0.05 cm in both cases; this value is somewhat lower than that stated in Chapter 6, which was a fairly high estimate. Column I further was operated with nitrogen and column II with hydrogen as carrier gas.

	Column I	Column II
Partition coefficient (k) of 2-methylpentane at 30°C	37	276
$k' = k \cdot F_{\text{liq.}}/F_{\text{gas}}$	7.668	40.558
$k'/(1 + k')^2$	0.102	0.0235
Film thickness (d_f)	6.8μ	5μ
$D_{\text{liq.}}$	0.4×10^{-6} cm²/sec	0.4×10^{-6} cm²/sec
$2\gamma D_{\text{gas}}$ (coeff. B)	0.075 cm²/sec for N_2	0.30 cm²/sec for H_2
A term $(2\lambda d_p)$	0.05 cm.	0.05 cm
Coefficient $C = \dfrac{8}{\pi^2} \cdot \dfrac{k'}{(1 + k')^2} \cdot \dfrac{d_f^2}{D_{\text{liq.}}}$	0.096 sec	0.012 sec
$H_{\text{min.}} = A + 2\sqrt{(BC)}$	0.22 cm	0.17 cm
u (at $H_{\text{min.}}$) $= \sqrt{(B/C)}$	0.885 cm/sec	5.017 cm/sec
Number of plate equivalents under optimum conditions	$\sim$3300	$\sim$4250

Before proceeding to the calculation of column pressure it should be mentioned that the value of $2\gamma D_{\text{gas}}$ refers to gas of 1 atm. pressure. The two columns are now supposed to operate at atmospheric outlet pressure, and for the linear gas velocity u_o (at the outlet) the value of u at $H_{\text{min.}}$ is chosen.

With the theory of Chapter 5 the inlet pressure and the elution times can be calculated. The permeability of the dry column (K) has been given in Chapter 5 (Figure 5.4); for 30/50 mesh ground fire-brick $K = 1.7 \times 10^{-6}$ cm². The permeability of the wet column (K') was then calculated by multiplying K by F_{gas}/F. The viscosities of N_2 and H_2 are expressed in poises, hence the pressures must be expressed in dynes/cm² (1 mm Hg = 1330 dynes/cm²).

	Column I	Column II
K' (wet column) in cm²	1.41×10^{-6}	1.49×10^{-6}
η in poises	1.8×10^{-4} for N_2	0.9×10^{-4} for H_2
$V_t = F_{\text{gas}} \times u_o$ in cm³/sec	0.17	1.02
p_o (1 atm.) in dynes/cm²	1.013×10^6	1.013×10^6
$V_t p_o L$ [Eq. 5 (p. 142)]	1.25×10^8	7.6×10^8
p_i in dynes/cm²	1.092×10^6	1.215×10^6
p_i in mm Hg	819	912
average column pressure in dynes/cm²	1.037×10^6	1.117×10^6
average column pressure in mm Hg	778	838
t_g (sec) [Eq. 10 (p. 145)]	847	158

In this table t_g is the residence time of a pure carrier gas molecule; the residence time of the solute is found by dividing the residence time of the carrier gas by the retardation factor $R_F = 1/(1 + k')$.

	Column I	Column II
t_g in sec	847	158
$R_F = 1/(1 + k')$	0.1154	0.0240
elution time in sec.	7340	6583
V_R (retention volume) in cm³ [Eq. 11 (p. 146)]	1254	6738

The elution time is slightly more than 2 hrs for column I and slightly less for column II.

The evaluation will be concluded with the calculation of the maximum permissible amount of 2-methylpentane. In Chapter 4 it was mentioned that the peak width is independent of the amount of a substance for very small samples only, viz., those less than $0.5\ V_{\text{eff.}}\ \sqrt{n}$, where $V_{\text{eff.}} = V_G + kV_L$, the capacity of one plate. The experiments of van Deemter *et al.* refer to a technique which is a combination of frontal analysis and elution development. For elution development with instantaneous introduction of the sample, the factor 0.5 appears to be much too large and will rather be of the order of 0.02, which value will be taken for the calculation below.

	Column I	Column II
V_G	0.042 cm³	0.035 cm³
V_L	0.009 cm³	0.005 cm³
$V_{\text{eff.}} = V_G + kV_L$	0.375 cm³	1.415 cm³
$0.02\ V_{\text{eff.}}\ \sqrt{n}$	∼0.43 cm³	∼1.84 cm³

It hence follows that column II is capable of handling samples four times as large as column I.

In spite of a number of uncertainties in the data, the evaluation of gas-liquid chromatographic columns is hence possible. When comparing the two columns mentioned above there is no doubt that for the analysis of the hexanes column II is superior in every respect, although in the latter hydrogen was the carrier gas:

(1) its efficiency is about 25 per cent higher;

(2) the time of analysis is about 10 per cent shorter;

(3) the size of the sample that may be used is four times as large.

(4) On account both of the nature of the carrier gas and the larger sample higher detector signals are obtained.

RECENT ADVANCES IN SEPARATING EFFICIENCY

The degree of resolution obtained in separations by G.L.C. is affected by a number of factors that have been discussed in previous pages of this book. From a practical point of view, these factors can be divided into two

groups, giving two lines along which an improvement in separating efficiency may be approached. The lines are: (a) a careful search for a stationary liquid giving a particularly favourable separating factor for the compounds in question, and (b) the choice of a suitable combination of the
other experimental parameters affecting the general column efficiency, with
the object of increasing the number of theoretical plates that it contains.
Both of these lines of approach have been followed recently by investigators dealing with critical separations, and both have led to remarkable
results.

A successful choice of the stationary phase, even with a column of moderate efficiency, has resulted in separations that would, in the early days of
G.L.C., have been considered impossible. Two examples, mentioned in
previous chapters, are the resolution of butene-1 from isobutene with a
solution of a silver salt as column liquid (p. 21), and that of meta- from
para-xylene by the use of tetrahalophthalate esters (Example G, Chapter 2).
It should be realized, however, that the introduction of a new stationary
liquid will usually offer a solution only for a specific problem. A general
improvement in column efficiency, on the other hand, affects all separations
equally, and is therefore a subject for investigation of wider interest than
the search for special column solvents. Furthermore, there is obviously no
reason why an efficient column should not be combined with a superior
stationary phase. As a rule, in fact, the use of columns with a large number
of theoretical plates will render the selection of the stationary phase less
critical and so limit the number of substances that have to be considered
for this purpose; secondary factors, such as thermal stability, elution time
and viscosity will then often determine the choice of the column liquid.

Recent advances in the design of efficient columns will be described in
the remaining pages of this chapter.

Improvements in Packed Columns

The following investigations were largely based on the rate theory discussed in Chapter 4.

Bohemen and Purnell[15] carried out experiments with the object of finding
out how the values of A, B and C in the simplified Van Deemter equation
for the H.E.T.P.

$$H = A + B/u + Cu$$

vary with certain experimental parameters. They showed that by using
narrow screen fractions for the support, by further reducing sample size
and by a proper choice of the carrier gas and its rate of flow, efficiencies of
1000 plates per foot can be realized in practice. In Table 7.9, the values of

TABLE 7.9. CALCULATED VALUES OF VAN DEEMTER EQUATION CONSTANTS FOR CYCLOHEXANE, ACETONE AND BENZENE, ELUTED AT 47°C BY NITROGEN FROM COLUMNS CONTAINING 20% WT. POLYETHYLENE GLYCOL 400.

Mesh size spread of support	Cyclohexane			Acetone			Benzene		
	A	B	C	A	B	C	A	B	C
	$\times 10^3$	$\times 10^3$	$\times 10^4$	$\times 10^3$	$\times 10^3$	$\times 10^4$	$\times 10^3$	$\times 10^3$	$\times 10^4$
20–30	39	149	102	36	230	77	39	198	100
30–40	27	142	78	26	203	61	26	227	66
40–50	33	129	55	18	200	47	2	242	60
50–60	−19	293	65	−3	285	41	16	168	31
100–150	−11	184	48	−10	254	26	−20	264	34

A, B and C measured by these investigators are given as a function of the mesh size spread of the support (Silocel) for three substances eluted with nitrogen. It proved that A was always small and in some cases even negative, from which fact Bohemen and Purnell concluded that A could in practice be omitted from the Van Deemter equation under the circumstances of their experiments. Different values would then, of course, have to be assigned to B and C.

Scott and Cheshire[16] and Scott[17], in their fundamental work on high separating efficiency, have principally studied the lengthening of the column and the problems which this measure involves. It was found that beyond a certain length the number of plates became appreciably less than proportional to the column length. This proved to be due to the high inlet/outlet pressure ratios that were necessary for obtaining a sufficient flow with pressures at the conventional levels. It then became obvious that the solution of the problem would involve high column pressures, so as to keep p_i/p_o close to unity, and the gas rate close to the optimum value. Like Bohemen and Purnell, Scott further studied the variation of A, B and C with operational factors. A was in this case also found to be small, but not negligible. The reality of A was substantiated by the finding that the number of plates increases with a diminution in the column diameter, owing to the resulting reduction in "path tortuosity". A further diminution in A was effected by rendering the packing more homogeneous. An important increase in plate number also resulted from the use of a very low ratio of stationary liquid to column support (5 or even $2\frac{1}{2}$ per cent). This extremely effective measure is possible only if residual adsorption by the support, as evidenced by tailing of the peaks, does not become serious*. Finally, Scott found that the use of high column pressures had the additional advantage

* See the footnote on page 157.

of diminishing the value of B by reducing diffusion in the gas phase. It should be pointed out, however, that with a reduction in diffusivity in the gas phase there is also an increase in the resistance to mass transfer in the gas phase, whilst a reduction in the thickness of the liquid film causes resistance to mass transfer in the liquid to diminish. The complete equation for the H.E.T.P. developed by Van Deemter is based on the assumption that the resistance to mass transfer is fully located in the liquid (see p. 135). The equation for the conditions maintained by Scott can, however, be represented just as well by $H = A + B/u + Cu$, but in this case B and C obtain a slightly different meaning.

Scott pointed out that a high-efficiency column as developed by him requires a very small sample and an extremely sensitive detector. We shall revert to the consequences of this point in the next section. As an example of Scott's results it may be quoted that a 50 ft. column, 2.2 mm I.D., charged with 5 per cent Apiezon Oil on 110–120 mesh firebrick, when employed at about 200 p.s.i. inlet pressure and at 78°C, proved to have an efficiency of about 30,000 theoretical plates for a 5μg sample of o-xylene, which was eluted in 240 minutes.

The Coated Capillary Column

An entirely unconventional type of high-efficiency column has been evolved by M. Golay.

Whilst a considerable part of the chromatographic theory so far developed was based on chemical engineering principles, in which a packed column is regarded as a bundle of long capillaries, Golay employed an electric analogy of resistances and condensers for his deductions. He applied this analogy first to a column packed with solid particles, comparing this also to a system of parallel capillaries, which were assumed to have an internal diameter in the same order of magnitude as the particle size. Theoretical considerations on the comparison column led him to the conclusion that its H.E.T.P. should be roughly the same as the size of the particles in the packed column. His predictions were in agreement with the properties of the packed column in several respects, but this did not apply to two important characteristics: a packed column, when compared to the analogy of ideal capillaries, has the H.E.T.P. that would be expected if the particle size (or channel diameter) were ten times as large, and the gas resistance corresponding to particles or channels ten times as small. These two factors of ten give the packed column a gas resistance that is $100^2 = 10,000$ times greater than an ideal capillary column having the same H.E.T.P.

This finding led Golay to experiment with well-defined capillary tubes internally coated with a very thin film of the stationary liquid. The coated capillary column has been treated by him theoretically in a number of publications[18], its practical applicability has been demonstrated with examples, in which not only short capillaries of glass, but also long ones of stainless steel (150 ft) were used. These were coated by the simple procedure of filling them with a dilute solution (1 per cent) of the liquid in a volatile solvent, closing off one end and moving the open end slowly into an oven heated to a suitable temperature, in which the solvent evaporates.

Figures 7.1 and 7.2 demonstrate that exceptionally good results may be so obtained. It proves possible, by the relatively simple procedure outlined above, to arrive at columns not only having plate numbers of 50,000 or more, but also permitting the analysis to be carried out in a far shorter time than required with packed columns of comparable efficiency. These two factors should, of course, be considered together when judging a column's performance. Golay has facilitated this by developing an expression called the Performance Index (P.I.), which he defines as:

$$\text{P.I.} = \left(\frac{\Delta t_x}{t_x - t_a}\right)^4 \cdot \frac{(t_x - t_a)^4 \cdot t_a}{t_x{}^4 \left(t_x - \frac{15}{16} t_a\right)} \cdot t_x \cdot \Delta p$$

in which

Δt_x = width of band measured as intercept of base line by tangents to inflection points;

t_x = passage time of band from beginning to end of column;

t_a = passage time of inert component (air);

$\Delta p = p_i - p_o$

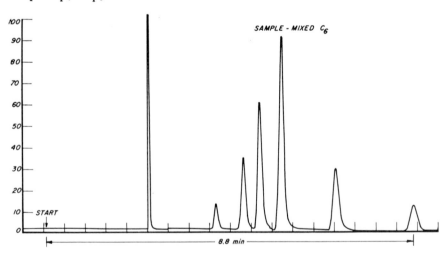

Figure 7.1.

Figure 7.1. Separation of C_6 paraffins with a coated capillary column (after Golay). 150' x 0.010" capillary; 1% didecyl phthalate; 20 p.s.i., 40°C; flow: 0.96 cm³/min (helium).

The first part of the formula is the fourth power of the relative band-width, whilst the factor $t_x \cdot \Delta p$ constitutes a measure of the price paid (in expended time) for a given resolution. The lower the P.I., the greater is the practical "goodness" of the column. Although P.I.'s considerably below unity are possible according to theory, values around 1 (as obtainable with Golay's capillaries) must be considered extremely good; a packed column of high efficiency may have a P.I. of about 6, a normal packed column a very much higher value. It should be emphasized that Golay's theory (like the rate theory) presupposes linear chromatography and that the P.I. should be calculated under conditions of optimum flow rate.

Golay's work has shown that high-efficiency columns can be constructed in a relatively simple manner. Their operation, however, involves a number of experimental difficulties. In the first place, optimum results are obtain-able only with minute samples, ($\sim 0.02 \ V_{\text{eff}} \cdot \sqrt{n}$ or less), because $V_{\text{eff}}(= V_g + kV_L)$ is very small. From Figure 7.2 it is found that in Golay's columns the H.E.T.P. is approximately 1 mm; the capillary diameter is about $\frac{1}{4}$ mm, so that the empty volume of the capillary is about 2×10^{-4} cm³ per plate. Putting V_{eff} at twice this figure, we find for the permissible size of the sample

$$0.02 \times 4 \times 10^{-4} = 8 \times 10^{-6} \ \text{cm}^3$$

a value corresponding to weights in the order of fractions of a microgram. The introduction of such very small samples is a difficult problem. One possibility is to take a sample of the usual size (1 to 2 mg) and to bleed the greater part of it outside the column, admitting only 1 per cent or less[20].

It is important to observe that with such small samples the elution

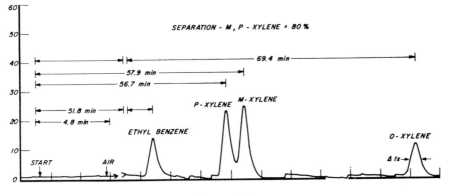

Figure 7.2.

Figure 7.2. Separation of C₈ aromatics with a coated capillary column (after Golay). 150' x 0.010" capillary; 1% didecyl phthalate; 10 p.s.i.; 70°C; flow: 0.48 cm³/min (helium). Number of theoretical plates 50,000.

curves can be registered satisfactorily only with highly sensitive detectors. Referring again to Figure 7.2 it will be seen that the time (Δt_x) for eluting the peak of the heaviest component was 22 secs at a gas rate of about 1 cm³ per minute; the material corresponding to this peak was therefore present in approximately $\frac{1}{3}$ cm³ of gas, and the average concentration in the peak works out to be in the order of 10^{-6} g per cm³ of carrier gas. It will also be clear that the gas volume of the detector should be only a fraction of the volume corresponding to the width of the narrowest peak.

The first practical application of coated capillary columns (of somewhat lower efficiency) has been published by Dijkstra and de Goey[19], who investigated their use for the separation of fatty acids.

Summarizing, we can say that Golay's coated capillaries offer a promising approach for the realization of high-efficiency G.L.C. columns; the development of these columns will, however, have to be accompanied by that of systems for introducing minute samples, and by the use of highly sensitive detectors, having an extremely low dead volume. As regards the detectors, the McWilliam flame ionization detector (Chapter 3) appears to be particularly suitable. (Golay worked with a thermistor-type katharometer of special construction.)

In practice the G.L.C. column of ultra-high efficiency will probably never replace the normal packed column in many of its applications, any more than the microscope will ever entirely replace the hand lens. There is no purpose in using a delicate, but more exacting instrument in cases where the simpler, though less sensitive one gives the required service.

REFERENCES

1. Martin, A. J. P., Symposium on Gas Chromatography, Society for Analytical Chemistry, Ardeer (Scotland), May 1955, *Analyst*, **81**, 52 (1956).
2. Littlewood, A. B., Phillips, C. S. G., and Price, D. T., *J. Chem. Soc.*, **1955**, 1480.
3. Herington, E. F. G., Symposium on Gas Chromatography, Society for Analytical Chemistry, Ardeer (Scotland), May 1955, *Analyst*, **81**, 52 (1956). *See also* Vapour Phase Chromatography, Desty, D. H. (ed.), London, 1957 (Proc. of London Symposium on V. Ph. Chr., May/June 1956), p. 5.
4. Hoare, M. R., and Purnell, J. H., *Trans. Faraday Soc.*, **52**, 222 (1956).
5. Porter, P. E., Deal, C. H., and Stross, F. H., *J. Am. Chem. Soc.*, **78**, 2999 (1956).
6. Pierotti, G. J., Deal, C. H., Derr, E. L., and Porter, P. E., *J. Am. Chem. Soc.*, **78**, 2989 (1956).
7. Brønsted, J. N., and Koefoed, J., *Kgl. Danske Videnskab. Selskab, Mat.-fys. Medd.*, **22**, No. 17, 32 pp., (1946).
8. Waals, J. H. van der, and Hermans, J. J., *Rec. trav. chim.*, **69**, 971 (1950).
9. Neckel, A., and Fohler, F., *Monatsh. Chem.*, **87**, No. 1, 176 (1956).
10. American Petroleum Institute, Project 44, "Selected Values of Physical and Thermodynamical Properties of Hydrocarbons and Related Compounds," Pittsburgh, Pa. 1953.
11. Maxwell, J. B., "Data Book on Hydrocarbons, Application to Process Engineering," New York, van Nostrand, 1950.

12. Bosanquet, C. H., and Morgan, G. O., Vapour Phase Chromatography, Desty, D. H. (ed.), London, 1957 (Proc. of London Symposium on V. Ph. Chr.; May/June 1956), p. 35.
13. Adlard, E. R., *ibid.*, p. 98.
14. Pollard, F. H., and Hardy, G. H., *ibid.* p. 115.
15. Bohemen, J., and Purnell, J. H., Gas Chromatography 1958, Desty, D. H. (ed.), London (Proc. of 2nd Symposium on Gas Chr., Amsterdam, May 1958), p. 6.
16. Scott, R. P. W., and Cheshire, J. D., *Nature* **180,** 702 (1957).
17. Scott, R. P. W., Gas Chromatography 1958, Desty, D. H. (ed.), London (Proc. of 2nd Symposium on Gas Chr., Amsterdam, May 1958), p. 189.
18. Golay, M. J. E., *Analyt. Chem.* **29,** 928 (1957); *Nature* **180,** 435 (1957);
19. Dijkstra, G. and de Goey, J., Gas Chromatography 1958, Desty, D. H. (ed.), London (Proc. of 2nd Symposium on Gas Chr., Amsterdam, May 1958), p. 56.
20. Desty, D. H., private communication.
21. Kwantes, A., and Rijnders, G. W. A., Gas Chromatography 1958, Desty, D. H. (ed.), London (Proc. of 2nd Symposium on Gas Chr., Amsterdam, May 1958), p. 125.

Chapter 8
GAS-SOLID CHROMATOGRAPHY

INTRODUCTION

Gas-liquid chromatography has, in the few years since its discovery, undergone a spectacular development and it now constitutes a separation method of the greatest versatility. This very fact, however, tends to make one forget that gas adsorption chromatography (G.S.C.) is the older technique of the two and that there are still several specific cases in which it possesses advantages with respect to G.L.C.

The latter, more modern method mainly owes its favorable features to two phenomena. Firstly, the linear course of the distribution isotherms gives rise to symmetrical peaks for the components (see Chapter 2). Secondly, a G.L.C. column, operated under optimum conditions, is extremely efficient, viz., it contains a large number of theoretical stages in a moderate length.

The efficiency of a gas adsorption column, in so far as it can be expressed in convenient terms, is usually of about the same order as that of a column for G.L.C. The striking difference between G.S.C. and G.L.C., then, lies in the fact that the distribution isotherm in adsorption is usually strongly curved. This phenomenon causes the peaks emerging by elution from the column to be very asymmetric; as a rule they show a sharp front flank, but a relatively long, drawn-out "tail." (See, for instance, Figure 8.7a.) This shape of peak in many cases mitigates against the efficiency of separation.

Two points should, however, be noted in this connection. (a) The curvature of the adsorption isotherms decreases with the boiling point of the compound in question, and (b) the steep front of the peak for a component may occasionally be put to good use. These points constitute the background for the two principal cases in which the adsorption technique has, to the writer's knowledge, advantages over G.L.C. They are:

(a) G.S.C. (using the elution technique, see below) may be employed to effect a reasonably good separation between components of low boiling point, such as the rare gases, CO, H_2, O_2, CH_4 and NO. So far no satisfactory stationary liquid is available for separating such mixtures by G.L.C.

(b) G.S.C. can sometimes be usefully employed for dealing with substances containing a very small amount of some admixture or impurity. While in G.L.C. this minor component will appear only as a diffuse peak of low height, it may in G.S.C., using the method of displacement, be pushed up as a relatively narrow band before the steep front of another constituent, so that it can be collected in fairly concentrated form. If desired, it may then be submitted to further analysis by G.L.C.

Some recent developments in adsorption analysis, which hold certain favorable aspects, will be referred to at the end of this chapter.

The main disadvantages of G.S.C. with respect to the more modern method of G.L.C., in cases where both can be used, are the following. The adsorption methods are frequently vitiated by the tailing of the bands already discussed; particularly in displacement development they also involve more time for the analysis, larger samples, somewhat more critical flow rates of the carrier gas, repeated replacement of the adsorbent and, in some cases, evacuation of the column before each run. In both the elution and displacement adsorption techniques the accuracy of the method largely depends on the identity in the adsorbing power of various batches of the column packing, a requirement difficult to realize. Furthermore, there is relatively little choice in adsorbents; G.L.C., which uses a liquid for partition, offers a far larger range from which to choose. Most of these disadvantages, however, are absent in the hybrid form of gas chromatography employing a solid adsorbent, "modified" by the presence of a small amount of a suitable liquid. (See "G.S.C. with Tailing Reducers", p. 212.)

Forms in Which G.S.C. is Carried Out

As we have seen in Chapter 1, there are three distinct ways in which chromatographic analysis may be carried out:

(a) by elution development,
(b) by frontal analysis and
(c) by displacement development.

On account of the nature of the partition process, G.L.C. nearly always employs the elution technique, the eluent being the carrier gas. The displacement technique is scarcely feasible in this system of separation, while frontal analysis offers advantages only in non-analytical applications.

In G.S.C., on the other hand, all three methods may be—and have been —adopted. In elution development the carrier gas is again the eluent. Displacement development uses a carrier gas which is saturated with the vapor of a strongly adsorbed substance. Both techniques employ a small sample for analysis. In frontal analysis, a larger sample is passed into the column in the gas phase, usually after admixture with a certain amount of a "neutral" gas.

In elution chromatography the band of each component travels through the column at a rate specific for that component under the conditions of the experiment; if two bands are completely separated, pure carrier gas emerges from the column between them. In displacement chromatography, on the other hand, all bands travel at the rate of the displacer and issue from the column without intervening gap. An essential condition for good separation by the latter technique is therefore that the fronts of each band shall be steep and sharp; in practice, a slight overlap is always inevitable.

A point of practical importance is that in employing G.S.C. with the displacement technique the adsorbent is left saturated with the displace, at the end of the experiment, so that in most cases the column must be charged with fresh solid before each run.

In frontal analysis the least adsorbed component appears first from the column and it is followed by the components, broadly speaking, in the order of their strength of adsorption; it will be shown further on, however, that the components after the first are not obtained pure.

A variation on the practical execution of G.S.C. lies in the use of local heating for desorbing bands of components from the column. In this method—which has been called "Chromathermography" and can be applied in principle to any of the three forms of analysis—a heater is moved up gradually from the end of the column toward the inlet. It is particularly useful for releasing bands so strongly adsorbed that they would move very slowly at normal temperatures.

THE EVOLUTION OF G.S.C.

The attempts to use selective adsorption for the qualitative and quantitative analysis of gases and vapors date back at least to 1930[1]. Most of the early work was carried out in the form of frontal analysis, but the effects caused by mutual displacement of the components were not taken into account. The heater-desorption technique mentioned above was employed in such separations by Zhukhovitskii, Turkel'taub and Georgievskaya[2] and by Aivazov and Vyakhirev[3], who showed it to be a useful method in spite of its serious limitations. Thermal desorption was also used in later work by Turkel'taub[4] and by Turner[5].

The first to give a satisfactory account of the theoretical aspects of frontal analysis and displacement development in G.S.C. were Tiselius[6] and Claesson[7]. On the basis of theory Claesson developed the displacement technique into a quantitative method for analyzing mixtures of hydrocarbons containing up to eight carbon atoms. Claesson, for detection, employed the thermal conductivity method, which was first advocated by him. For the separation of the hydrocarbons this investigator used several types of carbon of different surface activity, of which a large stock was kept so as to obtain reproducible column charges.

Claesson's displacement method was further developed and successfully applied by Phillips[8] in experiments on gas kinetics. Phillips studied the main operating parameters in the separation—particle size of the adsorbent, rate of flow, column dimensions, pretreatment of the adsorbent and column temperature—with the object of increasing the sharpness of the fronts. He further employed the method for separating a variety of organic compounds, including saturated, olefinic and aromatic hydrocarbons, halogenated hydrocarbons, nitroparaffins, ethers, ketones, alcohols, and esters.

The analysis of gas mixtures by G.S.C. with the elution technique was first studied by Cremer and co-workers[16] and was further developed by Janák[9]. In the latter's analyses a small sample of the gas mixture (containing components such as CO, H_2, CH_4, C_2H_4, C_2H_6, etc.) was introduced into the end of an adsorption column packed with charcoal or silica gel, and was developed with CO_2. The carrier gas was removed and the components were collected in a burette containing caustic potash solution, so that an elution curve of the integral type was obtained (see Figure 2.21). Patton, Lewis and Kaye[10] also employed the elution adsorption method for the separation of various gases and volatile liquids, using charcoal, silica gel and alumina as adsorbents and hydrogen, nitrogen or carbon dioxide as eluent. Charcoal effects a separation virtually according to boiling point, whereas silica gel has a polar character; as a consequence the order of elution of ethane and ethene is reversed. Cremer[17], who separated oxygen and nitrogen with active charcoal as adsorbent, showed that the order of emergence of the components may depend upon the eluent (carrier gas) used; in this case O_2 broke through before N_2 with hydrogen as eluent, whilst the order was reversed with CO_2. Ray[11] has used a combination of the elution adsorption and gas-partition techniques.

In the author's opinion many of the separations referred to above would at present be preferably carried out by G.L.C., the only undoubted exceptions being those of mixtures of low boiling-point constituents.

The Principles of G.S.C.

A brief account of the theory of frontal analysis and displacement development in G.S.C. will be given here. For further details the reader is referred to the original papers of Tiselius[6] and Claesson[7].

Frontal Analysis

Frontal analysis will be discussed first, since it is suitable for determining adsorption isotherms, which are required for interpreting displacement curves.

If a "neutral" (non-adsorbed) gas containing an adsorbable component in a concentration c_1 per unit of volume is passed through a column of an adsorbent, and some property (say the thermal conductivity) is plotted against the volume passed in, a curve as shown in Figure 8.1 will be obtained. The volume v_1 of gas that has entered the column until the component breaks through is the retention volume of that component. If a_1 is the amount of the component adsorbed, we have

$$a_1 = v_1 c_1 \qquad (1)$$

(The same relation holds if a_1 and v_1 refer to unit weight of adsorbent; the equation will further be given this interpretation.)

As a_1 is in equilibrium with c_1, the concentration of component in the vapor, a plot of a_1 against c_1 for various values of the latter gives the adsorption isotherm, which in fact can conveniently be determined in this way. In Figure 8.2 an adsorption isotherm of the type most encountered is shown. It follows from this curve that the retention volume (a_1/c_1) depends upon the concentration c_1 and decreases as this value increases, in contrast

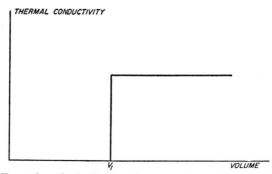

Figure 8.1. Frontal analysis diagram for one solute. ("Ideal" Chromatography).

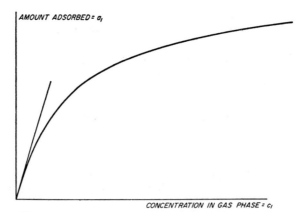

Figure 8.2. Adsorption isotherm (Langmuir type).

to the state of affairs in G.L.C., where the retention volume is independent
of the concentration. Very small values of c_1, however, produce an approximately constant retention volume, since the first part of the curve is almost
linear.

If the gas contains two adsorbable components, a curve with two steps,
as shown in Figure 8.3, will be obtained. While in the former case the
height of a step corresponds directly to the concentration of the component
in the original mixture, this is not generally the case when two components
are present, since there is a competition between the molecules of the
components for the adsorbing surface, which results in a mutual decrease
in adsorption. Consequently the concentration in the moving phase becomes larger than in the case of a single component and the height of the
step for this component is greater. After the second step the gas passes
through the column unchanged. If we denote the retention volume of the
first step in this case by v_1 and that of the second by v_2, the concentrations
of components in the gas by c_1 and c_2, the amount of component 2 adsorbed
in the column is obviously v_2c_2. The amount of component 1 is then (see
Figure 8.3)

$$v_2c_1 - (v_2 - v_1)c_{1.1} \qquad (2)$$

where $c_{1.1}$ corresponds to the concentration of solute 1 in the first flat
Provided that the adsorption isotherms are known, the quantities v_1,
v_2 and $c_{1.1}$ allow c_1 and c_2 to be calculated separately.

For the case of more than two solutes the reader is referred to the original
publications of Claesson. By assuming Langmuir type isotherms for mixed
adsorption this author succeeded in developing the method of frontal
analysis to a fairly accurate method for the analysis of multicomponent
systems.

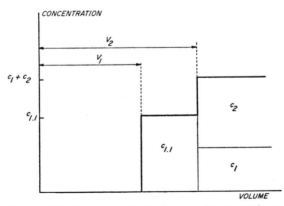

Figure 8.3. Frontal analysis diagram for two solutes.

Displacement Development

Higher accuracies, however, are obtained with the displacement technique. Tiselius has shown that qualitative and quantitative analysis amounts to the measurement of heights and lengths of the steps in the curve. Figure 8.4 represents the simplest case of displacement development, in which a narrow band of one component at the column inlet is displaced by the more strongly adsorbed substance contained in the carrier gas.

For the developer the conditions of frontal analysis apply and the component is forced to travel in front of the developer and at the same rate. This, of course, will only be possible at a certain concentration distribution of that component, which depends upon the concentration of the developer in the gas. Following Claesson we denote the amount of solute i, adsorbed per gram of adsorbent at equilibrium with a concentration c_i of that solute, by a_i. Then the adsorption isotherm may be represented by

$$a_i = f_i(c_i) \tag{3}$$

In order that the component i shall travel at the same speed as the developer d, the following relation must exist:

$$\frac{f_d(c_d)}{c_d} = \frac{f_i(c_i)}{c_i} \tag{4}$$

where subscript d refers to the displacer.

To satisfy this expression the concentration c_i has to establish itself in accordance with this equation and the chosen concentration of the developer. This implies that for a certain concentration of the displacer the component i will leave the column in the gas at a concentration that is constant and characteristic of that component. This concentration in the effluent is hence independent of the amount of that component.

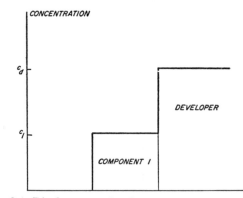

Figure 8.4. Displacement development diagram for one solute.

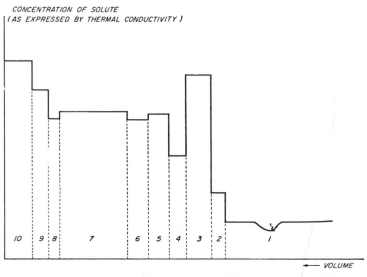

CONCENTRATION OF SOLUTE
(AS EXPRESSED BY THERMAL CONDUCTIVITY)

Figure 8.5. Displacement development. (After James and Phillips).

Successive components will normally emerge from the column in displacement G.S.C. with successively lower concentrations. If the detection device gave a signal only dependent on the concentration (and irrespective of the nature of the components), the diagram would therefore show a series of diminishing steps. Actually the detector gives a signal which is determined both by the concentration of a component and the property—for instance thermal conductivity—that is registered. These two factors may tend to compensate each other and it thus often happens that two "steps" appear at virtually the same level, even though separation is satisfactory. There are frequently, however, methods for circumventing this difficulty. Phillips[8a], for instance, describes a case in which butane and butene showed up as one step, though separation was good. The butene could here be eliminated by adsorbing it in sulfuric acid, and this procedure produced a gap between butane and the saturate below it (propane). In other cases it was possible to employ a substance as "marker" giving an intermediate step, for instance chlorobenzene for differentiating between equal steps of pyridine and o-xylene. Figure 8.5 shows a typical curve obtained in an analysis by G.S.C. according to the displacement technique.

Equation (4) for the various components gives the relation between the adsorption isotherms as determined, for instance, by frontal analysis and the step heights in the displacement diagram. The equation can easily be solved graphically by a method devised by Tiselius.

This method is based on a plot of the distribution isotherms of the components in the mixture ($f_1(c)$, $f_2(c)$, etc.) and that of the displacer ($f_d(c)$), as given in Figure 8.6, (I). If A' is the concentration of the displacer in the gas, point A on the isotherm of the displacer is joined to the origin by a straight line (full line a). It can then be shown that the intercepts C_3, C_2, etc. corresponding to the intersections with the isotherms for components

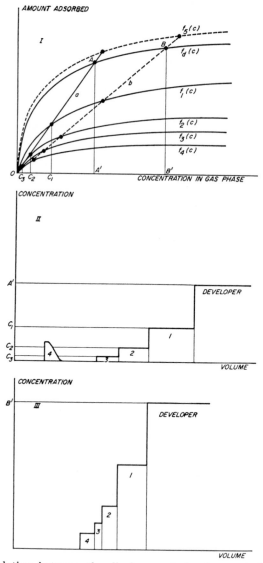

Figure 8.6. Relation between the displacement development diagram and the adsorption isotherms.

3, 2, etc. indicate the concentration at which these components emerge from the column, as shown in Figure 8.6 (II). It should be noted that line a does not intersect curve $f_4(c)$; this signifies that component 4 is so weakly adsorbed that the displacer cannot overtake it. Component 4 will be eluted by the (pure) carrier gas and thus will give rise to an "elution" peak, which will be followed by a band of pure carrier gas and then by the fronts of 3, 2, 1 and the developer. By choosing a higher concentration of the developer, however, as shown by point B (dotted line b), the isotherm $f_4(c)$ will be intersected, and 4 will behave as all the other components [Figure 8.6 (III)].

Curve $f_5(c)$ is the adsorption isotherm for a component more powerfully adsorbed than the developer; this component will hence not be displaced by it.

The success of the displacement method very much depends upon whether sharp fronts can be obtained. The requirements for homogeneous packing are very exacting. Fortunately, a disturbance in the front is automatically corrected owing to the fact that bands of low concentration travel more slowly than those of high concentration. This "self-sharpening" tendency applies to all successive bands; consequently displacement G.S.C. is sometimes particularly suitable for isolating a component or impurity occurring in a small concentration in a mixture. As the method usually employs a fairly large sample, it will frequently be possible to concentrate it in the manner indicated above and analyze it further, say by G.L.C.

NEW POSSIBILITIES IN GAS-SOLID CHROMATOGRAPHY

Since the evolution of the "classical" methods of G.S.C. described above—which, as we have seen, have in many cases largely been superseded by G.L.C.—there have been some developments that may possibly cause a more general revival of interest in the procedure.

"Molecular Sieves"

It has been found (see for instance Barrer[12]) that there exist certain silicates which provide regular net-works of channels with diameters no bigger than those of molecules. Such crystals can act as sieves and bring about a separation of molecular species by occluding small molecules, while not adsorbing larger molecules or molecules with shapes that do not "fit." "Molecular sieves"* are, for instance, prepared by outgassing finely powdered zeolites at temperatures within the range of thermal stability of the crystals. The conditions during outgassing may be varied so as to produce molecular sieves having different properties. Barrer, who has studied

---

* Molecular sieves of various types are now marketed by the Linde Air Products Company.

these substances extensively, divides them into the following three classes having successively smaller channel diameters:

(I) Those that do not adsorb isobutane and other isoparaffins, but adsorb propane and higher normal paraffins slowly at or above room temperature, and ethane, methane and molecules of smaller cross-section rapidly.

(II) Those that do not adsorb normal or isoparaffins, but adsorb ethane and methane slowly, and molecules of smaller cross-section (including N_2) rapidly.

(III) Those that give a negligible adsorption of ethane and methane, but rapidly adsorb smaller molecules.

Molecular sieves with modified properties can further be made by cation interchange and by burning out interstitial ammonia. The potentialities of these separate classes have not yet been fully investigated.

It is evident that these bodies have interesting features which open up new possibilities for the separation of complicated mixtures. Barrer has further observed that by operating at low temperatures major differences may develop in the rates of sorption of gases which have but small differences in molecular shapes and diameters, and which are all rapidly adsorbed at higher temperatures. It should be noted that molecular sieves are not true adsorbents in the sense that they do not adsorb gases on the outer surface only. In this respect they bear some resemblance to ion exchangers.

G.S.C. with "Tailing Reducers"

A characteristic and unfavorable feature of elution G.S.C. that has been referred to is the tailing of the peaks for all components except those of very low boiling point. It has, however, been found by Eggertsen, Knight and Groennings[13] that this effect may be considerably reduced by coating the adsorbent with a small amount of a strongly adsorbed liquid. This useful new development virtually gives rise to a method in some respects intermediate between G.S.C. and G.L.C. and having some of the advantages of both.

Eggertsen et al. tested various adsorbents and "tailing reducers." The best combination found was a furnace carbon black, "Pelletex"* and 1.5 per cent (wt) of squalane (a C_{30} branched hydrocarbon of low viscosity, see Appendix I).

The influence of the tailing reducer can be illustrated by an example. It is known (see Hirschler and Amon[14]) that adsorbents such as silica gel and carbon frequently adsorb a paraffin preferentially to a cycloparaffin when both have the same boiling point (for instance n-heptane with re-

---

* Pelletex is marketed by the Godfrey Cabot Company, Boston (Mass.).

spect to methylcyclohexane and 2,4-dimethylpentane with respect to cyclohexane), while G.L.C. usually retards naphthenes selectively with respect to paraffins (see Chapter 6). Figure 8.7 shows the effect found for dimethylpentane and cyclohexane. Figure 8.7 (a) is the curve obtained by Eggertsen *et al.* when using G.S.C. with helium as carrier gas and "Pelletex" as such. Figure 8.7 (b) gives the corresponding curve found when using "Pelletex" coated with 1.5 per cent of squalane.

From these curves it may be seen that squalane as tailing reducer affects the separation in three ways:

(1) The bands become sharper and more symmetrical;

(2) The adsorptivity of the solid is reduced, as evidenced by the lower temperature required for comparable emergence times;

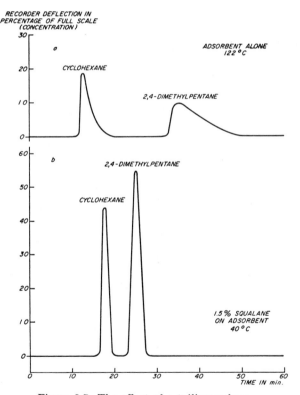

Figure 8.7. The effect of a tailing reducer.

Column: 10′ x ¼″; carrier gas: helium, 20 ml/min.; sample: 2,4-dimethylpentane + cyclohexane, 2:1, ca 1.5 mg; column packing: *a* Pelletex (14–48 mesh); column packing: *b* Pelletex (14–48 mesh) + 1.5% squalane. (After Eggertsen, Knight and Groennings).

(3) The paraffin/naphthene selectivity is somewhat reduced, as may be seen from the ratio of the emergence times.

The effectiveness of this new type of column packing may be demonstrated by an example taken from the paper by Eggertsen *et al.* Figure 8.8 is a reproduction of the chromatogram representing the resolution of a synthetic sample containing all the commonly encountered C_5 and C_6 saturates. The analysis was performed in a coiled 50 ft column, $\frac{1}{4}$ in. diameter, at 40°C. Not more than 3 mg of closely neighboring components could be charged. The duration of the whole analysis was 2 hours. The agreement between the results of the analysis and the composition was very satisfactory.

This method would appear to offer advantages with respect to G.L.C. in cases where certain characteristic features of adsorption can aid in effecting a resolution.

Effects closely related to that reported by Eggertson and co-workers have been found independently by E. Cremer and her students[18], who observed for instance that silica gel or active carbon carrying a certain amount of adsorbed moisture or carbon dioxide gives more symmetrical elution peaks and shorter elution times than the adsorbent with a clean surface.

Special Modifications of G.S.C.

It is to be expected that specific modifications of G.S.C. will enable certain analyses to be carried out accurately with very simple means. An

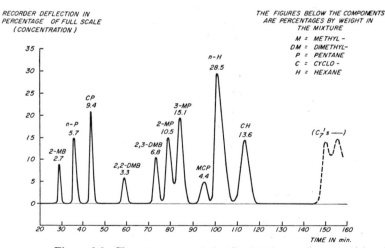

Figure 8.8. Chromatogram of the C_5 and C_6 saturates.

Column: 50′ x ¼″; carrier gas: helium, 20 ml/min; sample: ~10 mg; column packing: Pelletex (14–48 mesh) + 1.5% of squalane; Temp.: 40 ± 0.2°C; pressure inlet: 280 mm + atm. (After Eggertsen, Knight and Groennings).

example is furnished by a method that was demonstrated by Ray[15] for the rapid determination of small amounts of non-olefinic impurities (other than carbon dioxide) in ethylene.

The principle is as follows. A measured sample of the gas (25 cc) is carried in a current of pure carbon dioxide through a column which is composed of two parts. The first is packed with charcoal impregnated with bromine, which absorbs the ethylene and also retains the ethyl bromide formed; the unretained impurities pass into the second section of the column, packed with activated charcoal, where they are separated. The issuing gases are, as in Janák's method, collected in a micro-nitrometer over caustic potash solution and appear in two or more discrete fractions, with a sufficient interval between them to allow of separate measurement. In Ray's case, the first fraction contained any hydrogen, oxygen, nitrogen, carbon monoxide and methane present in the sample, the second fraction consisted of ethane only; any higher paraffins appeared in subsequent fractions. The complete analysis occupies only 15–20 minutes, and the smallest detectable concentration of any one impurity is 0.01 per cent. Sufficient bromine-impregnated charcoal can be accommodated in the column to last for about thirty analyses.

Separation of Isotopes

Whilst the heavier stable gaseous isotopes, such as those of neon[19], cannot easily be separated, but can be enriched, by G.S.C., Glueckauf and Kitt[20] have shown that very pure deuterium may be obtained from a 1:1 H_2-D_2 mixture by passage through a column containing palladium black on asbestos at room temperature. Glueckauf[21] has also demonstrated that when highly radioactive isotopes (krypton and xenon) are submitted to G.S.C. an interesting effect occurs. During the adsorption of such isotopes, the β-rays emitted produce a local rise in temperature. Owing to this fact, the rear of the radioactive band tends to move faster than the front and a contraction (sharpening) of the band results. The width that is finally established is not only independent of the width of the initial band, but beyond a certain distance also independent of the length of the column.

G.S.C. as a Means for testing Catalyst Activity

Cremer and Roselius[22] have employed G.S.C. for testing catalysts. Various pretreatments of the catalyst prove to affect the elution time when the substance is used as the adsorbent in a G.S.C. column under definite conditions. If we assume that the catalyst has a homogeneous surface and that catalyst "poisoning" is caused by the occupation of a part of the surface by the poisoning agent, we might accept as a first approximation that the retardation of an eluted substance, and hence its retention volume, are

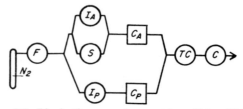

Figure 8.9. Block diagram of apparatus. (After Phillips).

proportional to the "active" surface present. Although the above assumption does not apply strictly, it has nevertheless been found that the retardation is a useful means for characterizing the catalyst surface. The method can also be applied to the quantitative determination of very small amounts of strongly adsorbed substances, by "poisoning" an adsorbent with the material in question and measuring the elution time of a reference compound.

Apparatus for, and Operation of G.S.C.

The apparatus used for G.S.C. will usually not differ essentially from that employed for G.L.C., since both are chiefly composed of an apparatus for percolation and a detector. It consists mainly of a thermostatted column and a detection device. The column is charged with the adsorbent; the sample is introduced and is moved down the column by a current of carrier gas. Granulated adsorbents are generally used, because the finer type of packing as employed in G.L.C. offers too great a resistance to the flowing gas.

In frontal analysis a fairly large sample, which is previously diluted with the carrier gas, is taken. Small samples are used in elution and displacement G.S.C.

Figure 8.9 gives a block diagram of the complete apparatus used by Phillips[8d] alternatively for displacement G.S.C. or for G.L.C. The mixture to be separated is placed in one of the introduction tubes I_A or I_P, and carried to the adsorption column C_A (or to the partition column C_P for G.L.C.) by a current of nitrogen from the cylinder. For the displacement technique (using the adsorption column) the current of nitrogen is passed through the saturator S, by means of which a constant concentration of displacer vapor is introduced into the nitrogen. After leaving the column, the gas passes through the thermal conductivity cell (TC) and the fraction collector (C). For the construction of the flow control (F), specially designed for gas chromatography, the reader is referred to the original literature.

REFERENCES

1. Peters, K., and Weil, K., *Z. angew. Chem.*, **43**, 608 (1930).
2. Zhukhovitskii, A. A., Turkel'taub, N. M., and Georgievskaya, T. V., *Doklady Akad. Nauk S. S. S. R. (Compt. rend. acad. sci. U. R. S. S.)*, **92**, 987 (1953).

3. Aivazov, B. V., and Vyakhirev, D. A., *Zhur. Priklad. Khim.* (*J. Appl. Chem. U. S. S. R.*), **26**, 505 (1953).

4. Turkel'taub, N. M., *Zhur. Anal. Khim.* (*J. Anal. Chem. U. S. S. R.*), **5**, 200 (1950).

5. Turner, N. C., *Natl. Petroleum News*, **35**, R-234 (1943).

6. Tiselius, A., *Arkiv. Kemi, Mineral. Geol.*, **16A**, No. 18, 11 pp., (1943).

7. Claesson, S., *Arkiv. Kemi. Mineral. Geol.*, **23A**, No. 1, 133 pp., (1946).

8. Phillips, C. S. G., (a) *Discussions Faraday Soc.*, No. 7, 241 (1949); (b) *J. Chem. Soc.*, **1953**, 1600; (c) *J. Chem. Soc.*, **1954**, 1066; (d) *J. Chem. Soc.*, **1955**, 1480.

9. Janák, J., *Collection Czechoslov. Chem. Communs.*, **19**, 684, 700 (in German) (1954).

10. Patton, H. W., Lewis, J. S., and Kaye, W. I., *Anal. Chem.*, **27**, 170 (1955).

11. Ray, N. H., *J. Appl. Chem. (London)*, **4**, 82 (1954).

12. Barrer, R. M., *Discussions Faraday Soc.*, No. 7, 135 (1949).

13. Eggertsen, F. T., Knight, H. S., and Groennings, S., *Anal. Chem.*, **28**, No. 3, 303 (1956).

14. Hirschler, A. E., and Amon, S., *Ind. Eng. Chem.*, **39**, 1585 (1947).

15. Ray, N. H., *Analyst*, **81**, 56 (1956).

16. Prior, F., *Thesis*, Innsbruck, (1947); Cremer, E. and Prior F., *Z. Elektrochem.* **55**, 66 (1951); Cremer, E., and Müller, R., *ibid.* **55**, 217 (1951).

17. Cremer, E., private communication.

18. See for instance: Müller, R., *Thesis*, Innsbruck (1949); Roselius, L., *Thesis*, Innsbruck (1957); Cremer, E. and Roselius, L., Advances in Catalysis, New York (1957), p. 659; *Angew. Chemie* **70**, 42 (1958).

19. Glueckauf, E. and Kitt, G. P., *Discussions Faraday. Soc.* No. 7, 199 (1949).

20. Glueckauf, E. and Kitt, G. P., Vapour Phase Chromatography, Desty, D. H. (ed.), London, 1957 (Proc. of London Symposium on V. Ph. Chr., May/June 1956), p. 422.

21. Glueckauf, E., Gas Chromatography 1958, Desty, D. H. (ed.), London (Proc. of 2nd Symposium on Gas Chr., Amsterdam, May 1958), p. 69.

22. Cremer, E. and Roselius, L., Advances in Catalysis, New York (1957), p. 659; *Angew. Chemie* **70**, 42 (1958).

Appendix I

THE CHOICE OF THE STATIONARY PHASE FOR G.L.C.

The considerations leading to the choice of a stationary phase for effecting a certain separation by G.L.C. have already been discussed from a general aspect in Chapter 2, and, from a more theoretical angle, in Chapter 6.

Since the introduction of G.L.C., the number of substances that have been employed as column liquids has steadily increased*. The introduction of new stationary solvents is in some cases justified by the fact that certain classes of compounds have special selective properties rendering them particularly suitable for performing specific separations. Notable examples that have been referred to in the foregoing pages of this book are: solutions of silver salts (effective solvents for separating some of the lower olefins) and the tetrahalophthalate esters employed by Langer, Zahn and Pantazoplos for obtaining an improved resolution between m- and p-xylene.

On the other hand there can be no doubt that the multiplication of column liquids has in many cases been unnecessary and undesirable. Investigators have probably often used a particular compound for this purpose because they happened to have it available, whilst a previously employed stationary phase might have given equally good results. This practice has a serious disadvantage: it renders the collection of comparable data by different investigators on retention volumes difficult or impossible. Furthermore, it may be pointed out that the gradual improvement in the efficiency of columns taking place at present tends to reduce the need for specially selective column liquids; as has been shown in Chapter 7 (under "Recent Advances in Separating Efficiency"), it is often more effective to increase the number of theoretical plates in a column than to change to a more "selective" stationary phase.

There is hence a definite need for limiting and standardizing the column liquids used in G.L.C. This desirability was recognized as early as 1956, during the first International Symposium on Vapour Phase Chromatog-

* The firm of May and Baker, Limited, Dagenham, England, has issued a booklet on materials for gas chromatography, in which all stationary phases that have been proposed for this purpose in publications up to 1957 are listed, together with their respective applications and references to literature.

220   *CHOICE OF THE STATIONARY PHASE*

raphy, held in London, and has since been considered by a special committee resulting from this Symposium. Unfortunately the standardization of solvents suitable for column temperatures higher than 150°C is still difficult. The committee have therefore in 1958 limited their recommendations for stationary liquids to two for the analysis of gases and three for the analysis of liquids up to 150° working temperature. The liquids in question, which are obtainable in adequate purity, have different polarities in view of the applications that may be involved. They are:

Application	Substance	Temperature
Gas Analysis	Squalane	0 and 25°C
" "	Dimethylsulfolane	0 and 25°C
Other Analyses	Squalane	50 to 150°C
" "	Dinonyl phthalate	50 to 130°C
" "	Diglycerol	50 to 150°C

The inclusion of the above list in the present book does not, of course, imply that the need for other column liquids may not arise, particularly since the range above 150°C is not considered and special cases may have to be dealt with. A more extensive list is therefore given by the author below. The main purpose in drawing up the abbreviated list was to promote the use of the liquids in question wherever possible in the range considered, and thereby assist in the collection of standard data for purposes of comparison.

The committee has also suggested that specific retention volumes measured with these solvents should be related to a suitable standard solute. The list of solutes recommended for this purpose in London in 1956 has been retained unchanged, viz.:

> n-butane
> iso-octane (2.2.4-trimethylpentane)
> benzene
> naphthalene
> methyl-ethyl ketone
> cyclohexanone
> cyclohexanol.

By working systematically along these lines it will become possible to draw up tables of retention data, which can then be published at regular intervals and should prove of great value in identifying substances encountered in gas-chromatographic analyses.

The committee further emphasizes a number of points that are of importance in determining retention data; it may be useful to repeat these here:

1. The sample size must be small enough not to overload the column.

Several determinations with varying sample size are desirable to check this point.

2. In determining relative retentions, measurements should be made from the "air" peak.

3. The supplier of the stationary phase should be stated and, where appropriate, the batch number.

4. The retention volume is proportional to the quotient (flow rate of carrier gas) : (weight of stationary phase) and errors in the retention volume are therefore directly dependent upon errors in the last two parameters. For accurate measurement of the carrier gas flow, a soap-film meter seems most suitable and this flow must be corrected to the outlet column pressure.

5. Inlet pressures must be known for the application of the pressure correction factor.

6. Account must be taken of the temperature of operation in assessing the life of the column before a significant change in the weight of the stationary phase occurs.

7. The temperature must be known and its variation with time and along the column should be specified.

The following more extensive list of stationary phases includes the most important types of substances that have been employed, together with their applications and the temperatures up to which they can be used. The temperatures are the maximum values that can be maintained if the column is utilized a number of times. For one or two analyses it is frequently permissible to employ the column liquid at 20–25°C or even more above the figure quoted. However, as was stated in Chapter 3, the use of modern hypersensitive detectors (such as the argon β-ray and flame ionization detectors), together with recent types of column requiring extremely small samples, may render the volatility of the stationary phase very noticeable; in such cases it will become necessary to limit the upper temperature to considerably lower values and so maintain base-line stability by sufficiently close thermostatting.

Organic esters

Esters of an aromatic carboxylic acid and an aliphatic alcohol:
Phthalates: e.g. Dinonyl (di-3,3,5-trimethylhexanyl-)phthalate;

Stationary liquids of very general applicability. The esters derived from aromatic acids, in particular, usually show no pronounced selectivity over a wide range of compound types, since they contain phenyl, aliphatic and polar groups. They separate many classes of solutes roughly according to volatility, and can be employed, if pure, for long periods up to about 140°C. (Less pure products up to 125°C.)

Mellitic esters (e.g. C_1-C_6);
Esters of 2,3,6,7-naphthalene tetra-carboxylic acid (e.g. C_5-C_6).
Esters of an aliphatic dicarboxylic acid:
Sebacic esters (e.g. C_8, "Octoil S").

Mellitic esters up to 160°C.

Paraffinic hydrocarbons
Pure normal paraffins (C_{12} and higher)
Mixtures (paraffin wax)

Excellent solvents for separating volatile hydrocarbons. Owing to "negative" deviations from Raoult's law the retention volumes of the latter are generally higher than predicted from the vapor pressures of the pure substances. With polar solutes the opposite effect may be present to a marked degree.

Temperature limits: dodecane 0°C; hexadecane 40°C; tetracosane 120°C; higher members up to about 160°C.

Squalane[1] (2,6,10,15,19,23-hexa-methyltetracosane, $C_{30}H_{62}$). Obtained by hydrogenating squalene, an unsaturated hydrocarbon from shark's liver oil.

Applicability roughly as above. Low melting point and volatility (approx.: 1 mm/210°C). Interesting as a *reference liquid*, since it can be obtained fairly pure. Max. temp.: approx. 140°C.

Petroleum fractions
Lubricating oils
"Liquid paraffin"
Apiezon grease
Bitumen

Besides paraffin chains, these contain cyclic groups. With a view to stability, highly refined (dearomatized) products are sometimes desirable. Applicability very similar to that of the paraffins.

Temperature limit for an average "liquid paraffin" (medicinal oil) about 150°C, for Apiezon grease and bitumen over 250°C.

Silicones

e.g. no. 703 (phenylsilicones), no. 550 (mixed silicones).
Silicone high-vacuum grease.

Volatility is lower and thermal stability higher than that of hydrocarbons, etc. Principally employed at high column temperatures.* Under these conditions they show no pronounced selective properties. Can be used regularly up to 200°C, occasionally up to 250 or even 300°C.

Benzyldiphenyl[2]

An aromatic compound (m.p. about 50°C, vapor pressure 100 mm at 286°C) which may prove valuable as a stationary liquid for reference purposes. Suitable, for instance, for separating aromatics and other hydrocarbons.
Temp. range: 50° to 100°C.

α-Naphthylamine[7]

M.p. 50°C. Gives an excellent separation of isomeric paraffins, with short retention times; shows a high naphthene-paraffin selectivity, the naphthenes being retained appreciably longer. Temp. range: 50° to about 150°C.

Aromatic nitro-esters

e.g.: the ester of dinitrodiphenic acid† and hexanol-1 (or other primary alcohols); the ester of trinitrobenzoic acid and polyethylene glycol 400.

These esters show a high selectivity among hydrocarbons, being good solvents for aromatics and very poor solvents for paraffins. Aromatics on elution emerge together with paraffins having about 4 to 6 C atoms more, so that G.L.C. can frequently effect a separation according to type. These solvents give rise to striking separations

* It has been found that the suitability of silicones for use at high temperatures varies with the make and possibly also with the batch of product.

$$\dagger \left[NO_2 - \left\langle \bigcirc \right\rangle - \underset{COOH}{} \right]_2 .$$

among aromatics having different substituent groups, owing to steric effects.

The nitro-esters are suitable for use up to 120°C, some up to 140°C. (Dinitrodiphenic acid even to 150–160°C.)

Picrates

e.g. that of *p*-nitroaniline and fluorene.

Behave in a manner very similar to that of the nitro-esters.

Generally unstable at 120°C and higher.

Polyglycols

(Marketed under various trade names.)

E.g. polyethylene glycol 400*

Strongly polar liquids. Good solvents (large retention volumes) for oxygenated compounds and nitrogen compounds; poor solvents (low retention volumes) for saturated hydrocarbons; moderate solvents for aromatics. Suitable for the analysis of samples containing water.

Temperature limit for polyethylene glycol 400: approx. 100°C,† somewhat less for other types.

High-boiling alcohols

(e.g. octadecyl alcohol)

Stationary liquids with a high solubility for the low-boiling members of their own types.

High mol. weight fatty acids

Maximum permissible temperature probably about 140°C.

Dimethylsulfolane‡ [4]
Dimethylformamide¶

Two solvents of very similar be-

---

* According to Adlard[3] there is little difference among these products from the aspect of separation. Polyethylene glycol 400 seems to have the best overall properties.

† It has been reported that this temperature can be 150°C if oxygen is completely excluded.

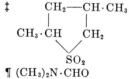

¶ $(CH_3)_2N \cdot CHO$

havior, which have been mainly used for analyzing hydrocarbon gases. Owing to their highly polar character the emergence of olefins is retarded very selectively. With dimethylformamide this effect is somewhat more marked than with dimethylsulfolane. The latter is suitable for use as reference liquid.

Temperature limits: dimethylsulfolane, approx. 40°C; dimethylformamide, about 0°C.

Tricresyl phosphate

Excellent selective solvent for chlorinated hydrocarbons.

Temperature limit: about 120°C (occasionally 150°C.)

Glycerol; diglycerol*

Highly polar liquids, giving a selective retention for water. Selective solvents for separating isomeric alcohols and amines. Moderate solvent power for ethers, esters and ketones.

Temp. limits: about 70°C for glycerol, approx. 110°C for diglycerol.

Solutions of silver nitrate
e.g. in polyethylene glycol[5] or (better) in benzyl cyanide[6]

"Super-selective" solvents for the resolution of overlapping peaks among the lower olefins, for instance for separating cis- and trans-isomers and butene-1 from isobutene.

Temperature below 40°C; above this limit the transient adducts with $AgNO_3$ are not formed and solutions are unstable.

Salts of Fatty Acids[8]
e.g. potassium stearate

Application very similar to that of silver nitrate solutions, but can be used up to about 250°C.

* $[CH_3OH \cdot CH_2OH \cdot CH_2]_2O$

Commercial Detergents of Arylalkyl Sulfonate Class[9, 10] **e.g. "Tide"**

Act as support plus stationary liquid. Convenient, and often give a good separation, e.g. of hydrocarbons. (Disadvantages: hygroscopic and variable in composition.) Temp. range: up to 250°C.

REFERENCES

1. Eggertsen, F. T., Knight, H. S., and Groennings, S., *Anal. Chem.*, **28**, 303 (1956).
2. James, A. T., and Martin, A. J. P., *Brit. Med. Bull.*, **10**, 170 (1954).
3. Adlard, E. R., Vapour Phase Chromatography, Desty, D. H. (ed.), London, 1957 (Proc. of London Symposium on V. Ph. Chr., May/June 1956), p. 98.
4. Pierotti, G. J., Deal, C. H., Derr, E. L., and Porter, P. E., *J. Am. Chem. Soc.*, **78**, 2989 (1956).
5. Bradford, B. W., Harvey, D., and Chalkley, D. E., *J. Inst. Petroleum*, **41**, 80 (1955).
6. Craats, F. van de, *Anal. Chim. Acta*, **14**, 136 (1956).
7. Boer, H., private communication.
8. Phillips, C. S. G., *I.S.A. Proceedings*, 1957 International Gas Chromatography Symposium, Michigan, August 1957, p. 59.
9. Gohlke, R. S. and McLafferty, F. W., presented at 29th A.C.S. Meeting, Dallas, April 1956.
10. Desty, D. H. and Harbourn, C. L. A., "Advances in Gas Chromatography" (A.C.S Symposium, New York, September 1957), p. D-157.

ELIMINATION OF UNCONDENSABLE GASES FROM COMMERCIAL CO$_2$

Carbon dioxide from normal commercial cylinders always contains uncondensable gases up to 1 per cent, which must be removed prior to its use as carrier gas in gas chromatography. Figure A shows a simple device, used by van de Craats,* that can be connected to the cylinder and by which the uncondensables are distilled off under pressure together with part of the CO$_2$. Carbon dioxide from the gas phase passes up through a packed column (I.D. about 1 in.) and is condensed in a cooler. Liquid CO$_2$ returns to the bottom of the storage cylinder. By venting part of the gases through the needle valve at the top of the cooler pure CO$_2$ remains in the cylinder.

The cylinder is kept at room temperature, the cooler is packed with ice.

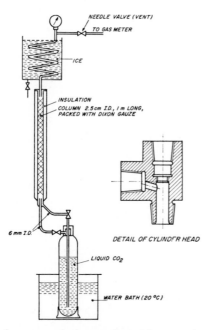

Figure A. Device for removal of uncondensable gases from carbon dioxide.

* F. van de Craats; private communication.

Top gas is vented at a rate of about 25 liters per hour. A cylinder with 8 kg of CO_2, if treated in the above manner for about 8 hours, contains carbon dioxide having less than 0.001 per cent of uncondensable impurities. The purity is determined by absorption in 30 per cent KOH in a gas burette. Only 5 per cent of the contents of the cylinder are lost in this way.

AUTHOR INDEX

Superscripts to page numbers indicate the bibliography reference number to the author's work cited on that page. In such cases the author's name does not appear on the page referred to.

Smart, J., 77
Smith, G. H., 28[7], 32[7]
Smith, V. N., 21[14], 32[14], 80[17]
Stamm, W., 3
Stern, O., 102
Stevenson, D. P., 80[17]
Stross, F. H., 65, 72[16], 91[16], 92, 155, 171, 174[15], 182[5], 184[5], 187, 187[5], 189, 189[5]
Stuve, W., 94
Synge, R. L. M., 9, 10, 111

Tatlow, J. C., 19[1a]
Taylor, B. W., 94
Thiele, E. W., 3
Thompson, R. J., 79[33]
Tiselius, A., 8, 9, 10, 204, 205, 208, 209
Tobin, H., Jr., 44, 45
Tompkins, E. R., 111
Tourneau, R. L. Le, 29[9], 47
Tswett, M., 9
Tunitskiĭ, N. N., 111
Turkel'taub, N. M., 9, 204
Turner, N. C., 9, 10, 204

Vaughan, G. A., 22
Vault, D. de, 110, 115
Voge, H. H., 45
Vyakhirev, D. A., 204

Waals, J. H. van der, 182[8], 184, 186
Weaver, E. R., 85[21]
Weil, K., 204[1]
Whitham, B. T., 47, 48, 49, 54, 55, 155[4]
Wiley, W. C., 56[28]
Williams, A. F., 93
Williams, R. J. P., 7, 167[13]
Wilson, J. N., 109, 110
Winterstein, A., 9
Wirth, M. M., 79

Zaal, P., 38[16]
Zahn, C., 49, 50
Zhukhovitskii, A. A., 204
Zlatkis, A., 77
Zucco, P. S., 21[14], 32[14], 80[17]
Zuiderweg, F. J., 66, 108, 111, 119[1], 124[1], 126[1], 129[1], 134, 156[8]

SUBJECT INDEX

Activity coefficient, 170, 182, 186

Band impurity, 126
Bracketing technique, 33, 35
"Building Block" theory, 174

Calibration of detectors, 32, 54
Capillary (coated) columns, 197
Carbon dioxide, purification of, 75, 227
Carrier gas, 12, 23, 58, 87, 140
Catalysts, examination by G.S.C., 215
"Celite" as support, 19, 61, 155
Chromatography, definition, 2
Chromatography, history, 9
Chromatography, "ideal", 108
Chromatography, nomenclature, 6, 9
Columns, chromatographic, 18, 60, 190, 195
Columns, coated capillary, 197
Columns, high-efficiency, 195
Columns, method of filling, 61
Countercurrent processes, 3
Craig extraction machine, 3, 116

Dead volume, 200
Deemter (Van) equation, 134, 148, 156
Detection by
    argon β-ray detector, 100
    combustion to CO_2, 76
    conductivity, 74
    density balance (comparator), 77
    dielectric constant, 76
    flame ionization, 101
    flame/thermocouple, 79
    flow through restriction, 76
    gas density balance, 77
    hydrogenation to CH_4, 77
    ionization with β-rays, 79, 100
    katharometer, 32, 84–99
    light-emissivity of flame, 82
    low-pressure electric discharge, 99
    surface potential, 76
    thermal conductivity, 32, 84–99
    titration, 74
Detection, differential, 13, 73, 76

Detection, integral, 12, 73, 74
Detector calibration, 32, 54
Detector, dead volume of, 200
Detector "noise", 73
Detector sensitivity, 73
Detectors, 12, 73
Detergents as stationary phase, 160, 226
Differential detection, 13, 73, 76
Diffusion (diffusivity) (eddy), 131
Diffusion (diffusivity) (molecular), 131, 152
Dilute solutions, 163, 170, 182, 186
Displacement development, 6, 8, 208
Distribution (partition) coefficient, 106, 173

Eddy diffusion, 131
Elementary process (step), 3
Elution curve (diagram), 15
Elution development, 6

Fire-brick as support, 19, 62, 155, 157
Fluorescent Indicator Adsorption (F. I.A.) technique, 47
Frontal analysis, 6, 7, 205

Gas Density Balance, 77
Gas Density Balance, electric analog of, 79
G.L.C., 6, 11
G.S.C., 6, 14, 202

Heat conductivity cell. See *Katharometer*
Heat of solution, 184, 190
Height equivalent to a theoretical plate (H.E.T.P.), 108, 124, 135
Henry's law, 163
High-efficiency columns, 195
High-pressure columns, 70, 152, 196
Hold-up, 16, 123

"Ideal" chromatography, 108
Ideal solutions, 162, 170
Identification of components, 26
Integral detection, 12, 73, 74
Ionization cross section, 81

233